H. HARRISON CLARKE, ED.D.

Research Professor
School of Health & Physical Education
University of Oregon

Application of Measurement

to

Health and Physical Education

THIRD EDITION

PRENTICE-HALL, Inc.
Englewood Cliffs, N.J.

PRENTICE-HALL PHYSICAL EDUCATION SERIES

Elmer D. Mitchell, Editor

First printing .... *May, 1959*
Second printing .... *June, 1960*

PRINTED IN THE UNITED STATES OF AMERICA

13911-C

To

my wife

FLORENCE OSBORN CLARKE

Preface

The Third Edition of *Application of Measurement to Health and Physical Education* constitutes a thorough revision of the earlier texts. It has been brought up to date with the most recent research available. New tests have been added and old ones reassessed in light of current information.

Every effort has been made to make this a practical publication. Ninety-five test batteries or evaluating instruments may be used directly from the text. In addition, many more tests are described and evaluated.

As was true for other editions of this text, the approach to measurement is in terms of improved health and physical education services. Measurement is presented as an administrative device enabling physical educators to serve pupils better than would otherwise be possible. Measurement is utilized to make physical education an effective force in the curriculum from elementary school through college.

The writer has considered tests in relation to the specific physical education objective for which they are utilized instead of in the usual functional classification. Thus, tests designed to meet the physical fitness objective are grouped together, as are those intended to meet the social objective and those directed toward the cultural and recreational objectives. Not only are desirable tests in each of these areas discussed and evaluated, but the procedures and methods employed to meet each objective are considered. Considerable emphasis is placed on the *use* of test results: *the application of measurement.*

Too frequently, measurement has been considered an academic appendage of physical education programs, the province primarily of the research worker and of the individual intellectually oriented toward physical education. Often, also, measurement has been discussed on a purely technical basis with slight emphasis on the use of the tests and practically none on necessary procedures for conducting follow-up programs. Actually measurement should be the nucleus of the physical education program; the physical educator should turn to it as readily and as naturally as he now turns to the various activities in his program. It should be the dynamic force in the development of physical education programs. Through the intelligent use of measurement, physical education can take its place as an indispensable phase of the educational process.

In making this approach to measurement, the selection of tests and the emphasis placed upon each were necessarily limited to those aspects of physical education that the writer considered of greatest significance. Consequently, many tests were omitted; only the best applicable tests were included. This lack of completeness in surveying tests in this field is done without apology in the interests of presenting effective procedures free from numerous nonessential details.

The current trends of physical education, a consideration of the desirable qualities to measure, and an explanation of definite administrative procedures to use in putting tests into practical use will be found in Part One. In the first chapter is a new orientation to the place of physical education in our culture. In the second chapter, criteria for selecting tests from a scientific point of view are considered, so that physical educators may be prepared to evaluate tests for themselves.

A separate part of the text is devoted to each of the objectives of physical education, so that the importance of each objective, the educational and administrative procedures for its realization, and the various phases of physical fitness testing are presented. In Part Three, social efficiency and motor ability tests are described, evaluated, and their uses indicated. A similar presentation is made for skill and knowledge tests in Part Four. Part Five is devoted to administrative problems and the process of inaugurating measurement programs.

Appendix A includes statistical procedures essential in construction of tests. Scoring tables necessary to the use of tests described throughout the text appear in Appendix B.

The writer wishes to express his gratitude to the many authors and publishers who have so generously permitted use of their materials.

H. H. C.

Contents

vii

CONTENTS

CONTENTS

Part III • Social Efficienecy

Part IV • Physical Education Skills and Appreciations

CONTENTS

Part V • Administrative Problems

Illustrations

ILLUSTRATIONS

Tables

TABLES

TABLES

PART ONE

Fundamental Considerations of Measurement

CHAPTER ONE

Approach to Measurement

The physical educator's approach to measurement should be in terms of improved service to boys and girls. Teachers with vision and the will to do have little time in this life to accomplish the work for which they are trained—that is, to contribute significantly to the growth and happiness of individuals in their care. Each child is a unique problem, with his own peculiar background and capabilities, differing from the others in innumerable ways. The fundamental function of the physical educator is *to understand each child's needs* in order to give him adequate guidance and to adapt programs to meet his needs.

If these functions are to be accomplished efficiently, measurement is indispensable, for orderly progress cannot be achieved without the guidance that intelligent use of measurement provides. By utilizing measurement properly, the physical educator may fulfill his destiny, giving the service that he should be qualified to give.

Successful measurement, then, involves defining and measuring the truly important outcomes of physical education—that is, the needs and capacities of individual pupils. The only justification of a testing program of any kind in the schools is that it insures and hastens children's growth. Of course, testing does not take the place of teaching. It does, however, make teaching more definite and concrete, and is itself a highly effective teaching device. To outline such an approach to measurement and to indicate a practical basis for the selection of tests are the purposes of this chapter.

Interest in Physical Education Measurement [1]

Early Measurement in Physical Education

Physical education has a rich heritage in measurement and evaluation. Since the early work of Hitchcock in 1860, research leading to the construction of evaluation instruments has been a consuming interest of many workers in the field. Tests in some areas of physical education are much more numerous and better constructed than in others. The history of physical education reveals the reason, for measurement emphases have been closely associated with the changing role of physical education in our society. The direction of measurement over the years has reflected the changing philosophy and objectives of this field.

Early influences. The earliest physical education in the United States was patterned after European systems, especially the German and Swedish. Although parts of these systems still exist and are of great value to physical education, none of them was generally adopted. A new country was being explored, settled, and developed; a new and powerful nation was being created; a new culture was evolving. It was to be expected that physical education would eventually reflect and support this unfolding culture. Although certain beginnings can be traced to this earlier period, the emergence of a culturally oriented physical education was not generally apparent until after World War I.

Between the Civil War and World War I, the primary objective of physical education was physical fitness. Most pioneer leaders of this era were trained in medicine. These men and women were attracted to the field because of the potential health values of proper physical activity. They gave major direction to physical education for a half century during its formative years.

Among the professional leaders of this period were many who were interested in research. These men early turned their attention toward studying the effectiveness of their programs and constructing tests to evaluate results. In keeping with their objectives, tests were designed to measure aspects of physical fitness. The earliest form of such testing was anthropometry, based upon the theory that emphasis should be placed on bodily symmetry and propor-

[1] H. Harrison Clarke, "Measurement and Evaluation," *American Academy of Physical Education, Professional Contributions No. 2* (April 1952), pp. 58-63.

tion with exercise prescribed to affect muscle size. Later, due to the research of Dudley A. Sargent, indicating that "capacity" of the muscles should be given value in judging an individual's fitness, interest changed to strength and its measurement. With the invention of the ergograph by Mosso and its use to study muscle fatigue and the efficiency of the circulatory system, still another shift in measurement occurred to determine the efficiency of the cardio-vascular system. As will be recognized, the measurement emphasis during this period was consistent with the physical fitness objective. The changes in the actual types of tests utilized were the results of increased knowledge of the factors involved.

Organismic concept. The concept of organismic totality was gaining favor in man's beliefs. Milestones in the growth of this concept were: the Greek education of the fifth century B.C., which recognized the need for balance in the mental, social, and physical education of the individual; the expressions of Locke, Rousseau, and other European philosophers that in a sane body lies a sane mind, a thought voiced later by Horace Mann, Henry Barnard, and Herbert Spencer; the early observations of physical educators that the care and development of the body contributes to the individual's mental, emotional, and social effectiveness; the experimentation of psychologists, such as James, Thorndike, and more recently Jones, who demonstrated the interaction of basic forces in the individual; and the dramatic findings of physicians that the "whole man" must be treated, not just the disease or the disability.

The cumulative impact of evidence verifying the organismic concept led to enlarged functions of physical education after the first world war. It also set the stage for an expansion in research with new emphases in measurement, necessary concomitants of changing philosophies and objectives.

Factors Shaping Modern Practice

Modern physical education dates from approximately the early nineteen twenties when it became an integral part of education. The leadership shift was to men and women prepared as educators. The objectives showed recognition of physical education as a part of the educational process. In the period of transition, great difficulty was encountered in making necessary adjustments and thinking through, adopting, and putting into practice effective education

5

procedures. At the same time, to further complicate the situation, physical education was undergoing tremendous expansion throughout the United States. While many factors shaped modern practice in physical education, five especially significant ones have been selected for consideration.

Educational balance. As mentioned above, new objectives were recognized as physical education struggled for a place in the educational curricula of schools and colleges. Initially, however, physical educators were prone to go to extremes in promoting their favorite objective, be it physical fitness, character development, or preparation for leisure pursuits. In practice, some programs were all sports and games designed to develop desirable personal and social behavior patterns; other programs catered almost entirely to the teaching of sports skills for leisure use; in still others, mass drills and apparatus exercises were dominant as the development and coordination of the body were stressed.

At the beginning, there was also a tendency on the part of some influential leaders to abandon the biological heritage of physical education. The understandings and tested practices of fifty years were frequently rejected in the rush to adopt new ideas and procedures. In general, improvement of physical fitness became a concomitant of an activity program designed to realize other objectives. The results of this repudiation of the historic role of physical education found our youth to be no better off physically in World War II than they had been in the previous world war.

Too often during this period, an "either-or" attitude was adopted. Intolerance and immature judgment marked many professional arguments. Perhaps World War II had a leavening influence, for there is now a tendency to seek for educational balance, so that physical education may make its fullest contribution to the lives of boys and girls, men and women. As the dean of physical education researchers, C. H. McCloy,[2] has written: "I have always felt that a well-equipped physical educator would have room in his mind for a reasonably large number of objectives, of ideas, and of questions —and that the addition of some new idea should simply mean some careful rearrangements—but that the *good* ideas, even though they dated back 4,000 years to the Egyptians and the Chinese—should

---

[2] C. H. McCloy, "Why Not Some Physical Fitness?" *The Physical Educator of Phi Epsilon Kappa,* Vol. XIII, No. 3 (October 1956), p. 83.

still be welcomed, constantly experimented with and improved—
and put to use."

Meeting individual needs. In efforts to plan programs that will
effectively realize educational objectives, the necessity to meet the
individual needs of students has become apparent. Individuals differ
in innumerable ways. Their muscular strength varies from weak
and puny to powerful and vigorous; their ability to learn skills has
a wide range; there are pronounced differences in social adjustment
and mental health.

Insofar as activities and methods and the training of personnel
will permit, physical education should meet the individual needs
of boys and girls who are handicapped in some respect, who have
functional defects or deficiencies amenable to improvement
through exercise or who possess other inadequacies which interfere
with their successful participation in the diversified and vigorous
activities of the general program. Specific procedures should be devised and materials selected in accordance with the needs of school
and college populations.

Educating for democracy. In this century, our democratic belief
met its first great challenge with the rise of fascism and national
socialism in Italy and Germany, culminating in World War II in
which the democracies were forced to defend their ideals of government. More recently, communism has constituted a similar
threat. If belief in democracy is to survive, it must be essentially the
result of informed public understanding and action. Schools and
colleges should not only be dispensers of knowledge pertaining to
democratic concepts, but should be laboratories in democratic
living. As Hopkins [3] expresses it, "the outstanding characteristic of
the democratic process is the emphasis upon *cooperative social
action.*" Leaders in physical education are alive to this problem as
it relates to their field, as evidenced by selecting as the topic of the
first Yearbook of the American Association for Health, Physical Education, and Recreation, *Developing Democratic Human Relations
through Health Education, Physical Education and Recreation.*
The processes of democracy, as revealed in recent research in group
dynamics, are being studied and applied to physical education, as
witnessed by the pioneer volume on this subject by the physical

---

[3] L. Thomas Hopkins, *Interaction: The Democratic Process* (Boston: Houghton
Mifflin Company, 1941).

7

education staff at the University of California, Los Angeles.[4] The need to determine the physical educator's contribution to education in a democracy is essential and constitutes a forceful challenge for the future of the field. Coupled with this is the need to develop international and interracial understanding. Physical education has rich potentialities for the realization of this purpose.

Threat of war.[5] An essential motivation of European systems of physical education has been preparation for war. Every European country has been bounded by potential enemies. Nationalism has been rampant. Universal military training has long been an accepted policy of these countries. Huge standing armies made of every nation an armed camp, with preparedness a national watchword. As for Great Britain, the insular character of the British Isles saved her from the necessity for keeping pace in land armaments with rivals on the continent, but she maintained a navy which was overwhelmingly greater than any other.

American culture never has subscribed to preparation for war as an objective of education, except during short periods of armed conflict. In fact, such preparation has not been a national necessity. The United States has not had powerful enemies on its borders. For many decades, it has not been interested in territorial aggrandizement. Great oceans have been effective barriers to invasion from major powers elsewhere in the world. Thus, a prime purpose for the promotion of physical education in other countries, extending to ancient and primitive times, has not been of significant purpose here. As a consequence, the presentation of physical education in educational institutions as preparation for national defense has not been effective and programs to achieve this end have not survived.

However, no longer is our geographical isolation an effective barrier to attack; no longer will we have time to prepare after conflict is joined as in the preceding world wars. With the development of aviation, all countries have become neighbors. Within a matter of hours, enemy aircraft with their lethal loads can be over military and industrial targets in this country. Invasion would be relatively

---

[4] Staff of the Physical Education Department, University of California, Los Angeles, *Group Process in Physical Education* (New York: Harper & Brothers, 1951).
[5] H. Harrison Clarke, "Physical Education and National Survival," *Education*, Vol. LXXV, No. 2 (October 1954), p. 75.

simple were not the United States fully prepared. These facts are recognized by America and this country is armed; and this country is committed to military action whenever and wherever deemed necessary.

There are many implications for physical education in this tragic situation. Not only must we educate for democracy, but we have an obligation to graduate young men and women who are organically sound, physically fit, emotionally stable, and socially well-adjusted. They must be able to contribute to the defense of their country, whether in the armed forces, in industry, on the farm, or in the home. It may be argued that these objectives are also appropriate in peace, and this is true, but the need is greater during periods of national emergency; without fail, it should be given high priority in physical education programs, especially for those individuals who are deficient in any essential aspect of their development.

Rise of spectator sports. A tremendous cultural phenomenon of our time is the rise of spectator sports. Literally millions of people annually watch school, college, and professional sports contests from the stands; millions more view these same contests from in front of television sets or listen to their accounts on the radio. Nearly every cross-roads hamlet in the nation has its school athletic teams; partisan fans support these teams in their contests against those of neighboring schools. Frequently, area, district, and state championships are organized; spectator interest and attendance constantly mount as the championship level is reached. Colleges and universities have their conference championships, bowl games, and rated teams; the paid attendance of spectators place many athletic departments in the realm of big business.

The rise of spectator sports has had marked effects, both positive and negative, on school and college physical education programs. On the negative side, the drive to field the best possible athletic teams has often pre-empted personnel, attention, facilities, time allotment, and budget. On the positive side, it has stimulated athletic participation, engendered support for physical education, and created interest in the activities of the physical education program; it has also frequently been responsible for the construction of improved athletic facilities, which are shared by the physical education program. As the realization becomes clear that a strong physical activity program for all students contributes dynamically to improved athletic teams, increased support is readily realized for physical education.

Implications for Measurement and Evaluation

As noted before, measurement and evaluation always show relationship to purposes to be achieved. It may therefore be expected that more and better instruments will have been developed to determine achievement of older objectives than there has been time to develop in relation to newer goals. The construction of tests in various phases of physical fitness has been in process for a century. A wide research experience and valid instruments are at hand, augmented by materials developed by scientists in physiology and related fields. On the other hand, tests of sportsmanship and other social outcomes are of recent origin and only limited research and the construction of relatively crude instruments have so far been possible.

A considerable time lag is inevitable between new program emphases and the construction of adequate measurement instruments. Initially, then, program justification may be largely based on logical hypotheses. Sometimes a body of knowledge and evaluative devices may be available in an allied field. This is exemplified by the sifting and utilization of research developed by social psychologists, particularly in group dynamics, as bases for proposing changes in physical education content and method. As research workers in our field undertake and complete investigations, a body of professionally oriented evidence will gradually become available.

Competent research is essential to the establishment of any field as a profession. As our culture changes and as new demands upon education are made, changed program emphases are inevitable. As new program areas are developed in response to social change, a number of research steps are required: survey of existing knowledge in the professional and allied fields; the development of acceptable hypotheses to justify and guide practice; construction of evaluative and measurement instruments; utilization of these instruments as tools for conducting more effective programs in the light of the information the instruments provide.

Philosophy will continue to be the fountainhead for program direction. Not until physical education objectives have been set and program procedures accepted is it possible to assess the place of measurement in the educational process. However, progress in physical education toward the attainment of objectives is dependent upon the quality of its research and the validity of its measurement procedures.

A PRESENT CONCEPT OF MEASUREMENT

As inferred above, to consider measurement impels one to philosophical analyses. Thus, in order to select tests, the teacher must first decide what to test, which requires that he first select aims and objectives. To do otherwise would be to place the cart before the horse or to start a journey without knowing either the direction or the destination. The carpenter does not cut boards or nail them together without definite ideas of what he is to build—or, in fact, without detailed blueprints of how the job is to be done. The gunner in warfare does not fire his gun at random in any direction that his whims suggest; if he did, he would promptly receive a one-way ticket to the firing squad, or be placed in a psychopathic ward. The physical educator without definite aims and objectives and without well-thought-out procedures for realizing them is in much the same untenable position as would be "crazy" carpenters and gunners.

Furthermore, to prepare an *adequate* physical education program, teachers must measure, for measurement is as indispensable to an adequate program as measurement is impossible without an adequate program. Moreover, no testing project should be undertaken unless it is part of an attack upon a clearly defined educational problem, the solution of which can be aided materially by the use of tests. This means that tests should not be given merely for the sake of testing, but only when there is some definite object in view. The follow-up program—the use of test results for program modification in order to serve the pupil better than would otherwise be possible—is the real justification for the administration of tests.

The following three questions should be answered by all physical educators planning physical education programs: (1) What are the objectives of my physical education program? (What am I trying to accomplish in physical education, anyway?) (2) What procedures shall I follow in meeting these objectives? (How am I going to do it?) (3) What types of tests are needed to make my program

11

effective and later to determine results? (What tests will help me to do it and prove that it has been done?) These questions indicate the logical sequence of steps to be followed in the establishment of any rational physical education program. The omission of any one will result in a program that is wasteful, weak, and ineffective.

The scientific or measurement approach to program planning is the only way the teacher has of insuring himself against waste. It is safe to assert that the physical educator who does not measure wastes 50 per cent or more of his efforts. If he does not test to determine the physical needs of individuals, how can he plan a program to meet those needs, and how will he know that they have been met? Can he show that his teaching is benefiting his pupils in any way whatsoever? How? In what ways and how much? Can he prove that certain phases of his teaching, if not all of it, are not definitely harmful? Can he demonstrate how well an activity has been learned? Could he defend his physical education program against an investigation by administrative officials—except through verbal rationalization, a mere burst of "oratory"?

The Importance of Physical Education

In considering the first question stated above, concerning the objectives of the program, there has been among physical educators a definite conflict both in theory and in practice as to the desirable goals to be achieved in the activities they lead. This conflict is partially due to the historical concept of physical education, which in the past has been largely designed to build strong bodies and to develop men for fighting. The activities of this program were body building in nature with generous doses of calisthenics, apparatus exercises, tumbling, track and field events, and the like. Later, there was a swing to sports and games—a swing that often resulted in the disappearance from the gymnasium of apparatus necessary for physical development, and corresponding rejection of formal work, especially calisthenics and gymnastics. In fact, the pendulum in some localities swung so far that many programs degenerated into "just throwing out a ball" for pupils to play with as they chose. *The whim of the moment dictated the program for the hour.*

Physical education today must undergo a renaissance. Its contributions to child development must be evaluated, and programs established to insure definite outcomes. Such a rebirth does not necessarily mean that physical education ideas of the past must be discarded, but rather that, through an evaluative process, desirable activities from any available source should be used as needed. Today, much is heard of educational objectives, and more and more programs are being planned for definite educational outcomes. The purpose of the school is to provide experiences for boys and girls by which they can *grow* physically, mentally, socially, and emotionally, and by which they can adapt themselves to changing conditions of living. Physical education has a large place in this scheme of things.

Today's mode of living, as contrasted with that of our ancestors, has changed radically. Modern life, in spite of its time-saving, labor-saving devices, is difficult for human beings. People are herded together in cities with innumerable social contacts daily. Life is speeded up, each individual doing many more things than formerly. Social interdependence is very real. All too frequently people are occupied with monotonous work. Machines have decreased the intensity of human effort and have increased the amount of leisure time. Diet consists more and more of delicate, refined foods. Infectious diseases have been repressed, but there is a definite increase in degenerative diseases and affections of the nervous system and the mind. Resistance to fatigue and worry has decreased. Socioeconomic conflicts have multiplied greatly. There has been a noticeable lessening of constraint, discipline, and effort, the inevitable effects on people living in a mechanical universe without proper guidance to help them live the good life.

These changes and their subsequent results point to needs in three major areas: the physical, the social, and the leisure; and in all these areas, physical education can make definite and indispensable contributions.

MAN: AN INDIVISIBLE UNIT

In considering physical education objectives, the individual should be regarded as an indivisible unit, acting and reacting as an integrated whole. Man cannot be divided into separate compartments. His muscles, other organs, blood, and mind contribute to functional unity. Strength, at least its application to one's activities, depends no less on character than on muscles and on the quantity and quality of blood circulating through these muscles; and the quantity and quality of the blood depends on the efficiency of the other organs of the body. Without the help of the heart, the nervous system, the liver, the thyroid, and all the other glands, the muscles of the greatest athlete in the world would remain impotent. A healthy mind is necessary too. No soldier has ever been really great if not led by faith in himself, in the cause for which he fought, in his leaders, and in his country. To fight, or even merely to work in time of stress, requires more than well-trained muscles.[6]

Furthermore, all physiological activities contain mental elements and effects, and all mental elements are bound to organic functions. It is now generally accepted by scientists that body disturbances create psychic disturbances and psychic disturbances create body disturbances. The more informed people become concerning symptoms of stress and strain, the more difficult it becomes to determine whether physical symptoms are due mainly to emotional disturbances or to physical causes. In fact, the whole question of resistance to disease is bound up with the emotional resilience of the individual. For example, the physical changes that take place under the influence of fear are familiar phenomena: effects on the skin, the respiratory system, the heart, the digestive-eliminative functions, and so on. Actually, no comprehensive evaluation of the individual is possible unless a thorough physical examination has been made and any symptoms of emotional upsets explored—especially if, after a reasonable time, the condition does not respond to physical remedies. Many children have carried the physical symptoms of mental disturbances to the point where they have undergone painful treatment and even hospitalization and surgery.[7]

In like manner, physical abnormalities have often been the cause of mental, social, and emotional difficulties. To cite a homely illustration, an individual cannot perform his best mental work (nor is he such a social being) when he has a splitting headache or is suffering from indigestion. In treating mental patients, psychologists

---

[6] Alexis Carrel, "What Type of Physical Fitness for America?" *New York State Journal of Health, Physical Education, and Recreation,* Vol. V, No. 1 (February 1941), p. 2.

[7] Edward Lies, "Physical Aspects of Emotional Problems," *Child Study,* Vol. XVIII, No. 1 (Fall 1950), p. 3.

routinely investigate physical conditions as sources of the ailment as regularly as—and even before—they seek obscure psychological reasons. Thus, a regular phase of the corrective treatment applied to truancy offenders by Children's Courts is the correction of any physical defects found. Likewise, intelligent parents consider physical reasons as possible causes of emotional upsets in their children. An important responsibility of the school health service is the discovery and elimination of physical defects in children in order that they may benefit from their education and be better able to take their places in society after graduation.

All these possibilities illustrate the necessity for considering human beings as entities rather than as dichotomies of physical and mental forces. The pupil, then, must not be separated into "body" and "mind," but should be regarded as a complicated and precise mechanism, the effective and unimpaired action and interaction of all the parts being essential for the well-being of the individual as a whole. Therefore—and this is of major importance to all teachers—every instructor must be concerned for the body, the mind, and the spirit, of his pupils.

OBJECTIVES OF PHYSICAL EDUCATION

As a consequence of these considerations, physical education objectives must be clearly stated. They are not susceptible of organization into separate entities. In fact, the entire school should be in harmony with this idea. It would be a serious mistake for physical educators to consider the individual as composed of several more or less isolated parts; and it also would be a mistake for this *or any other field* of education to operate as an independent unit without reference to other educational services. The place of physical education in this process may be clearly indicated, and the points of contact and means of integration with other school processes may be pointed out.

From the administrative point of view, however, the *determination* of physical education objectives in terms of the major contribution to each field in the growth and development of the child—such as physical, mental, and social—is the only reasonable way of clearly stating the purposes to be attained in this field. Such designations should be considered as a method of analysis; any tendency to accept them as mutually exclusive categories should be guarded against.

Physical education is identical with other kinds of education so far as its aims and purposes are concerned. As expressed by Champlin: [8] *Personal and social developments in terms of all-round fitness to live the good life in our democracy* are its objectives." This means physical fitness, social efficiency (including moral and spiritual qualities), recreational competency, and the cultural appreciations to serve others and the nation and to enjoy the satisfactions of responsible, democratic citizenship. The great difference from other programs of education is that the medium employed to educate is physical activity.

> 1. PHYSICAL FITNESS: The development and maintenance of a sound physique and of soundly functioning organs, to the end that the individual realizes his capacity for physical activity, unhampered by physical drains or by a body lacking in physical strength and vitality.

"Physical fitness" is herein used synonymously with "physical vitality." It is a positive quality, extending on a scale from death to "abundant life." By this definition all living individuals have some degree of physical fitness which varies considerably in different people and in the same individual at different times. It is more than "not being sick," or "merely being well." It is different from resistance to or immunity from disease. *The person with adequate physical fitness should be able to carry out his daily tasks without undue fatigue and should still have an ample reserve of energy to enjoy leisure time and to meet unforeseen emergencies.*

The history of human experience provides unequivocal evidence to support the assertion that frequently repeated muscular exercises, practiced in accordance with sound principles and extended over long periods of time, result in striking alterations and modifications of the body organs. Schneider, a noted physiologist, states: "The benefit of muscular work cannot be overestimated. Exercise is necessary for healthy existence, it is a physiologic need of a primitive kind which cannot be safely eliminated by civilization." [9]

---

[8] Ellis H. Champlin, "Physical Education and the Good Life," *Springfield College Bulletin* (November 1955).

[9] E. C. Schneider, *Physiology of Muscular Activity* (Philadelphia: W. B. Saunders Company, 1933).

Physical exercise of the right kind and amount develops vitality, stamina, vigor, and skills related to the development of these qualities. There are other factors, of course, which influence physical fitness, chief among which are sleep, diet, and the avoidance of infections; but vigorous physical activity must be included as an essential source of organic power. There is general agreement among physiologists concerning the importance of systematic physical exercise in relation to fitness. Such activity is the only known means for acquiring the ability to engage in tasks demanding sustained effort.

Bertrand Russell has stated that physical fitness is a safeguard against envy (which he calls one of the great sources of human misery) because it makes life pleasant. Many bad qualities are compatible with vitality, however—for instance, those of the healthy tiger and the gangster; and many of the best qualities are incompatible with its absence—Newton and Locke, for example, had irritabilities and envies from which fit bodies might logically have set them free. Possibly the whole of Newton's controversy with Leibniz, which handicapped English mathematics for over a hundred years, would have been avoided if Newton had been robust and able to enjoy ordinary pleasures.[10] In spite of its limitations, therefore, physical fitness is an essential quality in man. The businessman today may not need the muscular development and strength required of his pioneering forefathers, whose very life often depended upon them; but in intellectual as in physical work, a sound heart and lungs, good digestion, and a vigorous, well-developed physique are still great assets for effective accomplishment and for living a happy and satisfying life.

2. SOCIAL EFFICIENCY: The development of desirable standards of conduct and the ability to get along with others.

In the past, the terms "character" and "personality" have been used somewhat loosely to mean the same thing, their definitions being proposed in similar terms. In writing on character measurement, also, these designations have been applied to tests obviously intended to measure identical elements. These terms, however, do not indicate precisely the same concepts, regardless of the manner in

---

[10] Bertrand Russell, *Education and the Good Life* (New York: Boni and Liveright, 1926).

which they are defined. "Character" was originally thought of as morality, and "personality" as the impression the individual makes upon others. According to this belief, one could have a "sterling" character and still be thoroughly disliked. A "pleasing" personality, on the other hand, indicated readiness in favorably impressing others, regardless of the fact that the possessor of the personality might be a complete scoundrel. With the emphasis in education today upon the social aspect of living, resulting from men's interdependence, the definition of character has been extended to include these relationships, and the concept of personality has been defined to include morality. The attempt has been to redefine both "character" and "personality" as all-inclusive terms embracing both individual and social behavior.

In this book, the term *social efficiency* is used to indicate those traits included in the concepts of character and personality defined above. This term is dynamic and descriptive. It has a definite social implication, since in our present democratic society the effect of one's actions upon others is of primary concern. *Behavior* is emphasized, rather than "impressions." This effect is dependent upon: (1) individual traits, such as courage, initiative, morality, perseverance, and self-control; (2) group traits, such as sympathy, courtesy (sportsmanship), honesty, co-operation, and loyalty; and (3) their interrelations for the common good. *A socially efficient individual is one who functions harmoniously within himself, in his relationship with others, and as a member of the society of which he is a part.*

There is little doubt among educators today that physical education may contribute to the social efficiency of school children. The physical educator leads pupils in highly social activities and experiences containing more powerful annoyers and satisfiers, usually, than do other educational fields. At this period in life most boys would rather make the school team than the honor roll, and most girls would rather participate in school play days than attend meetings of the literary club; a touchdown in football is a source of greater satisfaction than is a perfect experiment in a laboratory, and to fall short of the touchdown is a far greater tragedy than failing in the laboratory experiment.

Thus, physical education activities are real to the child—they have meaning; they result in action; decisions must be made that affect not only the child himself but others participating in the contest. When the social studies teacher stresses the duty of the citizen to vote, this duty is, on the whole, a relatively abstract concept, and its reality is not experienced by school children for some time to come. When one boy shoves an opponent in a basketball game, the effect is immediately felt; it is a concrete situation that is meaningful to him, to the boy shoved, and, in varying degrees, to all members of both teams. Physical activities, therefore, *properly presented and conducted,* develop traits basic to future civic behavior—traits that are fundamental to the social development of the individual—courage, co-operation, persistence, initiative, resourcefulness, and will power; respect for the rights of others, for authority, and for the rules of the game; also, self-respect, loyalty, justice, self-confidence, sacrifice of self for the good of the group, aggressiveness, followership, and leadership. The transfer of such traits to other school activities and to life situations, especially if the total interest of the pupil is stressed throughout, occurs more often than even psychologists sometimes recognize.

May it be said, too, that social efficiency embraces moral and spiritual values. The Educational Policies Commission [11] has defined these values as those, which, when applied in human behavior, "exalt and refine life and bring it into accord with the standards of conduct that are approved in our democratic culture." Many of these values find political expression in the Constitution and Bill of Rights. Among these are: the supreme importance of the individual personality, moral responsibility for one's conduct, voluntary co-operation through common consent, devotion to truth, respect for excellence, moral equality, pursuit of happiness, emotional and spiritual experiences transcending the materialistic aspects of life. The student can learn to compare the worth of one desire as it conflicts with another, or his own desires as they conflict with those of other people. He can do this by facing athletic situations which involve a moral choice among competing courses of action, by thought and discussion about the possible results of one course of action as weighed against another, and by later re-examination of the results. Resick [12] has presented an admirable application to physical educa-

---

[11] Educational Policies Commission, *Moral and Spiritual Values in the Public Schools* (Washington: National Education Association, 1951).

[12] M. C. Resick, "Moral and Spiritual Values in Physical Education," *The Physical Educator,* Vol. XII, No. 3 (March 1955), p. 3.

tion of the moral and spiritual values presented by the Educational Policies Commission.

> 3. CULTURE: The enrichment of human experience through physical activities that lead to the better understanding and appreciation of the environment in which boys and girls find themselves; and the development of recreational competency for leisure.

Liberal culture. Traditionally, culture has been thought of as confined to the classical areas of human thought: literature, philosophy, art, and music. Only infrequently since the time of the early Greeks has physical education been considered to possess cultural potentialities. This lack of recognition is due in part to the general concept of culture still prevailing in the minds of educators in general, and in part to a similar lack of recognition by physical educators themselves. There are, however, great cultural potentialities in physical education, and their realization should be planned for as carefully and specifically as is the development of other objectives of the program.

A broad definition of "culture" is: *one's stock of appreciation, including all aspects of living that will improve one's understanding and enjoyment of those objects, people, and events that make up his environment, both local and world-wide.* Many activities included in the physical education program are cultural—in fact, any worthwhile activity executed skillfully enough to help pupils to understand each other and the world. For example, the grace, rhythm, and creative expression of the dance, together with its association with the present and past in this and other countries, its racial and folklore significance—these are truly and highly cultural. An understanding and appreciation of the human body, both biologically and aesthetically, is cultural. Appreciations of skilled performance on the part of others, be they amateurs or professionals, are cultural. The historical backgrounds of such age-old physical skills as archery, fencing, boxing, wrestling, and track and field events are cultural. Physical education has its own culture, also, and the thoughtful teacher in the field will attempt to inculcate in his students the culture peculiar to his subject.

Recreational competency. Changing conditions of modern living have greatly increased the need for recreative activities. Today, men do not engage in a wide variety of activities, but repeat the same movement to distraction. Then, bodies and minds require change—

20

not only for pleasure, but even more to re-create their vitality and capacity for joy. These ends are accomplished by cultural activities —singing, talking, and hobby work—and by games and sports.

In large measure, too, the demands upon the worker's physical and mental energies are less than before, but as a rule the nervous tension is greater, owing to the mechanization of industry; labor-saving devices have cut down the amount of work required in the home, drudgery is reduced, and children who formerly had many chores about the house now find few tasks to perform. That the American people are utilizing this free time for recreational pursuits is clearly evident. Chase [13] estimated that in 1927, out of a national income of 92 billion dollars, the American people expended 21 billions upon leisure-time activities and for commodities consumed during leisure. By 1950, Dewhurst [14] estimated that approximately twice this amount was being spent for one purpose or another by the American public in the pursuit of recreational interests. The provision of opportunities for participation in desirable recreational activities has become a national problem. Steps to meet this problem are being taken by municipal, state, and federal agencies.

Recreation is a very broad field, including all those numerous activities that adults and children engage in for the pleasure that can be derived from them. Thus, activities considered as recreational take a variety of forms: fishing, sailing, camping, music, dramatics, crafts, sports, photography, dancing, reading, collecting, nature study, swimming, and the like. Obviously, physical education can contribute to the development of one's recreational competency.

Postwar Physical Education

While physical education in the schools has been oriented to a peace-time culture, nevertheless, wars have influenced physical education in this country. The tragic lessons of World War I, when a large proportion of our youth was found physically unfit to defend their country from mortal danger, resulted in a tremendous expansion in the number of physical education programs in educa-

---

[13] Charles A. Beard, *Whither Mankind* (New York: Longmans, Green and Company, 1928), chap. 14.

[14] J. Frederic Dewhurst, *America's Needs and Resources: A New Survey* (New York: Twentieth Century Fund, 1955), p. 348.

tional institutions. During World War II, many physical educators were utilized by the armed forces in the physical conditioning of military personnel; still others were used in the physical reconditioning of battle casualties; and numerous schools and college programs were re-directed toward graduating physically fit boys and girls.

Although our own young men exemplified a great fighting spirit and an ability to go all-out in combat, yet the picture also had its dark side. Our optimism regarding physical fitness was falsely based on observation of our star athletes in action in both national and international contests. Army and Navy physical fitness test data disclosed alarming deficiencies in the essential qualities of strength, skill, and stamina so necessary for combat. Prior to the war, this nation, despite its tremendous resources, did not provide widespread and adequate training in physical education for all boys and girls. Only one half of our high-school population was enrolled in such programs.[15] The situation is much worse on the elementary-school level, where adequate physical education programs, in general, have been lacking.

Physical education in this nation has the same potentialities as ever. The war experiences of all countries should leave no doubt of the importance of physical education. Although the pressure of war is not directly apparent, still the international situation is such that physical education should continue to develop those traits essential in boys and girls should armed conflict again face our people.

The seriousness of this situation is well exemplified in the formation of a Council on Youth Fitness at cabinet level in the federal government and a national Citizens Advisory Committee on the Fitness of American Youth by President Dwight D. Eisenhower during his second term in office.

Until the fundamental job of developing the individual physically has been accomplished, there is no place for haphazard methods or for fads and frills. This is physical education's primary mission in peace or war. It should be emphasized, however, despite the urgency expressed, that physical fitness should not be considered the only objective of this field. Physical education activities should be selected and conducted so that the individual becomes a member

---

[15] David K. Brace, "Physical Fitness in Schools and Colleges," *Journal of Health and Physical Education,* Vol. XV, No. 9 (November 1944), p. 489.

of a group and acquires desirable social traits through his inter-action with other members of the group, and so that the individual develops proper attitudes and skills for the continued use of phys-ical education activities during his leisure hours.

Emphasis for Girls

Many great educators since Aristotle have suggested the com-plete separation of educational aims and objectives for men and women. This may very well be. However, in recent decades, there has been a drastic increase in civil, vocational, and intellectual free-dom for women, and this trend is still progressing. Aside from definite biological differences, the educational and physiological needs of women are converging with those of men. Thus, the gen-eralization may be advanced that the aims and objectives of educa-tion and physical education are essentially the same for boys and girls, differing primarily in emphases and details.

To illustrate the emphases recognized by women, Jane Shaw,[16] in a study of reasons for participation in a YWCA physical edu-cation program as expressed by out-of-school girls and women, found that they came to the gymnasium because they were not satisfied with their lives as they were living them; that they felt that something was lacking and sincerely wanted to better themselves. Reasons given for YWCA participation were as follows:

1. To reduce.
2. To gain weight.
3. To correct posture or some figure fault.
4. To learn to relax and take things easy after working all day in an office.
5. To learn skills, such as tennis, swimming, and so forth, so that they could play them on their vacation and in their spare time.
6. To learn social dancing so that they would become more popular and have more dates.
7. To participate in a recreation program.
8. To seek company, a desire brought on by lack of companionship.

After this analysis of felt needs, and after subsequent interviews with many of the girls, the following physical education objectives were proposed:

1. PHYSICAL FITNESS: Organic vigor and efficiency, knowledge of require-ments for healthful living, nutrition, exercise, and rest; relaxation; cor-rection of physical defects; and preparation for motherhood.

---

[16] Jane Shaw, "Expressed Objectives of Physical Education by Girls and Women." Unpublished study, Syracuse University, 1940.

2. PERSONAL APPEARANCE AND BEAUTY: Development of a beautiful and graceful body; development of good posture and physical poise; elimination of physical defects affecting appearance; knowledge and care of hair, complexion, nails, and so forth; and knowledge of appropriate, healthful, and becoming clothing.

3. HUMAN RELATIONSHIPS: Opportunity to make friends; development of democratic conduct and ideals; opportunity for a rich and varied social life; development of consideration for the well-being of others; development of courtesy, co-operation, and sportsmanship; and development of social skills that will add to their popularity and social adjustment.

4. RECREATIONAL SKILLS: Development of many skills that will be useful as leisure-time activities, and enjoyment of those skills and games of a recreational nature.

5. APPRECIATIONS: Appreciation of rhythm and music; appreciation of beauty, grace, and poise; appreciation of art, skill, and achievement; appreciation of ability in others; appreciation of personality; and appreciation of freedom and democracy.

Thus, the values of physical education which women recognize as essential, correspond well with the stated objectives propounded in this text. Certainly, the physical, emotional, and social stresses of modern life strike both sexes indiscriminately. Strength and endurance are needed by both sexes. Boys may have a more immediate application for these qualities to athletic participation; however, many working housewives have need for a greater absolute level of physical fitness than do their sedentary husbands. While body poise and grace are recognized as immediately desirable traits for girls, they might actually be cited as prime criteria for good motor performance in both men's and women's activities. Even "beauty," if replaced by a term to indicate the idea of "attractive physical appearance," appears as a vital need for both men and women.

SELECTION OF TESTS

Tests in physical education may be used for many purposes. All purposes, however, focus in one all-encompassing aim: to realize educational objectives; to serve boys and girls better than would otherwise be possible. If the preceding discussion in this chapter is sound, therefore, physical educators will then logically devise procedures, select activities, and adopt methods to develop physical fitness, social efficiency, and recreational competency adapted to the separate needs of boys and girls.

Procedures for meeting each of the physical education objectives will be contained in Chapters 3, 10, and 13, which introduce the various types of tests. Examples of the manner in which physical education tests may be selected on the basis of educational procedures are given below:

1. If individual physical fitness needs are to be met, tests measuring essential elements of physical fitness are necessary—in order to select those with such needs, to follow their progress, and to know when needs have been met.
2. If maintenance of physical fitness on the part of all students is desired, again tests measuring essential elements of this quality are needed as a periodic check on fitness status.
3. If nutritional status or physiological efficiency of pupils is to be given special attention, appropriate tests in these areas should be selected.
4. If pupils with postural defects are to be selected for remedial classes, a test of this quality is obviously necessary.
5. If homogeneous grouping of pupils for the physical education program is considered desirable for pedagogical purposes and to provide a desirable setting for the development of social efficiency, general motor ability tests might well be selected.
6. If pupils with tendencies toward social maladjustment are to be discovered, personality and character tests and rating scales are essential.
7. If emphasis is to be placed upon the general development of athletic ability, tests of general motor capacity and ability will be found most useful.
8. If homogeneous grouping by specific skill ability is desired, appropriate skill tests and achievement scales are necessary.
9. If skill and understanding of specific physical education activities are sought, skill tests, knowledge tests, and attitude scales would be selected.
10. If reports of pupil progress are to be prepared for administrators, boards of education, and the public, the most essential physical and social growth factors should be measured.

In considering the selection of actual tests that will be used in the physical education program, two points should be borne in mind. First, only those tests should be selected that will aid in making physical education effective. Second, only the best tests available for the job intended should be used. The use of poorly constructed or empirical tests, when scientifically constructed tests are available, is little less than folly and decidedly a waste of time.

CONCLUSIONS

The regular use of measurement is one of the most distinctive marks of the professional viewpoint in any human activity. This statement applies particularly to engineering, medicine, and education, and perhaps most to physical education, which affects pupils so immediately and so profoundly in their most impressionable years. Educational tests and the programs resulting from their use in physical education are coming to be regarded as synonymous with good teaching practice, for it is only through measurement that the effects of teaching can be determined at all—that progress can be known. Therefore, the physical educator contemplating the inauguration of any program should turn to measurement as a matter of course. It is not too much to say that the use of measurement in physical education may be considered as a prerequisite to the professional growth of the educator.

But although the progressive physical educator should use tests, his attitude toward testing should be both liberal and critical. A liberal viewpoint will allow him to use imperfect tests if and when they are the best available at the moment, in the hope that through their greater use better tests will eventually result. A critical viewpoint prevents him from being satisfied with present tests and insures a demand for progressively better tests.

The scientific construction of tests in the field of health and physical education is still so relatively recent that a willingness to use existing tests and to analyze them critically is essential to the growth of this movement and of the profession itself.

Selected References

Bovard, John F., Frederick W. Cozens, and Patricia E. Hagman, *Tests and Measurements in Physical Education*, 3rd ed. Philadelphia: W. B. Saunders Company, 1949.

Clarke, H. Harrison, "Physical Education and National Survival," *Education*, Vol. LXXV, No. 2 (October 1954), p. 96.

Gulick, Luther, "Measurement as Applied to School Hygiene," *American Physical Education Review*, Vol. XVI, No. 4 (April 1911), p. 239.

Hitchcock, Edward, "The Need for Anthropometry," *Proceedings*, Second Annual Meeting, American Association for the Advancement of Physical Education, November 26, 1886.

McKenzie, R. Tait, "The Quest for Eldorado," *American Physical Education Review*, Vol. XVIII, No. 5 (May 1913), p. 295.

Rogers, Frederick Rand, ed., *Dance: A Basic Educational Technique*, Chapter I. New York: The Macmillan Company, 1941.

Russell, Bertrand, *Education and the Good Life*. New York: Boni and Liveright, 1926.

Sargent, Dudley A., "Twenty Years of Progress in Efficiency Tests," *American Physical Education Review*, Vol. XVIII, No. 7 (October 1913), p. 452.

CHAPTER TWO

Test Evaluation

Measurement is neither a new nor an uncommon phenomenon. In all walks of life measurement is used. In fact, if all our various testing devices were suddenly destroyed, contemporary civilization would collapse like a house of cards.

For ages the ingenuity of man has been directed toward the control of his environment. His procedures have evolved from pure trial and error, and even chance, through intelligent appraisal of existing knowledge and a thoughtful consideration and testing of likely hypotheses, to the marvelous method of modern science, which measures weights in millionths of a pound, distinguishes between thousands of colors and shades, calculates time even in millionths of a second, and so forth. Aristotle was one of the first great scientists. Since his time, man's quantitative conquest of nature has expanded not only into all branches of physics and chemistry, but into organic and psychological phenomena as well. Education, and even more recently physical education, are but newcomers to the scientific procedure. It is safe to predict that the future effectiveness of education and physical education will be proportionate to the refinement and use of testing instruments available in these fields.

The Function of Measurement

Reduced to its simplest terms, the function of measurement is *to determine status*. Status must be determined before conclusions

27

concerning the thing measured can be drawn and before comparisons can be made. In this concept, several factors are involved.

Status

By measurement the status of the quality to be measured is determined. For example, the distance an athlete can jump may be measured with a steel tape; the speed he can run, with a stop watch; the amount he weighs, with scales; and the capacity of his lungs, with a spirometer. In each case, a quantitative measure indicates the status of the quality involved in terms of feet and inches, minutes and seconds, pounds, and cubic inches, respectively. Status is determined by the surveyor with level and compass, by the photographer with photoelectric cell, by the mechanic with vernier calipers, and by the bacteriologist with microscope. To determine status, therefore, is the first function of measurement.

Comparison

After the status of an object is known with reference to a particular quality to be measured, it is possible to compare it with: (1) the same quality in other objects of a like nature, (2) norms or standards, and (3) itself at different time periods. Take weight-testing as an example: A boy may weigh 200 pounds (his status). This score may be compared with a norm based upon his sex, height, and age —which, let us say, is found to be 160, showing that he is 40 pounds, or 25 per cent, overweight (*comparison with a norm*). He may also be compared with others in his group and with national standards and found to be obese (*comparison with a standard*). As his weight is high, he is given appropriate treatment to reduce, with the result that his weight is lowered to 180, an improvement of 20 pounds (*comparison with self at different times*). Thus, the round of measurement possibilities on an individual basis is complete. Similar processes are possible for groups.

The fact that the amount of change in status can be determined by measuring the same individual or individuals after a lapse of time is a highly important factor in physical education, for it becomes possible to measure the progress of the individual, the group, and the school, so that program and teacher efficiency are in turn rendered measurable. These measures of progress are also the basis for research.

28

TEST EVALUATION

CRITERIA OF TESTS

After the physical educator has decided upon the objectives of his program, after he has devised administrative and educational procedures to realize these objectives, and after he has determined the type of tests he will need for their full realization, he is ready to select the specific tests to be utilized for each essential task to be performed. In order to make satisfactory selections, *he should evaluate available tests in terms of their scientific attributes.* In other words, he should answer such questions as the following concerning each test considered, in order to be able to choose the best and the most useful for the job to be done: (1) Does the test measure the quality for which it is to be used? (*Validity*) (2) Can the test be administered accurately? (*Reliability, Objectivity*) (3) Can the test scores be interpreted in terms of relative performance? (*Norms*) (4) Is the test economical? (*Cost of instruments, Economy of time*) An understanding of these terms is essential before tests can be intelligently evaluated and wise choices made.

Test construction is based upon the use of *statistics*—mathematical procedures showing relationship between variables. A presentation of statistical processes appears in Appendix A.

VALIDITY OF TESTS

A *valid* test is one that measures accurately what it is used to measure. The need for this quality in a test is so obvious as to preclude argument. To use a test to measure something for which it is not intended is absurd. We do not weigh a person in order to determine his height; nor do we use a barometer to determine temperature. On the contrary, if we wish to know a person's weight, we use scales that measure weight; and if we wish to know his temperature, we use a thermometer that measures heat. Despite the obviousness of this concept, however, it is frequently violated in educational measurement.

Certain relationships can be readily seen. We know that scales measure weight; a stop watch, time; a steel tape, distance; and a thermometer, degree of heat. And, yet, originally, the validity of these measures had to be established. How do we know that the scales measure weight? That the stop watch measures time? That the steel tape measures distance? That the thermometer measures temperature? One might ask: What is a pound? A second? A foot? A degree of heat? At one time agreement on these concepts had to be reached. Today, we no longer question these measurement relationships, nor do we question the instruments that have been devised to measure them. Scientists have done a good job in establishing these basic measures and in developing precise measuring instruments. They are now accepted as established facts.

But how about less tangible, less mechanical concepts? On what basis may we believe that the Binet-Simon Test measures intelligence? that the Physical Fitness Index is a measure of physical fitness? that cardiovascular tests indicate the condition of the circulatory system? that a ball-volleying test is a measure of general tennis ability? The relationships here are not so obvious. One wants to be shown that they exist. One wants proof.

Consequently, in constructing tests, the researcher presents evidence to support his contentions regarding the elements or traits that his tests measure. In order to do this, he establishes a criterion of the element being measured and compares the new test with this criterion measure. If the two have a high relationship—if they go together, if the test and criterion agree—the researcher may logically conclude that his test measures the same quality as does the criterion. In determining the validity of tests, therefore, the physical educator should evaluate two elements: (1) the degree to which the criterion measure represents the quality being measured; (2) the amount of relationship shown between the test and the criterion.

The Criterion

Physical education researchers have used considerable ingenuity in devising criteria in the validation of tests. In some instances, more than one criterion is used. In general, the following five types of criteria have been utilized:

Critical thinking. The basis for the construction of many general motor ability and motor fitness tests has been critical thinking, although other criteria have also been used. This process consists in analyzing the activity in terms of its fundamental elements. For example, in constructing his athletic ability test, Cozens, through critical thinking, specified the following seven components: arm and shoulder girdle strength; arm and shoulder girdle coordination; hand-eye, foot-eye, arm-eye coordination; jumping strength, leg strength, leg flexibility; endurance; body coordination, agility, and control; and speed of legs. Cozens then went on in his research to select test items to measure these elements. However, the critical decisions made in the selection of the seven elements played a leading role in the validation of his test.

Established test. A simple criterion is to utilize a test of the same quality the validity of which has been established. If the correlation [1] between the old and the new tests is high, they measure essentially the same thing. This is the practical application of the basic algebraic rule that, when two different measures agree with a third, they also agree with each other. Of course, the degree of agreement of the criterion test with the quality measured limits assurance of the validity of the new test. The new one may or may not be more valid than the criterion, but the experimenter cannot know this from his experiment. This practice of validating a new test with an established procedure has not been followed to any extent in physical education. However, several established tests have been revised in this manner, i.e., by using the original test as the criterion. Thus, we have the Iowa Revision of the Brace Test, the Metheny-Johnson Test of Motor Educability, and the Oregon Simplification of the Strength Index.

Subjective judgment. In the utilization of subjective judgment as the criterion, ratings of the relative ability of the subjects in the activity to be measured are made by experts. This criterion has been used extensively in constructing tests in team sports, such as basketball, soccer, field hockey, volleyball, and the like. In such activities, it is otherwise impossible to isolate the quality of the individual's performance from that of his team mates.

Composite score. The composite score is the sum of all the scores made by each individual on all the tests included in the experimental situation. These scores are usually expressed in standard score form, as, otherwise, such values as distance in the standing broad jump, number of chins, and speed in the 50-yard dash could not be added. This criterion has been in common use in the valida-

---

[1] Coefficient of correlation: A mathematical procedure for determining the degree of relationship between two variables.

tion of motor fitness tests, including those developed by the Army, the Navy, and the Army Air Forces during World War II.

Functional evidence. This criterion consists of functional evidence of the element for which the test is constructed. As examples of the application of this criterion in test construction, the following may be mentioned: Dyer used round-robin play to validate her tennis test; Cureton used a manikin as a criterion of posture and a footprint in specially prepared sand as the criterion for determining the validity of footprints as a measure of the height of the longitudinal arch of the foot; Rogers used major sports letter men and major sports captains and "best players" as representing athletic ability.

These examples indicate the methods used and the sort of process that must be evaluated in determining the validity of physical education tests.

Relationships

If the relationship between a test and its criterion measure is low, little value can be attached to the test, unless there are extenuating circumstances. One such condition would be the use of a criterion measure that is itself inaccurate. For example, certain judgment ratings are known to be inconsistent; to use such ratings as a criterion for test results, as has been frequently done in the construction of skill tests, would impair the value of the results. One would naturally, therefore, expect to get lower validity coefficients when such criteria are used.

Then, too, tests themselves may be somewhat inaccurate but still superior to any other available methods. To illustrate, Cureton, in constructing posture tests, obtained reliability and objectivity coefficients that were for the most part well below ordinarily accepted standards for satisfactory measurement. Yet, he was able to show that his objective procedures were much more accurate than the results of subjective inspections of experts. Therefore, the use of the objective posture scheme may be justified in lieu of a better testing instrument.

Obviously, too, not everything can be measured with the same degree of precision. Such elements as jumping distance, running speed, and muscle strength can be recorded with considerable accuracy, whereas character traits, appreciations, and attitudes still lag behind in the objectivity with which they can be determined. Consequently, these factors should be taken into account in evaluating present-day tests in physical education.

Relationship is usually shown by correlational methods, in which the proposed test is related by mathematical procedures with the criterion measure. In these instances, the most desirable standards are .90 and above, although correlations above .80 are considered significant. Validity coefficients obtained by this method in constructing certain of the tests mentioned above, for example, were as follows:

Experimenter	Element Measured	Criterion Measure	Correlation Coefficient
Cozens, F. W.	General athletic ability of college men	41 motor ability tests	.97
Cureton, T. K.	Height of arch by footprints	Height of footprints in sand	.90
Dyer, J.	General tennis ability	Round-robin play	.92
Rogers, F. R.	General athletic ability by Strength Index	Track and field events	.81

Relationship may also be indicated by comparing the successes in the test obtained by contrasting groups: those rated as "good" and those rated as "poor." For example, the performance on the test of the upper quarter or third of the group, selected according to the criterion measure, may be compared with the performance of the lower quarter or third. Validity for the McCurdy-Larson Organic Efficiency Test was determined by this method, three contrasting groups being selected as follows: (1) good-condition group, varsity swimmers at the 440-yard distance; (2) poor-condition group, infirmary patients; and (3) average group, all Springfield College freshmen over a two-year period. The criterion for the Washburne Social Adjustment Inventory was also established by this procedure, the following four groups being chosen: (1) well-adjusted high-school pupils; (2) average-adjusted pupils; (3) maladjusted high-school pupils; and (4) second-term reform school offenders.

Validity, of course, is absolutely essential for a good test, since without it one does not know what the test measures. In fact, to use an unvalidated test is worse than useless: it is positively misleading.

ACCURACY OF TESTS

Need for Precision

The accuracy with which things are measured, or with which differences are perceived, depends first upon the precision of the measuring instruments. An alarm clock is a valid measure of time, but one would scarcely use it as a measure of speed in the 100-yard dash, because it is not precise enough: it does not register time with sufficient precision to be usable for this purpose. Neither could a wrist watch be used, even if it were equipped with a second hand. Today, in important track meets, even the stop watch is unsatisfactory, accurate timing being based upon electrical devices free from human error. In like manner, a foot rule measures distance, but one would hesitate to use it for measuring the distance one can throw the discus or javelin. Even human ability to perceive the winner of a close race is often questioned; therefore, the photographic lens is replacing the human eye in many track meets.

Many men consider themselves able judges of weight; and, indeed, weight should be one of the easiest of the physical measurements to estimate. It is surprising, however, to note the great range of variation among any group of physical educators in estimating the weight of one of their members. To estimate the *amount* of difference in weight between two individuals when one is small and the other is large leads to even less satisfactory results. To perceive that one individual weighs more than the other is, of course, quite simple in this situation; but the more closely two individuals approach the same weight, the more difficult even this becomes.

Thus, the existence of a difference is quite easy to note when two objects are at opposite extremes, although the amount of the difference is not so simple unless *precise measuring instruments are used.* And, too, estimating the amount of an individual's change in weight after the lapse of a period of time is even more inaccurate. A pair of scales, however, would solve this problem simply and easily.

In measurement, we make sure rather than guess or take for granted; moreover, the more refined the testing instrument, the better the results. Of course, some individuals can attain a great degree of precision, at least of some qualities, as, for example, the "circus man" who guesses the weight of individuals within three pounds, and the athletic coach who, with many years of experience in observing his players in a large number of situations, selects the members of his athletic teams on a judgment basis. (Incidentally, this specialist regularly and frequently corrects his mistakes in judgment by substitutions.) But a convenient index of the condition of the players on the day of a game would be a great help to any coach in selecting his starting players, and also in determining substitutions. The need for precise measuring instruments is thus readily seen. Certainly, if guessing such tangible physical factors as weight is so obviously lacking in accuracy, how much more difficult must it be to judge such intangibles as physical fitness, motor ability, and social efficiency!

Reliability

The reliability of any test may be defined as the degree of consistency with which a measuring device may be applied. The common procedure is to repeat the full test with the same subjects and under the same conditions, and to correlate the results of the two tests. When this method is followed, test accuracy is expressed in terms of "coefficients of correlation." It is possible, however, for this correlation to be high without the test being really reliable, which would be the case if the subjects had consistently higher scores on the second administration of the test than they had on the first.[2] The presence of this condition may be detected by taking into account both the correlations and the difference between the average scores of the two groups.

It may now well be asked: What significance should be attached to various reliability coefficients? Garrett [3] states that "most makers of general intelligence tests demand a reliability of .90 between duplicate forms of their tests for unselected groups of the same chronological age. To be a reliable measure of capacity, a mental or physical test should, generally speaking, have a minimum reliability coefficient of at least .90." Ruch and Stoddard [4] have offered the following suggestions as "rough guides" for educational tests:

---

[2] C. H. McCloy, *Tests and Measurements in Health and Physical Education* (New York: F. S. Crofts and Company, 1939), p. 8.

[3] Henry E. Garrett, *Statistics in Education and Psychology* (New York: Longmans, Green and Company, 1930), p. 269.

[4] G. M. Ruch and George D. Stoddard, *Tests and Measurements in High School Instruction* (Yonkers-on-Hudson, N. Y.: World Book Company, 1927), p. 56.

Reliability
Coefficients

.95–.99 . . . . . Very high: rarely found among present tests.

.90–.94 . . . . . High: equaled by a few of the best tests.

.80–.89 . . . . . Fairly high: fairly adequate for individual measurement.

.70–.79 . . . . . Rather low: adequate for group measurement but not very satisfactory for individual measurement.

Below .70 . . . . Low: entirely inadequate for individual measurement although useful for group averages and school surveys.

Objectivity

Objectivity as a concept has different meanings. The common term, objective tests, usually refers to written examinations scored from a key, as for true-false and multiple-choice questions. In test construction, however, objectivity means the degree of uniformity with which various individuals score the same tests. In other words, a perfectly objective test is one in which no disagreement occurs among competent persons in scoring any given subject while using the same test. Objectivity in grading essay-type examinations has been notoriously low. Frequently great differences occur among scores assigned to the same paper by different readers. For example, Starch and Elliott [5] had facsimile copies made of actual examinations taken by a pupil in English and in geometry. These copies were sent to 142 teachers, who assigned to the identical paper in English values varying from 50 per cent to 98 per cent. The paper in geometry was graded by 114 teachers with assigned scores varying from 28 per cent to 92 per cent. The writer at one time examined the grades assigned independently by two instructors to answers made by forty college students to an essay question in educational psychology. The correlation coefficient was .60. Essay examinations, however, can be scored with greater consistency if proper precautions are taken in the preparation of check lists and in the training of scorers.

With the newer types of objective tests, however, great consistency is possible, although their validity may be questioned as measures of, say, appreciations, ability to express oneself, and vari-

---

[5] Daniel Starch and E. C. Elliott, "The Reliability of Grading High School Work in English," *School Review*, Vol. XX, No. 7 (September 1912), p. 442.

Daniel Starch and E. C. Elliott, "The Reliability of Grading Work in Mathematics," *School Review*, Vol. XXI, No. 4 (April 1913), p. 254.

ous social traits. In physical education, on the other hand, scoring is usually a fairly simple procedure, since scores are frequently recorded in units of time, distance, or height, in readings on a dynamometer dial, in the number of times a particular exercise or skill is successfully performed, and the like.

A slightly different concept of the meaning of the reliability and objectivity of tests is indicated in physical education performance. Rogers,[6] for example, states that "a measure is reliable if two or more *measurements* of the same object or function by the same measuring device yield similar scores"; and that it is objective "if two or more different *individuals*, using the same instrument, or procedure, secure similar results." In this case, tests with high objectivity will also have high reliability; since an individual will agree more readily with himself in administering tests than he will with others. Frequently, therefore, in constructing tests, objectivity only is computed; the assumption is that, if this is satisfactory, reliability is automatically assured. A test, however, can have a high degree of reliability without an appreciable degree of objectivity. For example, in establishing the footprint angle as a measure of the height of the longitudinal arch of the foot,[7] one of the lines originally drawn was defined as a "line of best fit." Reliability for this form of the test was .90, no objectivity coefficient being given. Thus, the individual was able to place the line consistently in the same place, but his idea as to where it should be did not agree with the position in which it was placed by others. By defining this line carefully, the reliability of the test was increased to .97 and the objectivity coefficient became .95. Many judgment ratings have yielded similar results. In test construction, therefore, every effort should be made to secure high objectivity, so that physical educators may compare their test scores with the test scores of other teachers or with universal norms.

Objectivity in measurement is secured by the following means: [8] (1) accurately phrased and fully detailed instructions in measuring procedures; (2) simplicity of measuring procedures; (3) the use, wherever possible, of mechanical tools of measurement; (4) reduc-

---

[6] Frederick Rand Rogers, *Fundamental Administrative Mesasures in Physical Education* (Newton, Mass.: Pleiades Company, 1932), p. 17.

[7] For the footprint angle, see Chap. 6.

[8] Frederick Rand Rogers, *op. cit.*, p. 19.

tions of results to mathematical scores; (5) selection of intelligent measurers, carefully trained; (6) maintenance of professional or scientific attitudes by testers; and (7) unremitting supervision of measuring procedures by administrative officers. Only by these practices may the objectivity of measures be maintained at a high level.

Norms

Is a weight of 125 pounds satisfactory? Is a Strength Index of 1500 good? How may a time of 25.5 seconds on the obstacle race in Scott's Motor Ability Test for college women be interpreted? What can be expected in athletics from an individual with a score of 190 on McCloy's General Motor Ability Test? These questions cannot be answered without additional information concerning the individuals so measured. A weight of 125 will be satisfactory for certain individuals; for others it will indicate a serious underweight condition; and for still others it may mean obesity. With norm charts based upon sex, height, and age, a satisfactory answer can readily be reached. The same is true of the Strength Index. Thus, a Strength Index of 1500 may indicate adequate strength, great strength, or general weakness, depending upon the sex, age, and weight of the individual. The obstacle race time of 25.5 seconds becomes meaningful when it is discovered that it has a T-scale score of 51, representing the average performance on the test for college women. In order to understand the McCloy score of 190, one must know the norm for that individual, the norm in this case being based upon a classification index (age, height, and weight).

Norms, therefore, are necessary in order adequately to interpret test scores. In physical education, norms may be based upon various combinations of age, height, and weight, as indicated above. In this situation, average scores are usually given with standards to indicate the significance of variances from this point. To illustrate: in the use of age-height-weight tables, usually an individual 10 per cent below the average weight for his age and height is considered to be underweight; and, if 20 per cent above, he is considered obese by these standards. In the case of the Strength Index, the boy or girl whose Strength Index equals the norm for his or her age and weight has a Physical Fitness Index of 100; this, then, is a median score based on sex, age, and weight. A lower score of 85 is at the first quartile according to the norms; and a higher score of 115 is at the third quartile. Thus, these variations from average may be interpreted.

Commonly used in physical education, also, are scoring scales based upon absolute performances, rather than relative performances as above. A little used scale is the percentile, which gives the percentage of individuals scoring below points on the scale in the sample upon which the scale was constructed. Thus, 50 per cent score below the 50th percentile, 27 per cent below the 27th percentile, etc. While easily constructed and readily understood, this scale has the disadvantage of unequal values for differences in scale points. Actually, the percentile scale is crowded largely around the mean performance, approximately with two-thirds of the scale within the middle one-third of the distribution.

Scales based upon standard deviation values of normal distributions [9] have been used extensively in health and physical education. Four of these are generally recognized: standard score, T-scale, sigma-scale, and Hull-scale. In the standard-score scale, the mean is zero; the other scores are expressed in terms of plus and minus standard-deviation distances from the mean. Thus, a score of -1.5 is 1.5 standard deviations below the mean. For the other three scales, the mean is 50; they differ in the positions of 0 and 100. Zero and 100 in the T-scale are minus and plus five standard deviations from the mean; for the sigma and Hull-scales, these distances are three and 3.5 standard deviations below and above the mean respectively.

There are strong advocates of certain of these scales. Montoye [10] has pleaded the case for the percentile scale largely on the grounds that it is easily understood. Miller [11] has advanced the standard score as the logical scale, as it provides for an unlimited distribution especially necessary in physical education where zero and ultimate performances are unknown. Massey [12] countered by argu-

---

[9] The construction of these scales is presented in Appendix A.

[10] Henry J. Montoye, "A Plea for the Percentile Rank in Physical Education," *The Physical Educator*, Vol. VIII, No. 4 (December 1951), p. 112.

[11] Kenneth D. Miller, "A Plea for the Standard Score in Physical Education," The Physical Educator, Vol. VIII, No. 2, (May 1951), p. 49.

[12] Benjamin H. Massey, "The Use of T-scores in Physical Education," *The Physical Educator*, Vol. X, No. 1 (March 1953), p. 20.

ing the case for the T-scale, indicating that its spread of five standard deviations is adequate for any reasonably normal distribution and that its understanding is relatively easy to master. It is true that occasional high or low scores will exceed the sigma and Hull scales. On the other hand, the ends of the T-scale are seldom used, as approximately 99.5 per cent of the cases in a normal distribution will fall between T-scores of 20 and 80.

Norm charts themselves must be evaluated, too, to determine their propriety. Several general evaluative factors are discussed briefly below to indicate the nature of this process.

1. Sampling procedures for the construction of norms should be based upon a wide distribution of the population. In physical education, quite frequently, such samples are definitely limited to rather small geographical areas. Typically, researchers have been restricted to their own general location in the collection of test data. To attempt a broader sampling has its hazards. Not only is it costly; it would depend upon the utilization of many testers. The proper instruction and training of such testers in order to obtain comparable results are particularly difficult where performance tests are concerned.

2. The testing sample should be representative of the population for which the test is intended. For example, data for skill test norms collected from athletes would be representative of athletes, but not of the population as a whole. Norms for weight charts based upon boys and girls residing in favored neighborhoods might not properly reflect the status of all classes of children.

3. Norms should be used for the specific groups for which they are prepared. As an illustration, the Dyer Tennis Test was originally constructed for college women and the norms were based upon a sampling of women in a number of colleges. To use these norms, therefore, for college men, or for any other group, would be definitely inappropriate and misleading.

4. The normality of each test item should be known before norm charts are constructed. The curve of normal distribution has been accepted so universally in test construction that frequently its essential characteristics are overlooked. Certain types of test data are not normally distributed in specified populations, and norms, such as sigma, Hull, and T-scales, based on the assumption that they

are, may be fallacious. For example, Ehrlich [13] found that, when male freshman students at a single institution were tested on the following items, the scores were positively skewed: 100-yard dash, Cozens' maze run, chins, dips, bar vault, and bar snap. Cozens and associates recognized this problem in the construction of their achievement scales, and corrected the process of establishing norms when data were found to depart from normality.

5. Norms for standard tests should be based upon a relatively large number of cases. An arbitrary assignment of a specific number for this purpose is impossible, however, as the reliability of the sample depends in part upon the variability of the test data, i.e., the range of scores in nature for the element being tested. The greater the variability of scores, the larger the number required to reduce the standard error of estimate to a negligible quantity. To illustrate: The heights of individuals in a defined population do not vary so greatly as weight or strength for the same population, and, as a consequence, in the development of norms they will vary within narrower limits.[14] The possibility of securing reliable norms for this trait is much better, therefore, and can be accomplished with a smaller sample of the population.

Economy of Tests

In considering the economy of tests, two factors should be kept in mind: (1) money costs, and (2) time required of subjects and testers. Other things being equal, of course, tests costing little in money and time should be used. Thus, the cost of apparatus may be a prohibitory factor in the use of certain tests in schools. For example, this is the chief reason why the X-ray and basal metabolism tests are not generally used. Cost, however, should not be the major consideration, but rather the value of the test in the physical education program. The cost of certain types of testing apparatus may be justified in the light of the value received.

The amount of time required for administering tests, as well as

---

[13] Gerald Ehrlich, "An Analysis of the Mathematical Curves Underlying Some Physical Education Test Items," *Research Quarterly*, Vol. XVII, No. 4 (December 1946), p. 270.

[14] Perhaps it should be added that this is true for absolute variability, but is not necessarily so for relative variability, i.e., the ratio of variability to its measure of central tendency.

the energy and degree of effort required, is an important factor in test economy. It has been estimated by various authorities that one-tenth of program time spent in testing is justifiable. Consequently, tests that may be quickly administered are preferable. One fault of many skill tests, for example, is that they require a great deal of time to give. The physical educator, however, should not form too hasty conclusions as to the amount of time required to administer certain tests, as many tests that appear difficult and time-consuming can be administered economically if proper organization techniques are employed.

Objective Written Examinations

Objective written examinations have not been utilized in physical education nearly so widely as in general education. However, such tests have been prepared to determine the amount of information acquired and the understanding developed in health education and in the rules, techniques, and strategy of certain sports.[15] The procedures for constructing tests of this sort differ somewhat from those employed with the more generally used skill and performance tests. Also, some physical educators prefer to construct locally the written tests they use; a distinct advantage of this procedure is that it permits adaptation to local needs, local course content, and specific types of teaching. A general understanding of the precautions to be taken in constructing such "homemade" tests and of the techniques employed in this type of test construction should therefore be beneficial to the physical educator.

Types of Examination Questions

Too frequently in practice, objective written examinations have taken the form of true-false statements exclusively. Consequently, in the minds of many the true-false test is "the" objective test. Actually, there are many types of written objective tests. These may be classified into two general categories: (1) *recognition*, including such types as true-false, multiple-choice, and matching; and (2) *recall*, including simple recall and completion. Several of these test forms are discussed briefly below.

Coupled with the overemphasis on true-false tests has been their

---

[15] See Chap. 15.

careless construction and use, resulting in a misunderstanding of the true potentialities of objective written tests in general and a reluctance to use them in educational practice. Actually these tests, when properly used, may be adapted to many types of thought reactions, such as memory, application of principles, reasoning, judgment, discrimination, and problem-solving.

True-false. In this common type of objective written test, a statement is made which the student marks as true or false. The following examples are taken from Heath and Rodgers' Soccer Knowledge Test [16] for fifth- and sixth-grade boys:

The letters T and F have been placed before each statement given. Draw a circle around the letter T if the statement is TRUE; and around the letter F if the statement is FALSE or PARTIALLY FALSE. *Do not guess.* You will be penalized for each statement marked incorrectly by taking one point or credit from the number of statements marked correctly.

Examples are given below. Read them carefully and then proceed to answer the others in like manner.

T F Soccer is a game in which there is much running.
    (*Answer:* Draw circle around T.)
T F In playing soccer, the ball is thrown from one player to another.
    (*Answer:* Draw circle around F.)
T F   1. The game is begun by a kick-off from center by the center forward in the direction of the field of play.
T F 13. The center halfback plays behind the center forward for support on the attack.
T F 46. Toe kicks send the ball straight along the ground.
T F 81. Fullbacks should seldom dribble the ball.

Unusual care must be exercised in phrasing true-false statements so that their meanings are clear without obvious clues to their answers. The following specific suggestions should be followed in constructing this type of test:

1. Avoid ambiguous statements.

2. Avoid tricky questions.

3. Do not use double negatives; in fact, avoid negative statements as much as possible.

4. Use *all* or *never* statements very cautiously.

5. Omit statements that express opinionated views, at least without definite reference to source.

---

[16] Marjorie L. Heath and Elizabeth G. Rodgers, "A Study in the Use of Knowledge and Skill Tests in Soccer," *Research Quarterly*, Vol. III, No. 4 (December 1932), p. 33.

6. Avoid statements that are partly true and partly false.
7. Utilize short, concise statements as much as possible.
8. Avoid trivial and meaningless items.

Scoring may be done by counting the number of statements answered correctly or by subtracting the number of wrong answers from the number right ("rights minus wrongs"). The latter method was devised to discourage guessing and is widely used. Actually, for college students at least, there is apparently little difference in the relative score received. Keislar [17] obtained correlations of .96 and .99 between the way the same college students answered true-false questions scored by number right and rights minus wrongs. Votaw [18] found that submissive students under "Do not guess" instructions, with right minus wrongs scoring, omitted more items than did ascendent students. Soderquist [19] and Swineford [20] also indicate the possibility that "Do not guess" instructions result in the measurement of some personality variable, such as "tendency to gamble."

In scoring, a copy of the test may be pasted upon cardboard and the T's and F's representing the correct answers punched out. When this key is placed over the student's paper, the number of correct answers can be determined quickly by counting.

True-false statements can be used to test for factual information, for the application of general principles, and for reasoning. They are also well adapted to testing the persistence of popular misconceptions and superstitions.

Multiple-choice. In the multiple-choice form, a statement or question is given with three or more responses, only one of which is correct or definitely better than the others. Examples of this type of question are:

Read each question carefully. Select the one item which best answers the question. Put the number of that item selected in the space in front of the question.

---

[17] Evan R. Keislar, "Test Instructions and Scoring Methods in True-False Tests," *Journal of Experimental Education,* Vol. XXI, No. 3 (March 1953), p. 243.

[18] David F. Votaw, "The Effect of Do-Not-Guess Instructions upon the Validity of True-False or Multiple-Choice Tests," *Journal of Educational Psychology,* Vol. XXVI, No. 9 (December 1936), p. 698.

[19] Harold O. Soderquist, "A New Method of Weighting Scores in a True-False Test," *Journal of Educational Research,* Vol. XXX, No. 4 (December 1936), p. 290.

[20] Frances Swineford, "The Measurement of a Personality Trait," *Journal of Educational Psychology,* Vol. XXIX, No. 4 (April 1938), p. 295.

_____ 4. In which direction is the force applied in any swim stroke? (1) In the direction in which the swimmer is moving, (2) at right angles to the direction in which the swimmer is moving, (3) opposite to the direction in which the swimmer is moving, (4) toward the surface of the water, (5) toward the bottom of the pool.

_____29. If a poor swimmer stands up and unexpectedly finds herself in deep water, how is she most likely to be successful in taking care of herself? (1) By trying to assume a face float, (2) by trying to assume a back float, (3) by trying a side stroke, (4) by exhaling, (5) by keeping her arms high in the water to pull with.[21]

In preparing multiple-choice questions, care should be taken to avoid the inclusion of irrelevant or superficial clues and to measure other than memorized knowledge. Following are suggestions for preparing appropriate statements of this type:

1. Use four, and preferably five, choices whenever possible.

2. Make all choices plausible; if obviously wrong choices are included, the real thinking situation is reduced accordingly.

3. Be sure only one of the choices is correct.

4. Keep the choices short where possible.

5. Word questions simply.

6. Scatter the position of the correct choices and avoid any set pattern.

7. Use unfamiliar phrasing rather than that out of the text.

8. Avoid statements acknowledged to be disputed by authorities, or which vary from time to time, unless authority or time is stated.

9. Score by counting the number of correct responses.

The multiple-choice type of test is regarded as one of the most useful of the test forms. It is especially valuable in testing judgment, reasoning ability, and fine discrimination between various shades of meaning.

Matching. Two varieties of matching questions are as follows: (1) *sentence completion matching*, in which completion of a sentence is required by matching it with a column of items, only one being chosen as correct; and (2) *column matching*, in which words, sentences, numbers, or phrases arranged in two opposite columns are matched. In these instances, the student merely shows which

---

[21] M. Gladys Scott, "Achievement Examination for Elementary and Intermediate Swimming Classes," *Research Quarterly*, Vol. XI, No. 2 (May 1940), p. 100.

items go together. Examples of matching questions from the Hewitt tennis test [22] are as follows:

Column A		Column B
1. Out	15. Allison	44. Knocking the ball over the head of the opponent. ....
2. Kill	16. Let	
3. Fifteen All	17. Chop	45. Ball hits net on the serve and falls into the correct service court. ....
4. Game	18. Continue Play	
5. Advantage Receiver	19. Reverse Ball	
	20. Fault	46. Both sides winning one point. ....
6. Cahill	21. Footfault	47. Winning point after deuce while serving. ....
7. Tilden	22. Lenglen	
8. Smash	23. Service Line	48. American man tennis player who was famous for his cannon ball service and is now a leading professional. ....
9. Jacobs	24. Perry	
10. Advantage Server	25. Lob	
	26. Permissible	
11. Moody	27. Let	49. Ball spinning backward to its flight. ....
12. Love All	28. Service	
13. Vines	29. Deuce	50. Any served ball hitting outside legal boundary. ....
14. Thirty All		

Scoring: Number right

Score. . . . .

The following suggestions should prove helpful in constructing matching-type questions:

1. Include more items among the choices, so that they may act as distracters: all distracters, however, should make sense.

2. Be sure that only one word in the choices applies to each situation.

3. Alphabetize the choices and arrange dates chronologically. (*Note:* In the illustration above, this rule is not followed.)

4. Have one of the lists to be matched composed of single words, numerals, or brief phrases.

5. Score by counting the number of correct answers.

The matching type of objective written examination has definite limitations. It is not well adapted to the measurement of understanding. It is likely to include irrelevant clues to the correct response, and, unless carefully made, is time-consuming in its administration. It is useful, however, in checking on precise information,

---

[22] Jack E. Hewitt, "Comprehensive Tennis Knowledge Test," *Research Quarterly,* Vol. VIII, No. 3 (October 1937), p. 74.

such as events, places, and dates; terms, definitions, and rules; and tools, equipment, and facilities and their use.

Simple recall. The simple recall test is one in which the answer is not suggested but must be recalled. There are three main forms of this test, as follows: (1) short answers; (2) test items that require identification or specific information; and (3) a word or phrase requiring definition. This test form permits the use of maps or diagrams with numbers to indicate the parts to be identified. The following examples of simple recall questions are again taken from the Hewitt Comprehensive Tennis Knowledge Test: [23]

Directions. Enumerate the names for the following lines and spaces of a tennis court.

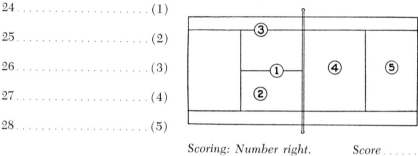

24 . . . . (1)

25 . . . . (2)

26 . . . . (3)

27 . . . . (4)

28 . . . . (5)

Scoring: Number right.   *Score* . . . . . .

Following are suggestions to be observed in constructing simple recall questions:

1. State the test items so that the answer can be given briefly and concisely.

2. As a general rule, use direct questions rather than statements.

3. Allow, in the key, for different ways in which the question can be answered.

4. Preferably, provide numbered spaces for responses in a column on the right, the numbers to correspond with the recall items.

5. Make minimum use of textbook language.

6. Score by counting the number of correct answers.

The simple recall type of question is particularly valuable in the identification of various items and in problem-solving requiring computation. Many of the questions included in the essay-type examination may be broken into recall questions.

---

[23] Jack E. Hewitt, *op. cit.*

Completion. In the completion test, sentences are given in which certain important words or phrases have been omitted, the resulting blanks to be filled in by the pupils. Such sentences may be disconnected or organized into a paragraph. In these questions, recall rather than recognition is required. Hewitt's tennis test [24] supplies the questions illustrated below:

Directions. In each statement, fill in the space or spaces with the proper word:

23. Hitting a ball directly overhead with attempt "to kill" is called a . . . .
25. All balls hitting boundary lines are . . . .
28. A cut makes the ball spin . . . .
31. Should a ball become broken in hitting, a . . . . is called.

Scoring: Number right. Score . . . .

The greatest difficulty in preparing this form is to make the sentences definite and clear. Suggestions for their construction are as follows:

1. Supply sufficient information so that the meaning of the sentence is clear to the reader.

2. Avoid phrasing the sentences so that the answer is perfectly obvious.

3. Use only two or three blanks in any one sentence; avoid over-mutilated statements.

4. Make such blanks as will call for one correct word or phrase, and not for a large number of similar words and phrases.

5. Provide blanks for all key words and omit blanks for those that are unimportant, such as *a, an,* and *the.*

6. Allow in the key for all different answers that may be used correctly, such as synonyms, and so forth.

7. Compose sentences around certain key words or phrases; avoid lifting sentences from the text.

8. Arrange, if desired, spaces for pupils' answers in a column at the right of the sentence; in this case, number the blanks and the spaces to correspond.

9. Score by counting the number of correct responses.

The completion type of objective written examination is useful in determining the amount of factual information known and in problem-solving.

---

[24] Jack E. Hewitt, *op. cit.*

Evaluation of Written Tests

The requirements of a satisfactory objective written examination are the same and are fully as necessary as for the various performance tests usually employed in physical education. Thus, the test must be valid; it must be reliable; it must be objective; it must have norms; it must be economical; and it must contribute toward the realization of physical education objectives. The techniques for determining these factors, especially the validity and accuracy of such tests, however, vary somewhat.

Validity. In educational practice, the validity of written tests is determined by two well-established methods, both of which should be employed in validating tests. These methods are: (1) curricular or content validity, and (2) statistical validity. To determine *curricular validity*, it is necessary to define carefully the extent of the test and then to insure that this range covers the course content. Sources of validity, therefore, would include courses of study, textbooks, and analyses of examination questions. If a standardized test for nation-wide use is being constructed, the sources must embrace a broader base, representing a cross section of practice in the subject throughout the country. Frequently, tests of this sort include understanding of materials only and have been based upon the memorizing of facts and familiarity with a body of knowledge. Recently constructed tests, however, have included attempts to test also the mental reactions desired in the course. The evaluation of curricular validity depends upon a study of the subject matter that the test aims to cover and also the procedures followed in constructing the test. Because of this indefiniteness, such test evaluation is very difficult to make.

Statistical validity may be determined by relating the test to other evidence of the quality being measured, such as other valid tests, the opinions of experts in the specific field of the tests, or pupil grades in the subject. Such criteria are only fairly adequate because of their admittedly inadequate subjectivity.

Statistical validity, however, may take another form—that of determining the difficulty and discriminative value of each item in the test. This is known as *item validity*. Item validity is determined by computing the percentage of pupils passing each item; the fewer passing the item, the more difficult the question, provided, of course, that the item itself is satisfactory and correctly phrased. For item discrimination, an appreciably larger percentage of the more competent pupils than of the less competent in a grade should answer it correctly, and an appreciably larger percentage of pupils in any grade should answer it correctly than in the next lower grade. Item discrimination may also be shown by comparing the percentage of correct answers on the item given by the upper third or fourth of the group on the entire test with the percentage of correct answers given by the lowest third or fourth. In all instances, items showing little or no discrimination, or those that show a percentage of successes in favor of the poor groups or the lower grades, should be either eliminated or examined for vagueness and ambiguity and reworded.

Various indices of discrimination are in use. Among these is the Flanagan technique [25] based upon a discrimination of test items as shown by the variance in the scores of the upper and of the lower 27 per cent from the total score made on the test. It is a simple method to operate, as a conversion table is available.[26]

Items which are too difficult or too easy are apt to have poor discriminatory value. When the test is intended to cover more than one school grade, a good rule to follow is to choose items that vary in difficulty rating from just above zero to close to 100 per cent, with the average at approximately 50 per cent. Items for a test covering a narrow range, as would be the case in many written tests on physical activities discriminate best when their difficulty is such that each item is passed by at least 50 per cent of the pupils in the group.[27] In any event, questions missed by all students or answered correctly by all students are of no differentiation value and should be eliminated. It is frequently desirable to establish difficulty limits. Such limits may be set at any desired point. In health and physical education, these limits have been variously established at 10 and 90

[25] John C. Flanagan, "General Considerations in the Selection of Test Items and a Short Method of Estimating the Product-Moment Coefficient from Data at the Tails of a Distribution," *Journal of Educational Psychology*, Vol. XXX, No. 9 (December 1939), p. 674.

[26] This table will also be found in M. Gladys Scott *et al.*, "Test Construction and Analysis Methods," Chapter 16 of *Research Methods Applied to Health, Physical Education, and Recreation* (Washington: American Association for Health, Physical Education, and Recreation, 1949), pp. 402-404.

[27] Clay C. Ross, *Measurement in Today's Schools* (Englewood Cliffs, N.J.: Prentice-Hall, Inc., 1941), p. 87.

per cent (i.e., by dropping those questions answered by less than 10 per cent and by more than 90 per cent), 7 and 93 per cent, and 5 and 95 per cent.

Accuracy. The reliability of objective written tests may be determined in several different ways, as follows:

(1) *Correlation between equivalent forms of the test.* Frequently, in constructing objective written tests, two or more equivalent forms of the test may be prepared so that the test may be administered repeatedly without duplication of the questions. If the two forms actually are comparable, it is possible to give both forms to the same subjects and correlate the results. Correlational standards of reliability coefficients are the same as discussed previously in this chapter.

(2) *Correlation between chance halves.* When only one form of the test is available, coefficients of correlation may be computed between odd- and even-numbered items on the test. The resulting correlation, however, would be for one-half of the test. Since the length of the test affects its reliability, the correlation must be corrected for the full length of the test. This is done by use of the Brown-Spearman prophecy formula.[28]

(3) *Correlation between repeated tests.* This procedure is the one generally followed in determining the reliability of physical performance tests. It is not so satisfactory with written tests, as pupils will usually improve their scores on the repeated test. The correlation, however, does show the degree of agreement between the two sets of scores, although the average scores of the two groups, and perhaps their variability, will differ.

Construction of "homemade" tests. The physical educator may wish to construct his own objective written tests in order to center his examination procedures around his own course of study. The following steps may be found helpful in preparing these tests:

1. Outline the scope of the proposed examination, listing the important topics and the types of thought reactions to be tested.

2. Under each topic, list the most significant items to be included.

3. Compose test items, selecting the type of objective form best

---

[28] See Appendix A, "Elementary Statistics," for an explanation of the Brown-Spearman prophecy formula.

suited for each. Keep items of the same objective form together; this may be done while composing by using separate sheets of paper for each type.

4. Arrange test items in approximate order of difficulty.

5. Give clear directions for taking the various test types.

6. Specify the scoring procedure for each test type.

7. Prepare scoring key.

8. Compute the reliability of the test.

SELECTED REFERENCES

McCloy, C. H., *Tests and Measurements in Health and Physical Education*, Chapter II. New York: F. S. Crofts and Company, 1939.

Richardson, M. W., J. T. Russell, J. M. Stalnaker, and L. L. Thurstone, *Manual of Examination Methods*. Chicago: University of Chicago Bookstore, 1933.

Rogers, Frederick Rand, *Fundamental Administrative Measures in Physical Education*, Chapter II. Newton, Mass.: The Pleiades Company, 1932.

Ross, Clay C., *Measurement in Today's Schools*. Englewood Cliffs, N.J.: Prentice-Hall, Inc., 1941.

Ruch, G. M., and George D. Stoddard, *Tests and Measurements in High School Instruction*. Yonkers-on-Hudson, N. Y.: World Book Company, 1927.

Scott, M. Gladys, *et al.*, "Test Construction and Analysis Methods," Chap. 16, of *Research Methods Applied to Health, Physical Education, and Recreation*. Washington: American Association for Health, Physical Education, and Recreation, 1949.

PART TWO

Physical Fitness

CHAPTER THREE

Education and Fitness

In Chapter 1, "physical fitness" was defined as a positive quality, extending on a scale from death to "abundant life." Another concept regards a person's fitness as his "distance from death."[1] All living individuals have some degree of physical fitness; and this degree may be interpreted in terms of their capacity for performance and their endurance in physical activities. Thus, physical fitness is a qualitative element, with many, many variations among individuals and even within each individual at different times of life. It should not be considered in the two categories "sick" and "well," as, unfortunately, is so generally done.

The physician traditionally and properly is concerned primarily with deficiencies likely to impair organic function and to cause early death; and medical practitioners rightly devote themselves largely to protecting the organism from disease and to prolonging life. The physical educator, on the other hand, accepts the individual free from organic drains and handicapping defects—*his essential starting point if he is to be effective*—and, through his activity program, develops a body that is physically strong and capable of prolonged effort without efficiency-destroying fatigue.

In our "push-button" society, people frequently question the need for much physical fitness, as doing one's job many times requires only a minimum of physical strength and endurance. The present

---

[1] Arthur H. Steinhaus, "Health and Physical Fitness from the Standpoint of the Physiologist," *Journal of Health and Physical Education,* Vol. VII, No. 4 (April 1936), p. 224.

55

chapter will show the relationship of physical exercise—the physical educator's stock in trade—to physical fitness and will indicate the importance of exercise as applied to this objective.[2]

The Physical in Physical Education

Little doubt exists today that the right kind and amount of exercise will develop muscular strength and endurance, body flexibility, and circulatory-respiratory endurance. In fact, properly directed exercise is the only known means for acquiring the ability to engage in tasks demanding sustained physical effort. However, it is gratifying to demonstrate the presence of such benefits as a consequence of existing physical education programs.

Whittle [3] studied two groups of 81 twelve-year-old boys who were comparable in such maturity factors as chronological age, skeletal age, weight, height, and Wetzel developmental level. One group of these boys had participated for at least three years in good physical education programs; the other had little or no physical education in elementary school. Pronounced differences were found between the two groups in various affective factors. The means on the Rogers Physical Fitness Index (PFI) test [4] for the boys in the good and poor physical education programs were 121 and 103 respectively. The boys in the good programs also produced higher means on the Metheny-Johnson Test of Motor "Educability," the Indiana Motor Fitness Test, and the vertical jump.

A further interesting disclosure of the Whittle study was that boys in each group who participated a "lot" in out-of-class physical activity showed strong superiority over those who participated a "little." Again, in terms of the PFI tests, a very high mean of 132 was scored by those participating a lot in outside activity from the good programs, while the mean for those engaging a little was 109. Of special import for those interested in the development of strong

---

[2] This is in accordance with the general plan of the book to present a separate chapter to introduce measurement as applied to the objectives of physical education.

[3] H. Douglas Whittle, "Effects of Elementary School Physical Education upon Some Aspects of Physical, Motor, and Personality Development of Boys Twelve Years of Age," Microcarded Ph.D. Dissertation, University of Oregon, 1956.

[4] The Physical Fitness Index is presented in Chapter 8. A PFI of 100 is the median for the test; scores of 85 and 115 reflect the first and third quartiles respectively.

athletic programs is the comparison between the boys from both programs who participated a lot in out-of-class activities. The PFI means were 132 and 116 for the boys in the good and poor programs respectively. Comparable results were obtained for other tests included in the study.

Utilizing PFI tests, Clarke [5] reported that male students entering the University of Oregon with four years of high school physical education had a higher average than did those entering with two years or less. In another study by the same investigator,[6] the results of the Oregon Pilot Physical Fitness Project were presented. In this project, 100 boys and 100 girls in each of eleven high schools were tested with the PFI test before and after a three-months physical fitness program. The median PFI for all boys increased 10 points, from 98 to 108; the median PFI increase for all girls was 13 points, from 93 to 106. A number of other schools elsewhere have reported similar results.

Shaffer [7] reduced failures on the Kraus-Weber Test of Minimum Muscular Fitness to a marked degree in a few weeks through body and conditioning exercises. Forty-two per cent of 2,281 junior high school boys and girls in Johnstown, Pennsylvania, failed one or more of the six Kraus-Weber test items in September; in November, the failures dropped to 8 per cent. At the end of the term, only 4 per cent failed one or more of the test items.

Organic Soundness

Kraus and associates [8] state: "Study, treatment and prevention of physical inactivity as an important etiological factor of many disabling diseases is imperative for our national welfare." In *Hypokinetic Disease*,[9] such information as the following was presented as gleaned from many sources: coronary heart disease is twice as fre-

---

[5] H. Harrison Clarke, "Physical Fitness of University of Oregon Male Freshmen," *Physical Fitness News Letter*, No. 4, University of Oregon, (March 1955).

[6] H. Harrison Clarke, "Oregon Pilot Physical Fitness Project," *The Physical Educator*, Vol. XIV, No. 2 (May 1957), p. 55.

[7] Gertrude Shaffer, "Editor's Mail," *Journal of Health, Physical Education, and Recreation*, Vol. XXVIII, No. 2 (February 1957), p. 6.

[8] Hans Kraus, *et al.*, *Hypokinetic Disease: Role of Inactivity in Production of Disease* (New York: Institute for Physical Medicine and Rehabilitation, New York University-Bellevue Medical Center).

[9] *Loc. cit.*

quent in the sedentary as in the active; other diseases more frequent in the sedentary than in the active are diabetes, duodenal ulcer, and other internal and surgical conditions; 80 per cent of low back pain is due to lack of adequate physical activity; lack of physical exercise goes parallel with emotional difficulties; the physically active show better adaptability to stress, less neuromuscular tension, and lesser fatigability; active individuals age later, do not tend toward absolute and relative overweight, have lower blood pressure, are stronger and more flexible, and have greater breathing capacity and lower pulse rate.

Morris and Raffle [10] studied the incidence of coronary heart disease among 25,000 drivers and conductors, aged 35 to 64 years, of the red busses, trams, and trolley busses of the London (England) Transport Executive. Nearly all the conductors' work was on double-decker vehicles, which required considerable physical activity as contrasted with the drivers' relative physical inactivity. The standard mortality rate per 1,000 from coronary heart attack was at least twice as high for the sedentary drivers at three days, three months, and three years after the onset of the first clinical episode. As a consequence of these and other observations, the authors advanced the following hypothesis: "That men in physically active jobs have a lower incidence of coronary heart disease in middle age than men in physically inactive jobs. Most important, the disease is not so severe in physically active workers, tending to present first in them an angina pectoris and other relatively benign forms, and to have a smaller case fatality and a lower mortality rate."

Luongo [11] studied the health habits of adults who had suffered heart attacks. The evidence showed that sedentary living and poor health habits were the real culprits and not hard work, over exercise, or occupational stress. The author contended that proper health habits, including proper nutrition and adequate exercise, should be carried on into middle and old age. Dr. Paul Dudley White [12] prescribed exercise for President Dwight D. Eisenhower following his

10 J. N. Morris and P. A. B. Raffle, "Coronary Heart Disease in Transport Workers," *British Journal of Industrial Medicine*, Vol. XI (October 1954), p. 260.

11 Edward P. Luongo, "Health Habits and Heart Disease," *Journal of the American Medical Association*, Vol. CLXII (November 10, 1956), p. 1021.

12 "Exercise: What It Does for Ike and What It Can Do for You," *U.S. News and World Report* (August 23, 1957), p. 50.

heart attack; he has written: "Proper exercise is as essential to good health as eating and sleeping." [13]

Zankel and others [14] obtained Physical Fitness Indices of diabetic patients in the Crile Veterans Administration Hospital, Cleveland, Ohio. The median PFI score was 53. After an average 33-day period of treatment, the median improvement was 20 per cent. In another study,[15] 19 additional diabetic patients were treated from nine to 60 days. Nine of these patients received regular supervised exercise and ten did not. The patients receiving exercise showed an average PFI increase of 12 points, or 29 per cent; the patients not receiving exercise showed an average decrease of 2, or −3.7 per cent. Thus, proper diet and insulin therapy alone were not adequate to improve the level of strength of diabetic patients; an increase in strength occurred only when exercise was included in the treatment regime.

Gallagher [16] has stressed the value of athletics and other physical activities in the adolescent's development and the frequency with which strengthening activity rather than rest is the appropriate recommendation when the person is below par in health. For medical practice, he states: "The evaluation of strength, the determination of the disproportion between strength and probable stress, and the increase of strength through exercise can at times constitute better management than a regime which focuses upon the ailment, emphasizes rest, and ignores the facts regarding strength development in exercise." During World War II in the hospitals and convalescent centers of the Army, Navy, and Air Force and since the war in Veterans Administration and other hospitals, exercise was and is being used extensively in speeding the recovery of patients. Early ambulation, the basis of which is exercise, is now a standard procedure following surgery of many kinds; even with extensive

---

[13] Paul Dudley White, "Man's Best Medicine," *New York Times Magazine* (June 23, 1957).

[14] H. T. Zankel, *et al.*, "The Physical Fitness Index in Diabetic Patients," *Journal of the Association for Physical and Mental Rehabilitation,* Vol. X, No. 1 (January-February 1956), p. 14.

[15] H. T. Zankel, *et al.*, "Physical Fitness Index Studies (PFI) in Hospitalized Diabetic Patients," *Archives of Physical Medicine and Rehabilitation,* Vol. XXXVIII, No. 4 (April 1957), p. 250.

[16] J. Roswell Gallagher, "Rest and Restriction," *American Journal of Public Health,* Vol. XLVI (November 1956), p. 1424.

abdominal surgery, the patient is frequently out of bed within 24 hours after the operation.

MENTAL ALERTNESS

A number of researches support the contention that physical fitness is related to mental achievements. The great psychologist, L. M. Terman, concluded after 25 years of studying intellectually gifted children that: "The results of the physical measurements and the medical examinations provide a striking contrast to the popular stereotype of the child prodigy, so commonly predicted as a pathetic creature, over-serious, undersized, sickly, hollow-chested, nervously tense, and bespectacled. There are gifted children who bear some resemblance to this stereotype, but the truth is that almost every element in the picture, except the last, is less characteristic of the gifted child than of the mentally average." [17] In Terman's initial monumental study,[18] when his gifted subjects were young, symptoms of general weakness were reported by the school nearly 30 per cent less frequently for the gifted than for the control group.

Jarman [19] investigated the academic achievement of boys at ages nine, twelve, and fifteen years, who had high and low scores on the Strength Index and the Physical Fitness Index. For each age and for each test, the high and low groups were equated by Intelligence quotients. Quite generally, the boys with the high scores on each of these physical tests had significantly superior grade-point averages in their class work and significantly higher means on standard scholastic achievement tests. Earlier, Rogers [20] studied two groups of Stanford University men with nearly equal I.Q. averages, but differing in average muscular strength. The scholarship of the high strength group (I.Q. = 107) was considerably superior to the low strength group (I.Q. = 111).

[17] Lewis M. Terman, Ed., *Genetic Studies of Genius. IV. The Gifted Child Grows Up* (Stanford: Stanford University Press, 1947), p. 24.

[18] Lewis M. Terman, ed., *Genetic Studies of Genius. I. Mental and Physical Traits of a Thousand Gifted Children* (Stanford: Stanford University Press, 1925), p. 211.

[19] Boyd Jarman, "Academic Achievement of Boys Nine, Twelve, and Fifteen Years of Age as Related to Physical Performances," Master's Thesis, University of Oregon, 1959.

[20] F. R. Rogers, "The Scholarship of Athletes," Master's Thesis, Stanford University, 1922.

Page [21] found that 83 per cent of the freshman male students dismissed from Syracuse University because of low grades had Physical Fitness Indices below 100; 39 per cent had PFI's below 85. These same students had scholastic aptitude scores well above the average; their median score was at the 72nd percentile. Coefield and McCollum [22] at the University of Oregon found that the 78 male freshmen with lowest PFI's during the 1954 fall term were definitely low in scholastic accomplishment, as compared with all freshmen at the university. As in Page's study, the low fitness students were above average in scholastic aptitude.

In the 1941 annual report of the Brookline, Massachusetts, public schools,[23] the average PFI for the 126 boys whose names appeared on the high school scholarship role was 117; thus, the PFI's of these honor-roll boys generally exceeded the score of 115, which is typically the third quartile for normal populations. Studies in Manchester, England,[24] revealed that only 2.4 per cent of students with good scholarship were below the average in physique, as evidenced by body measurements, but that 39.7 per cent with poor scholarship were physically below the average.

Some studies have reported little or no relationship between physical measures and mental achievement.[25,26] These investigations, however, have been correlational in nature and have ignored the levels of intelligence of the subjects. By contrast, in the studies showing physical-mental relationships, it is essential to recognize that certain of these considered only the low level of fitness and that others equated the groups in accordance with the intelligence of the subjects.

As a consequence of this type of evidence, it may be contended

---

[21] C. Getty Page, "Case Studies of College Men with Low Physical Fitness Indices," Master's Thesis, Syracuse University, 1940.

[22] John R. Coefield and Robert H. McCollum, "A Case Study Report of 78 University Freshman Men with Low Physical Fitness Indices," Microcarded Master's Thesis, University of Oregon, 1955.

[23] "Reports of the School Committee and Superintendent of Schools of Brookline, Massachusetts," Year Ending December 31, 1941.

[24] David K. Brace, "Some Objective Evidence of the Value of Physical Education," *Journal of Health and Physical Education*, Vol. IV, No. 4 (April 1933), p. 38.

[25] Robert R. Jorgensen, "The Relationship of Physical Fitness to Optimum Scholastic Achievement," Master of Science Thesis, State College of Washington, 1955.

[26] Robert J. Weber, "A Study of the Relationship of Physical Fitness to Success in School and to Personality," Doctor of Philosophy Dissertation, State University of Iowa, 1952.

that a person's general learning *potential* for a *given level of intelligence* is increased or decreased in accordance with his degree of physical fitness.[27] Thus, the individual is more prone to be physically and mentally alert, to be vigorous in his applications, and to suffer less from efficiency-destroying fatigue than when he is unfit.

SOCIAL ADJUSTMENT

Physically unfit boys and girls experience difficulty in day by day personal adjustments with others and in developing good social habits and attitudes. As a part of a longitudinal study of growth in adolescence at the Institute of Child Welfare, University of California, Berkeley,[28] scores on dynamometric strength tests were related to biological, social, and psychological characteristics. Among the findings were the following: (1) As compared with "dynamic" strength (dash, jump, throw), static dynamometric strength is more closely associated with biological growth, suggesting a dependence upon constitutional factors expressed in physical measurements and in physiological maturity. (2) Among boys, a positive relationship of strength to "prestige" traits is apparent, which is regarded as evidence of the role of physical prowess in the adolescent value system. (3) Superior strength in boys is part of a complex of physical characteristics valued highly during the adolescent period; the absence of this trait is a handicap which can be overcome only by strongly compensating personal traits in other areas also highly valued. (4) Boys high in strength tend to be well adjusted socially and psychologically; boys low in strength show a tendency toward social difficulties, feelings of inferiority, and other personal maladjustments.

In a study by Popp,[29] the PFI test was administered to approximately 100 sophomore boys at Marshfield High School, Coos Bay, Oregon. The 20 boys with the highest PFI's and the 20 boys with the lowest PFI's were arranged in a single alphabetical list. Five judges (principal, vice-principal, dean of boys, and two physical

---

[27] F. R. Rogers, "Rogers' Law of Learning Capacity," *Physical Fitness News Letter,* University of Oregon (January 31, 1955).

[28] Harold E. Jones, *Motor Performance and Growth* (Berkeley: University of California Press, 1949).

[29] James Popp, "Case Studies of Sophomore High School Boys with High and Low Physical Fitness Indices," Master of Science Thesis, University of Oregon, 1959.

educators) each independently selected the ten most desirable boys (those most nearly like sons they would like to have) and the ten most undesirable boys (those least like sons they would like to have). Sixteen boys were named by at least one judge in the "desirable" classification. Of these, 11, or 69 per cent, had high PFI's and five, or 31 per cent, had low PFI's. In selecting the "undesirable" boys, again 16 boys were chosen. Of this group, four, or 25 per cent, had high PFI's and 12, or 75 per cent, had low PFI's. Thus, the five judges, without knowledge of each boy's PFI, generally recognized in the boys with high scores on this test the many and varied traits they would like most to see in a son of their own.

Studies conducted at the United States Military Academy by Appleton [30] indicate that physical proficiency measures are useful predictors of non-academic aspects of military success, particularly at the lower range of motor fitness. Ninety per cent of applicants in the bottom 10 per cent on Academy fitness tests made below average cadets. A high positive correlation, curvilinear in nature, was found at the lower extreme of the physical ability range between entrance physical achievement and the ability to graduate from the Academy; this relationship was definitely apparent below the 12th percentile and increased in degree below this point. Furthermore, Appleton found that 12.9 per cent of the cadets in the lower seven per cent on the West Point motor fitness test needed psychiatric help; this percentage exceeded the number of cadets given psychiatric care from the upper 93 per cent on the physical efficiency test.

In a paper before the International Symposium of the Medicine and Physiology of Sports and Athletics at Helsinki, Finland, Cureton [31] reported that personality itself is responsive to physical training in view of the changes that can be made in the autonomic nervous system and in the cardiovascular state. He concluded that men are more energetic, more buoyant and optimistic, more action-minded, more playful, more aggressive—in general, they appear more extroverted and more healthful when they are physically trained than when they are physically untrained. And, as men go

[30] Lloyd O. Appleton, "The Relationship Between Physical Ability and Success at the United States Military Academy," Microcarded Doctor of Philosophy Dissertation, New York University, 1949.

[31] Thomas K. Cureton, "Physical Training Produces Important Changes, Psychologically and Physiologically," *Proceedings of the International Symposium of the Medicine and Physiology of Sports and Athletics at Helsinki,* 1951.

63

through progressive training, they tend to tackle harder and harder tasks; and they are able to work relatively harder and longer.

Need for Objective Tests

The physical educator is under a moral compulsion to select activities for, and to adapt methods in, conducting his program that will meet all the objectives of physical education: the physical, the social, and the cultural. The physical fitness objective, however, is basic, and all pupils should be assured of at least a minimum amount of this essential quality. Without this basic assurance, other phases of the program are ineffective. Consequently, definite steps should be taken to ascertain the physical fitness of each pupil in school and to institute individual remedial and developmental programs for those who require them—for those who are physically unfit.

But individual needs cannot be known accurately, nor can the effects of individual programs—*in fact, the effects of the general program as well*—be known without tests *and re-tests* of the individuals themselves. Therefore, measurement of physical fitness is essential for the physical educator in his attempt to improve the fitness of school children: to determine their status and to measure their progress. In fact, a knowledge of the physical fitness of boys and girls is the logical *starting point* for conducting effective physical education programs.

Measurement of general physical fitness by physical educators should include primarily tests of strength and endurance. In the following chapters, the measurement of these elements will be considered, as well as various specialized aspects of physical fitness, such as the medical examination, posture and foot tests, sensory tests, and the like.

Conclusion

In this chapter, it was not intended to present physical fitness as a panacea, as, obviously, there are many other important factors contributing to our various performances. However, evidence was provided to show that, *other things being equal,* we will be more effective as a consequence of an adequate level of physical fitness. We should have the strength and stamina to carry on the duties of the day without undue fatigue and with an ample reserve to enjoy leisure and to meet unusual situations and emergencies; we should realize in an adequate measure our capacity for physical activity as well as for mental accomplishments unhampered by efficiency-destroying fatigue. The functions of measurement are to determine the physical fitness status of boys and girls and to evaluate their progress toward adequate standards.

Selected References

Clarke, H. Harrison, "Physical Fitness Benefits: A Summary of Research," *Education*, Vol. LXXVIII, No. 8 (April 1958), p. 460.

Coefield, John R., and Robert H. McCollum, "A Case Study Report of 78 University of Oregon Freshman Men with Low Physical Fitness Indices." Microcarded Master's Thesis, University of Oregon, 1955.

Jones, Harold E., *Motor Performance and Growth*. Berkeley: University of California Press, 1949.

Kraus, Hans, *et al.*, *Hypokinetic Disease: Role of Inactivity in Production of Disease*. New York: Institute for Physical Medicine and Rehabilitation. New York University-Bellevue Medical Center.

Page, C. Getty, "Case Studies of College Men with Low Physical Fitness Indices," Master's Thesis, Syracuse University, 1940.

Whittle, H. Douglas, "Effects of Elementary School Physical Education upon Some Aspects of Physical, Motor, and Personality Development of Boys Twelve Years of Age," Microcarded Doctor of Philosophy Dissertation, University of Oregon, 1956.

CHAPTER FOUR

Medical and Sensory Tests

Fundamental to the physical fitness of the individual is the effectiveness of his physiological or organic functions. In considering the individual as a whole, it is readily recognized that all factors that influence his life also affect his organic system. This includes many things: the presence of disease and organic drains, the condition of the muscular system, the degree of emotional, psychological, and social adjustment, and so forth. In this chapter measures bearing directly on the organic system itself, measures that may appropriately be used in school programs, will be considered.

HEALTH APPRAISAL

Physical inspection in the schools, first employed in Boston in 1894 following a series of epidemics among school children, was originally directed toward the discovery of contagious disease. The first state law relating to medical inspection, passed in Connecticut in 1889, required teachers to test the eyesight of each pupil every three years. The first school nurses were employed in New York in 1902. Eye, ear, and throat examinations were made compulsory in Vermont in 1904. In 1906, Massachusetts adopted a similar law.[1]

Since these origins, the role of the school physician has changed

---

[1] Thomas D. Wood and Hugh G. Rowell, *Health Supervision and Medical Inspection of Schools* (Philadelphia: W. B. Saunders Company, 1928), Chap. 1.

through the years. Sellery[2] has traced this change through six "eras." The first era was his function in communicable disease control, as indicated above. The second, following World War I, was typified as medical inspection, during which school doctors examined children for such obvious physical defects as diseased tonsils, decayed teeth, heart abnormalities, and the like. The third era, in the 1930's, emphasized the improvement of the medical examination given in schools. In the fourth era, the school physician became a health educator by making the medical examination an educational experience for children and parents. Due to the shortage of physicians during World War II, the school physician became a medical advisor in the fifth era, during which he relied more and more on screening inspections conducted by others while he examined only those children referred by the school nurse or classroom teacher. In the present, or sixth era, the school physician is becoming a medical educational consultant, as related to the presence in children of physical defects, physical retardation, mental retardation, psychological maladjustment, and the like.

In 1947, a Conference on the Cooperation of the Physician in the School Health and Physical Education Program was sponsored by the American Medical Association through its Bureau of Health Education. The participants in the conference were representatives from state departments of education, state departments of health, state education associations, state medical societies and associations, and national voluntary health agencies. This conference strongly recommended the employment of school medical advisers rather than school medical inspectors, and that such medical personnel should not be used for functions that teachers and school nurses can perform. It was also recommended that routine medical examinations be required every three years, and that, in so far as possible, these examinations should be given by family physicians. According to these proposals, pupils in need of interim examinations should be screened by teachers and nurses.[3]

The term "health appraisal" is suggested as a replacement for the narrow concepts implied in "medical inspection" and "health ex-

---

[2] C. Morley Sellery, "Role of the School Physician in Today's Schools," *Journal of School Health*, Vol. XXII, No. 3 (March 1952), p. 69.

[3] Dean F. Smiley and Fred V. Hein, eds., *Physicians and Schools* (Chicago: American Medical Association, 1947).

aminations" by the Joint Committee on Health Problems in Education of the National Education Association and the American Medical Association.[4] Health appraisal is defined as "the process of determining the total health status of a child through such means as health histories, teacher and nurse observations, screening tests, medical, dental, and psychological examinations." Representatives of education, medicine, and public health [5] have agreed that health appraisal should be designed (a) to contribute to the maximum effectiveness of the child as an individual and a member of the community, (b) to assure the child's maximum fitness to receive an education, (c) to inform school personnel, parents, and the child regarding his health status, (d) to suggest adjustments in the school environment or instructional program based on individual needs, and (e) to serve as learning experiences for children, teachers, and parents which will be basic to lifelong programs of healthful living.

The medical examination has two very distinct values for the physical educator. *First,* pupils with serious defects, of such a nature that vigorous exercise would be harmful to them, are discovered. Such pupils should be exempted from any physical tests of a vigorous nature, and should be placed in physical education classes in which exercise is restricted to individual capacities and modified to meet individual needs. The medical examination thus becomes a safeguard for the individual and a guide for the physical educator in prescribing physical activities for him.

Second, the medical examination, including the annual examination and individual re-examinations when considered advisable, is helpful in discovering physical defects that result in physiological disturbances that may be the cause of low physical fitness in those pupils so classified by other testing techniques employed by the physical educator. The school health service personnel can be of great value in discovering the cause of this condition and in suggesting remedies for its amelioration.

The school physician also has a special function in relation to teachers of physical activities: to notify them of findings and to help them conduct physical education programs in conformity with

---

[4] Charles C. Wilson, ed., *School Health Services* (Washington: National Education Association, 1953), p. 7.

[5] American Medical Association, *Report of the Third National Conference on Physicians and Schools* (November 1951).

modern medical science. The school physician should be considered the physical educator's medical adviser, and should be called on repeatedly for help and guidance in classifying pupils for activity programs, in conducting individual and adapted physical education, and in handling the "excuse" problem. Informed physicians, who understand modern concepts of physical education, in general thoroughly believe in its importance for growing children and youth and give enthusiastic support to programs that are well conducted.[6] The physical educator *should take the initiative* in developing proper and effective relationships with his school medical officer.

Validity and Accuracy of the Medical Examination

The validity of the medical examination as a measure of health is obvious. There is sufficient clinical evidence to support the contention that a physical defect *causing organic disturbances,* such as diseased tonsils or abscessed teeth, constitutes a drain on the individual, lowering his vitality and his capacity for physical activity, impairing the function of his vital organs, and reducng his efficiency as a total being. As previously stated, health is more than *either* being sick *or* being well; more than having a fever or not having a fever. Health is a positive quality extending from death to abundant life. Therefore, any defect that impairs the function of the body as a whole reduces its capacity for physical activity.

Although the validity of the medical examination is unquestioned, frequently questions may be raised concerning its accuracy and thoroughness as conducted in public schools. The fact that this examination is, of necessity, based upon the judgments of physicians usually without the assistance of laboratory tests or other objective techniques, places it in much the same category of subjectivity as judgment in other types of observations. When subjective judgment becomes the basis for decisions, differences of opinion are apt to exist. The need for care on the part of school physicians in giving medical examinations is clearly indicated. A hurried examination actually may be worse than none at all if it fails to detect defects, thus giving pupils a false sense of security, as well as giving them an erroneous notion that medical examinations are relatively unimportant.

---

[6] Dean F. Smiley and Fred V. Hein, *op. cit.*

Standards for the School Medical Examination

New York State Regulations.[7] In attacking the problem of improving school medical examinations, the Bureau of Health Services, New York State Education Department, has established official regulations governing health services. The regulations provide that the following shall be the responsibilities of all boards of education throughout the state:

1. To provide and maintain a continuous and satisfactory program of school health service.
2. . . . to require each child enrolled in the public school to have a satisfactory annual health examination either by the family physician of the child or by the school physician and to require such health examinations as may be essential.
3. To require that the results of the health examination . . . shall be recorded on approved forms which shall be kept on file in the school.
4. To require the physician making the examinations to sign the health record card and make approved recommendations.
5. To advise, in writing, the parent or guardian of each child in whom any aspect of the total school health service program indicates a defect, disability, or other condition which may require professional attention with regard to health.
6. To keep the health records of individual children confidential except as such records may be necessary for the use of approved school personnel and, with the consent of the parents or guardians, for the use of appropriate health personnel of cooperating agencies.
7. To require adequate health inspections of pupils by teachers, school nurse-teachers and other approved school personnel.
8. To maintain a suitable program of education for the purpose of informing the school personnel, parents, nonschool health agencies, welfare agencies and the general public regarding school health conditions, services and factors relating to the health of school children.
9. To provide for adequate guidance to parents, children and teachers in procedures for preventing and correcting defects and diseases and in the general improvement of the health of school children.
10. To provide suitable inspections and supervision of the health and safety aspects of the school plant.
11. To provide adequate health examinations before participation in strenuous physical activity and periodically throughout the season for those so participating.

In New York State, essential data must also be carried on school medical record cards, which must first be approved by State Bureau of Health Services. An attempt is thus made to obtain a reasonable

---

[7] *Regulations of the Commissioner of Education Governing Health Service,* New York State Education Department, 1956.

uniformity in examining and recording, and the minimum extent of the examination in all schools is defined.

Medical Record Forms

As indicated above, the use of proper forms on which to record the results of medical examinations is of considerable value both in defining minimum standards and in securing adequate examinations. A large number of these forms have been prepared by schools throughout the country. The most valuable and acceptable health records are those designed jointly by representatives of the persons who will use them.[8] These include teachers, physical educators, the school nurse, the school physician, and local private physicians and dentists. Both the Fourth and Fifth National Conferences on Physicians and Schools [9] suggested that school health records include: (a) a personal history of diseases and immunizations, (b) data from the examinations of the physician and dentist, (c) observations noted by teachers concerning health behavior and appearance, (d) the data from visual, hearing, and nutritional screening tests, and (e) recommendations from professional people who serve the child.

Numerous school systems and several states have developed health appraisal forms by cooperative means or through research. One such form will be presented below and certain other ones briefly described.

Oregon School Health Appraisal.[10] Recommended Oregon school health appraisal procedures were developed cooperatively by such state groups as the State Department of Education, the State Board of Health, the Oregon Dental Society, the Oregon Medical Society, and the University of Oregon.[11] In carrying out the recommended procedures, the State Department of Education and the State Board of Health recognize mutual interest and responsibility for the health examinations of Oregon public school children. With the advice of

---

[8] Donald A. Dukelow and Fred V. Hein, eds., *Health Appraisal of School Children,* 2nd ed. (Chicago: American Medical Association, 1957), p. 8.

[9] American Medical Association, "Report of the 4th Nat'l Conference on Physicians and Schools: Coordinating Health Records and Examinations," 1953; "Report of the 5th Nat'l Conference on Physicians and Schools: Use of Health Records," 1955.

[10] *Health Services for the School-Age Child in Oregon* (Salem: State Department of Education; Portland: State Board of Health, 1951).

[11] Information received orally from Dr. Franklin B. Haar, School of Health and Physical Education, University of Oregon.

Oregon Pupil Medical Record

TO BE FILLED IN BY PARENT BEFORE PHYSICAL EXAMINATION:

.... (Name of school) .... (Grade)

Pupil's Name .... Sex: M...... F..... Birth ....
(Last) (First) (Middle) (Mo.) (Day) (Year)

Address .... Home phone ....
(Street or rural route) (Town or location)

Name of
Parent or guardian .... Occupation: of Father .... of Mother ....

Name of physician to be called in an emergency ....

Birth and Infancy—Mention anything unusual such as premature birth, convulsions, "blue spells", feeding difficulty ....
....
....

Habits:

Hour of rising ....

Hour of going to bed ....

Appetite: Good ☐ Fair ☐ Poor ☐

How many times per day does your child have:

Milk .... Fruit .... Vegetables ....

Bread and cereal .... Meat, eggs, fish ....

Cod liver oil or vitamin preparation ....

What kind .... How much ....

Personality and Behavior—Describe for teacher's understanding ....
....
....

Illness—Give year in which your child had any of the following:

Measles . . . . . 19.......	Pneumonia . . . . . 19.......	"Running ear" . . . . 19.......
Mumps . . . . . . 19.......	Diphtheria . . . . . 19.......	Hearing difficulty . . . 19.......
Chickenpox . . . . . 19.......	Scarlet fever . . . . 19.......	Frequent colds . . . . 19.......
Whooping cough . . . 19.......	Poliomyelitis . . . . 19.......	Frequent sore throat . . 19.......
German measles (3-day) . 19.......	Rheumatic fever . . . 19.......	Vision difficulty . . . 19.......

Immunization—Give year your child was vaccinated or had "shots" to prevent:

	Completed Immuniza- tion	Latest Booster Dose		Completed Immuniza- tion	Latest Booster Dose	Tests:	Date	Result
Diphtheria . .	19.......	19.......	Smallpox . . .	19.......	19.......	Tuberculin test .	19.......	....
Whooping cough .	19.......	19.......	Others:	19.......	19.......	Chest x-ray . .	19.......	....
Tetanus . . .	19.......	19.......	....	19.......	19.......	Other test . .	19.......	....
				19.......	19.......			

Additional Information About Your Child—Allergy, heart trouble, diabetes, speech difficulty, loss of consciousness, fainting spells, seizures, behavior difficulties, serious illness, accident, operation (include tonsils and adenoids), or other condition.

....
....
....
....

Has your child been exposed to tuberculosis? Yes ☐ When? .... No ☐

- -

IDENTIFICATION FOR HEALTH DEPARTMENT

.... (Name of school) .... (Grade)

Pupil's Name .... Sex: M...... F..... Birth ....
(Last) (First) (Middle) (Mo.) (Day) (Year)

Address .... Home phone ....
(Street or rural route) (Town or location)

Date .... Signed ....
(Parent or guardian)

ADDITIONAL HISTORY—For use of physician as indicated.

Figure 4.1.

Medical Examination

Information on this record, especially recommendations, guides teachers and nurses in the school health program.

Information for the HEALTH DEPARTMENT

Please indicate condition by code and give details below.

Code—   O = omitted   N = no defect   + = defect found   ++ = requires immediate attention

1. Eyes	6. Teeth	11. Genitals	16. Skin
2. Ears	7. Lymph nodes	12. Posture and feet	17. Nutrition
3. Hearing	8. Heart	13. Gait	18. Endocrine
4. Nose and throat	9. Lungs	14. Nervous system	19. Urine
5. Mouth	10. Abdomen—hernia	15. Musculo-skeletal	20. Other

Positive Findings:

Recommendations for Health Department:

Is medical treatment planned?   Yes ☐   No ☐   Completed ☐
Was dental referral advised?   Yes ☐   No ☐

....
(Signature of examining physician)

This record should be sent directly to the local health department, except in those counties where a committee of the county superintendent of schools, county health officer, and a representative of the medical profession decides on an alternate plan of distribution. If sent to the health department first, the form should be separated at the perforation by the health department and the larger portion sent to the school. Reports for children entering school for the first time should be at the school for registration day. Reports received at the health department during the school year should be forwarded to the school promptly.

Information for the SCHOOL

	Both Eyes	Right	Left
Height Weight Vision—With glasses	20/	20/	20/
Without glasses	20/	20/	20/

Does the pupil's condition permit participation in all usual school activities?   Yes ☐   No ☐

Recommendations for classroom adjustment, special health instruction or limitation of physical activities if indicated.   (Please estimate duration)

Immunizations given at this visit ....

Is medical treatment planned?   Yes ☐   No ☐   Completed ☐

Was dental referral advised?   Yes ☐   No ☐

Parent present during examination?   Yes ☐   No ☐

Date ....
(Signature of examining physician)

Comments from Health Department ....

Date ....   Signed ....

Figure 4.1. (Continued)

the Board of Health, the Superintendent of Public Instruction has the duty to prescribe a program of health examinations of pupils.

In Oregon, health examinations are required of all pupils entering an Oregon public school for the first time. Also, all pupils must receive an examination either at the ninth grade or at the seventh and tenth grades, as the local school provides. In addition, all pupils referred through teacher-nurse screening throughout the school year must be examined; all pupils taking part in interscholastic athletic contests are examined before participation in the sports program each year. The medical part of the examination is performed by a private physician, school physician, or local health officer and his assistants.

Public health departments and schools may cooperate in sending a letter to parents asking that children be examined before school opens and including the standard form, *Oregon Pupil Medical Record*. As will be seen in Figure 4.1, the information required for this form includes the following: history of birth and infancy, habits, personality and behavior, illnesses, tests, and unusual conditions; medical examination findings, height and weight, and vision testing.

When the *Oregon Pupil Medical Record* is completed and on file in the school, essential information is transferred to the Oregon School Health Record Form, as shown in Figure 4.2. This is a cumulative record form, designed to follow the pupil throughout his public school attendance from the first grade in elementary school to his graduation from high school. The annual height, weight, vision, and hearing tests are administered by nurses or teachers; observations of the teacher relative to each pupil's eyes, ears, oral cavity, nose and throat, general condition and appearance, and behavior are recorded annually.

The Connecticut Cumulative Health Record.[12] Byler [13] described a new cumulative health record to be used in conjunction with the school health service program in Connecticut. In constructing this form, medical record cards in use in the local school systems of the state, plus a wide sampling of forms recommended by other states

[12] Division of Health and Physical Education, State Department of Education, Hartford, Connecticut.
[13] Ruth V. Byler, "The Cumulative Health Record," *Journal of the Association for Health, Physical Education, and Recreation*, Vol. XX, No. 7 (September 1949), p. 444.

were analyzed. Regional meetings of all school health personnel concerned were held throughout the state.

This form has several unique features, as follows: (a) space is provided for recording, each September and February, the date of the pupil's last visit to a dentist; (b) a record is provided for pre-school health notes and a complete list of preventive treatments and tests; (c) both chronological age and mental age may be entered on the card; (d) considerable space is devoted both to teachers' notes on the pupil's physical, mental, and emotional health and to nurses' notes on health counseling; (e) following each examination, physicians must answer the following four questions as an aid in advising the school and parents relative to follow-up treatment: Does the pupil need medical care? Is further examination or a laboratory test recommended? Does any irremediable defect exist? Are there problems relating to growth, development, or nutrition, with which teachers and parents should be acquainted? When any of these questions are answered in the affirmative, the examining physician is asked to write his significant findings and specific recommendations in space provided for this purpose.

The Springall Cumulative Health Record.[14] Arthur N. Springall, M.D., Council on Medical Education and Hospitals, American Medical Association,[15] studied school health record forms with the intention of suggesting such a form for common use in the elementary and secondary schools of the United States. Fifty-nine forms were obtained as follows: 36 forms from state departments, 20 from boards of education, and one each from the Y.M.C.A., the Y.W.C.A., and the Boy Scouts. After analysis, the compiled data were sent to a jury of 14 individuals designated by various health organizations as being especially well qualified in child health work. On the basis of those who voted to include the item, the values of the various items were judged as follows: 75 to 100 per cent, essential; 50 to 75 per cent, recommended; 25 to 50 per cent, optional; zero to 25 per cent, not considered for inclusion. Thus, the Springall form represents a compilation of the 59 forms analyzed, modified by the opinions of outstanding workers in the field of child health, and interpreted by the investigator.

---

[14] Arthur N. Springall, "A Suggested Cumulative Health Record Form for Use During the Elementary and Secondary School Years," Microcarded Master of Science thesis, George Williams College, 1954.

[15] Physicians' Record Company, 161 West Harrison Street, Chicago, Illinois.

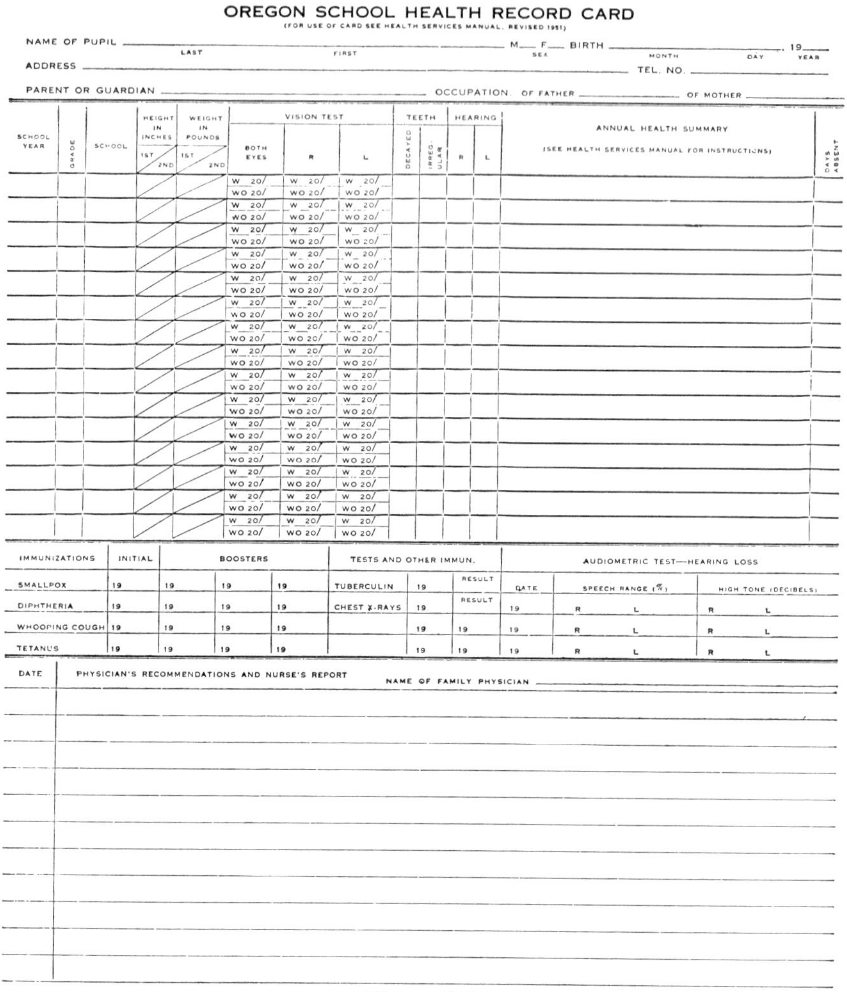

Figure 4.2.

VISION TESTS

Visual defects if not discovered and compensated for, greatly impair pupils' general physical fitness. Many physical ailments, such as headaches, indigestion, and neuromuscular hypertension are traceable to eyestrain caused by noncompensated visual defects. Such defects also affect children's school achievement. Stump [16]

---

[16] N. Franklin Stump, "Visual Performance and Educational Success," *The Optometric Weekly* (September 4, 1952).

HISTORY OF PAST AND CURRENT ILLNESS. ACCIDENT. DISABILITY. AND ABSENCE

OBSERVATIONS BY TEACHER

		19	19	19	19	19	19	19	19	19	19	19	19	19	19	19
SCHOOL YEAR																
GRADE IN SCHOOL																
EYES	STYES OR CRUSTED LIDS															
	INFLAMED EYES															
	CROSSED EYES															
	FREQUENT HEADACHES															
	SQUINTING AT BOOK OR BLACKBOARD															
EARS	DISCHARGE FROM EARS															
	EARACHES															
	FAILURE TO HEAR QUESTIONS															
ORAL CAVITY	INFLAMED GUMS															
	INFLAM OF LIPS, CHEEKS, PALATE															
	FAULTY ORAL HYGIENE															
NOSE AND THROAT	PERSISTENT MOUTH BREATHING															
	FREQUENT SORE THROAT															
	FREQUENT COLDS															
GENERAL CONDITION AND APPEARANCE	FAILURE TO GAIN WEIGHT															
	EXCESSIVE GAIN IN WEIGHT															
	DOES NOT APPEAR WELL															
	TIRES EASILY															
	POOR MUSCLE COORDINATION															
	POOR POSTURE															
BEHAVIOR	EMOTIONAL DISTURBANCES															
	SPEECH DEFECT															
	TWITCHING MOVEMENTS															
	UNDUE RESTLESSNESS															
	SHYNESS															
	NAIL BITING															
	EXCESSIVE USE OF LAVATORY															
	EXCESSIVE DROWSINESS															
	POOR FOOD HABITS															

CODE   V≡DEFECT   T≡UNDER TREATMENT   C≡CORRECTED   R≡REFERRAL   NT≡NO TREATMENT NEEDED

STATE PRINTING

Figure 4.2. (Continued)

in 1952 compared the visual performance of "best" and "fair" students in 11 school subjects; the average scholastic advantage in visual performance for the best students ranged from 11 to 35 per cent for the various subjects. Kephart [17] demonstrated that a significant relationship exists between the visual status of school children and their academic success and that improvement of visual

[17] Newell C. Kephart, "Visual Skills and Their Relation to School Achievement," *American Journal of Ophthamology*, Vol. XXX (June 1953).

skills through professional attention leads to more rapid progress in school achievements.

Visual demands made on school children are very great. It has been estimated that more than three-fourths of all our learning comes through use of the eyes.[18] Reliable judgments indicate that 40 per cent of all school children have a visual handicap serious enough to require the attention of an oculist.[19] Annual tests, therefore, should be made in the schools both to discover new and to indicate additional corrections of previously determined deficiencies in vision.

The diagnosis and treatment of pathological conditions of the eyes, of course, is the physician's responsibility. Teachers, especially, and physical educators, to some extent, should be alert to detect signs of visual discomfort in the appearance and behavior of children. Among the symptoms to look for are the following: bloodshot, swollen, watery, or discharging eyes; inflamed eyelids; complaints of sleepiness, fatigue; headache, nausea, and dizziness; blurred, double, or distorted vision; pain or feelings of dryness, itching, burning, or grittiness in the eyes; squinting, strained and tensed facial expression, and frequent or continuous frowning; rapid blinking or twitchings of the face; inattention during reading periods or shutting or covering one eye or holding the head to one side while reading; poor alignment in written work. Holding books close to the face for reading may indicate nearsightedness (myopic vision); holding them at a distance may reveal farsightedness (hyperopic vision). Such signs as these should be reported to the school nurse or physician.

In view of the great importance of vision, it would be ideally desirable for every child to have a periodic examination by an eye specialist. Since the expense of such a practice is prohibitive for most schools, however, it becomes necessary to utilize tests that will select or screen out those who require careful examinations. Screening tests are not intended to diagnose the nature of eye defects; thus, such tests may be given by non-medical personnel. In schools, classroom teachers and physical educators should de-

---

[18] "20 Questions About Eye Health," Bureau of Health Services, University of the State of New York, 1956.

[19] Delbert Oberteuffer, *School Health Education*, revised ed. (New York: Harper & Brothers, 1954), p. 332.

velop competency in using one or more of the vision screening tests currently available.

In evaluating vision tests for screening purposes, Hitz [20] proposes the following four criteria:

1. The test should pick up most errors without finding minor transient psychic effects.
2. The test should be easy to operate without the need for specialized training or technical knowledge.
3. The test should not be more discriminating than the accepted thorough examination utilized by the majority of competent well-trained ophthalmic physicians.
4. If the principles upon which the test is based are different from those accepted by competent ophthalmologists, then at least the findings must agree fairly accurately with the findings of a thorough ophthalmic test.

These criteria will be applied to the tests considered below for determining the visual efficiency of school children.

The Snellen Letter Chart

In 1862, Professor H. Snellen of Utrecht presented a practical method of determining visual acuity. Since that time the Snellen Letter Chart has become the accepted method of testing vision in schools. This chart consists of several rows of letters, each succeeding row from top to bottom being reduced in size, thereby requiring a consecutively greater amount of visual acuity in order to read them.

The E Chart, or Snellen Egyptian block letter chart, is similar to the Snellen letter test and is of particular value in testing the vision of young children, although in some respects it may be considered for general use. On this chart only the letter E is used, facing in different directions. The procedures for administering and scoring this test are the same as for the Snellen test, except that a single symbol is shown at a time, seen through a hole in a card held by an assistant. The subject by pointing indicates the direction of the "E", whether up, down, to the right, or to the left. This chart may, therefore, be used with young children who do not know the alphabet, and it eliminates with older subjects the possibility of memorizing a sequence of letters on the chart.

---

[20] H. B. Hitz, "An Evaluation of Vision Testing Methods in Schools," *American Journal of Ophthalmology*, Vol. XXI, No. 9 (September 1938), p. 1024.

The techniques for testing the eyes with the Snellen test are as follows:

1. The child should stand or sit 20 feet from the chart, with the "20-foot line" on the chart approximately level with the eyes. If standing, the child's heels should touch a line drawn on the floor 20 feet from the chart; if seated, the back legs of the chair should touch this line, with the child sitting erect in taking the test.

2. The chart should be illuminated with ten foot-candles of light, evenly diffused over the chart with no glare. This amount of illumination should be checked through use of a light meter. General illumination in the vision-testing room should not be less than one-fifth of the chart illumination and should not be more than the illumination on the chart. There should be no bright light in the child's field of vision.

3. Each eye should be tested separately, the other being covered with a square of cardboard held obliquely against the nose so as to cover the eye completely, avoiding any pressure on the eyeball. Both eyes should be kept open. If the child wears glasses, these should be removed and a test made first without glasses, followed by a test with glasses. If only one test is recorded, it should be with the glasses. Test the right eye first, then the left eye, then both eyes.

4. Generally in testing, begin with the 30-foot line on the chart and follow with the 20-foot line. It is not necessary to test below the 20-foot line, as visual acuity is considered satisfactory at this point. If the child is suspected of having poor vision or fails the 30-foot line, start the testing with the 20-foot line. Vision at a given test line is considered satisfactory if the child reads correctly three out of four letters.

5. The vision testing room should be quiet and the atmosphere friendly for best results. Only one subject should be in the room at a time in order to eliminate any opportunity for memorizing the letter sequences prior to testing. If the tester suspects subjects of such memorizing, he may ask the child to read lines backward.

6. The scoring is in fractions, the numerator being the distance the subject is from the chart (20 feet, usually), and the denominator the number on the chart which indicates the distance that would be read by the normal eye. If the subject's vision is just normal, then his acuteness of vision will equal 20/20. A score of 20/30, 20/40, or 20/50 indicates that the child can just see at 20 feet letters large enough for the normal eye to see at 30, 40, or 50 feet, respectively.

The Snellen Test, and this applies to other tests of the same general type, has been criticized, as analyses of its limitations as an adequate visual screening test show:

1. That the eyes are not appraised at reading distance (ten to sixteen inches).
2. That the co-ordination of the two eyes is not tested. Some individuals have normal visual acuity in each eye, but do not have good two-eyed vision.
3. That the test does not provide even a crude index of the degree of farsightedness. Somewhat farsighted people who should have glasses for near work read perfectly at twenty feet.

4. That the test is not critical in detecting astigmatism because an individual can with conscious effort force his eyes to read small enough type to pass the test even though his refractive error is such as to make sustained reading difficult and uncomfortable.[21]

In studying the results of the visual acuity of 32 children as determined by the Snellen test, the Betts test, and a careful examination by an ophthalmic physician, Hitz [22] found that 50 per cent of the children had visual defects by the Snellen test, 69 per cent by the specialist's examination, and 89 per cent by the Betts test. The investigator concluded that the Snellen test was unsatisfactory because of the large proportion of defects it failed to uncover. The test, then, violates the first criterion for the selection of a visual screening test, as proposed by Hitz, since it does not pick up sufficient visual errors.

Investigations in visual acuity at the Medical Research Laboratory, New London Submarine Base, revealed that the Snellen charts made by commercial concerns are notoriously poor. For example, letter sizes from a given line differed by as much as 25 per cent, depending upon the manufacturer. Also, the difficulty of reading different lines on the chart varied. [23] As a result of these studies, New London Vision Charts were constructed, which are modifications of the ordinary commercial chart, but with precision reproduction of letters according to Snellen's specifications. By the selection of letters and modifications of the series, the items on each line are partially equalized in difficulty. Three charts are available in the series, one each for the right eye, the left eye, and both eyes. Reliability coefficients of .88 were obtained for single eye acuities and .82 for binocular acuity.[24]

A handy practical device for shielding the eye not being tested is the occluder, proposed by the Army-Navy-NRC Visual Committee. Specifications for this instrument are given in Figure 4.3. It should

---

[21] Emmett A. Betts, *The Prevention and Correction of Reading Difficulties* (Evanston, Ill.: Row, Peterson and Company, 1936), p. 150.

[22] H. B. Hitz, *op. cit.*

[23] C. E. Feree and G. Rand, "A New Visual Acuity and Astigmatism Test Chart," *American Journal of Ophthalmology*, Vol. XX (January 1937), p. 21.

[24] John H. Sulzman, Ellsworth B. Cook, and Neil R. Bartlett, *Comparison of Various Screening Devices with Standard Visual Procedures*, Progress Report No. 2. New London, Conn.: Medical Research Department, U. S. Submarine Base (April 22, 1948).

be constructed from rigid material, such as wood, translucent plastic, or metal.[25]

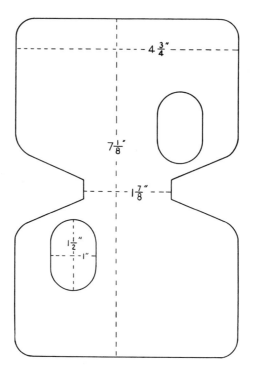

Figure 4.3. The Occluder.

Commercial Screening Devices

There are a number of commercial devices for testing visual acuity which are designed for school use by non-medically-trained personnel. Among these are the following: the Keystone Ophthalmic Telebinocular, the Ortho-Rater, the Sight Screener, and a kit of instruments for the Massachusetts Vision Test. Each of these will be discussed briefly.

Keystone Ophthalmic Telebinocular.[26] The Telebinocular is a modification of the Brewster stereoscope with stand, attached mov-

[25] *Manual of Instructions for Visual Acuity,* Army-Navy-NRC Vision Committee (October 1, 1947).

[26] Keystone View Company, Meadville, Penn.

82

able slide holder, and light. The construction of the instrument separates the fields of vision and permits each eye to see only its half of the slide. The vision of both eyes may be tested together or either eye may be tested separately. A special arrangement whereby measurements can be made at reading-distance equivalents ranging from 12 inches to infinity (ordinarily, infinity is considered 20 feet and beyond) is also provided. The telebinocular is shown in Figure 4.4.

The *Keystone Visual Survey* Tests consist of fourteen stereographic cards, which provide information on the pupil's visual efficiency covering a wide field of important functional aspects of vision. Instead of testing visual acuity by occlusion, the usable vi-

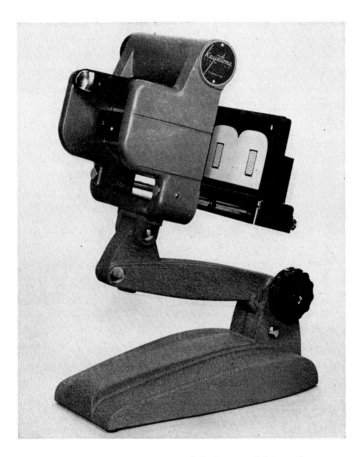

Figure 4.4. Keystone Ophthalmic Telebinocular.

sion of each eye is tested with the other eye open and seeing; stress is placed on binocularity, with the two eyes working together. The fourteen tests included are for the following: simultaneous perception, vertical posture, lateral posture at far point, fusion at far point, usable vision of the right eye at far point, usable vision of the left eye at far point, depth perception (stereopsis), color perception (two cards), lateral posture at near point, fusion at near point, usable vision of the right eye at near point, usable vision of the left eye at near point. Before referral to an eye specialist, it is urged that such pupils be re-tested with great care.[27]

School Vision Tester.[28] This vision tester, developed by Bausch & Lomb Optical Co., has been approved as a vision screening device by the Bureau of Health Services, New York State Education Department. As for the telebinocular described above, this instrument employs the stereoscopic principle with optical equivalents for far and near distances. Six visual performance tests may be given from slides, as follows: monocular acuity of each eye, farsightedness of each eye, simultaneous testing of vertical and lateral muscle balance at far distance, and gross muscular imbalances at near point. A gross color test for traffic light recognition is also included.

Sight Screener.[29] Again, this instrument employs the stereoscopic principle at the optical equivalent of distance; near vision is tested without the interposition of lenses. The targets for right and left eyes are superimposed on Polaroid vectograph film. The visual functions tested are: superimposition and abduction, depth perception, right acuity, left acuity, binocular acuity, vertical phoria, and lateral phoria.

Massachusetts Vision Test.[30] The kit for this test consists of a standard Luckiesh-Moss Illuminator; an improved form of the Snellen E chart; a house card mounted on a frame with an electrical unit and light source; a near phoria tester, also with an electrical unit and light source; spectacles with plus sphere lenses, others with Maddox rods; and a central switch for controlling the lights. In addition to the usual test for visual acuity, the series also provides tests for latent hypermetropia and for muscle imbalance. The test

[27] G. E. Hamilton, "The Keystone Visual-Survey Service," *The Science Counselor* (December 1956).

[28] Bausch & Lomb Optical Co., Rochester 2, New York.

[29] American Optical Company, Southbridge, Mass.

[30] Welch-Allyn Company, Auburn, N. Y.

equipment is approved by the Council on Physical Medicine of the American Medical Association,[31] and is recommended especially for school vision testing in the state of Massachusetts.[32]

Eames Eye Test.[33] The Eames eye test examiner's kit contains a lens, visual acuity card, near-vision card, two stereographic cards, card for testing stereoscope and astigmatic chart. The following visual tests may be administered with this kit: visual acuity at far distance, by conventional use of Snellen Test; hypermetrophia, by reading Snellen chart through a convex lens; near vision test, by reading a set of test letters and characters at reading distance; eye coordination test, vertical or horizontal imbalance, by use of a hand stereoscope; fusion test, also by use of the hand stereoscope; astigmatism, by use of astigmatic chart; test of eye dominance, by sighting through a ring.[34]

Evaluation of Commercial Screening Devices. A number of studies have been made on the relative merits of the various commercial screening devices. A number of these are summarized below.

The reliability and validity of scores obtained on the Telebinocular, the Ortho-Rater, and the Sight Screener were studied at the U.S. Submarine Base, Groton, Connecticut.[35] Reliability coefficients by the test-retest method compared well for the three instruments, ranging from .81 to .84. In checking far and near vision against visual targets developed by the investigators, an early model Telebinocular proved inferior to the other devices. Hitz [36] found that the old-model Telebinocular was more discriminatory in detecting visual defects than is the ophthalmic examination; the tests with this instrument produced 20 per cent more visual cases than did the specialist's examination. Similar results were obtained by Oak and Sloane,[37] utilizing 200 boys and girls ranging in age from 6 to 15

---

[31] *Apparatus Accepted by the Council on Physical Medicine of the American Medical Association.* Chicago: American Medical Association (January 1, 1949).

[32] Lura Oak, "The Massachusetts Vision Test," *American Journal of Public Health,* Vol. XXXII, No. 10 (October 1942), p. 1105.

[33] World Book Company: Yonkers, New York.

[34] Thomas H. Eames, "A Visual-Ocular Screening Test," *The Physical Educator,* Vol. XIII, No. 3 (October 1956), p. 101.

[35] John H. Sulzman, Ellsworth B. Cooke, and Neil R. Bartlett, *op. cit.*

[36] H. B. Hitz, *op. cit.*

[37] Lura Oak and Albert E. Sloane, "The Betts Visual Sensation and Perception Tests," *Archives of Ophthalmology,* Vol. XXII (November 1939), p. 832.

years. Gates and Bond [38] found that Telebinocular tests sometimes give inconsistent results when used with young children. These investigators concluded, however, that this situation may be due to fluctuations in attention and distractibility in young children rather than to any fundamental defects of the tests.

Gutman [39] compared the Massachusetts Vision Test and the Snellen Test as school vision screening devices. 6500 school children in three Oregon counties were screened with one or both methods; 1533 children were tested by both methods. The author concluded that both tests coupled with observation will, when given by a trained operator, yield an equivalent number of referrals for professional eye examinations. One component common to both tests, the Snellen Test, had a high degree of efficiency with but one "over-referral" in seven when failure to read 20/30 with either eye was used as the criterion for referral; it disclosed from two-thirds to three-fourths of all cases meriting professional care. The subsidiary tests of the Massachusetts Vision Test produced an additional small group of cases, but did so with a high ratio of over-referrals.

A comprehensive study of visual screening procedures was conducted in the St. Louis schools with the joint support of the National Society for the Prevention of Blindness, the Children's Bureau of the Federal Security Agency, the Division of Health of the State of Missouri, the St. Louis Board of Education, the Department of Ophthalmology of Washington University School of Medicine, and the Bureau of Naval Research.[40] The children tested were 606 first-grade and 609 sixth-grade pupils; all subjects were given a complete ophthalmological examination, along with a number of screening tests, including the Snellen, the Massachusetts, the Telebinocular, the Ortho-Rater, and the Sight-Screener. The Ortho-Rater, Sight-Screener, and the Telebinocular correctly referred about 75 per cent of the pupils referred by the ophthalmologist;

---

[38] Arthur I. Gates and Guy L. Bond, "Reliability of Telebinocular Tests of Beginning Pupils," *Journal of Educational Psychology*, Vol. XXVIII, No. 1 (January 1937), p. 31.

[39] Eleanor B. Gutman, "School Vision Screening: A Comparison of Two Methods," *Sight-Saving Review*, Vol. XXVI, 1956, p. 212.

[40] Marian M. Crane, *et al.*, "Study of Procedures Used for Screening Elementary School Children for Visual Defects: Referrals by Screening Procedures vs. Ophthalmological Findings," *The Sight-Saving Review*, Vol. XXII, No. 3, 1952.

however, these screening tests referred incorrectly an even larger number of pupils. The Massachusetts Vision Test and a combination of high standard Snellen with teacher judgment, both correctly referred about two-thirds of the students who need care. While this proportion is not quite so high as was obtained with the other screening procedures, there were fewer incorrect referrals. This was particularly true of the Massachusetts Vision Test's incorrect referrals, which, for sixth grade, were between half and two-thirds of the number of correct referrals, while for the first grade correct and incorrect referrals were in about equal proportion. The investigators concluded that none of the vision-testing methods provides more than a rough screening procedure.

AUDITORY TESTS

Auditory defects are serious handicaps in all phases of individual growth. It has been shown that even slight losses of hearing in school children cause speech defects, retardation, inferiority complexes, and unsocial behavior. Hearing losses are also an important cause of reading difficulties, frequently resulting in inability to distinguish between words that sound alike: if the child does not hear the difference between two words, he will have difficulty in distinguishing between their printed symbols.[41]

There is reason to believe that about five per cent of children have impaired hearing which may interfere more or less seriously with health and behavior. Many of these defects can be prevented by early diagnosis and medical treatment. Cameron [42] found that a newly discovered hearing loss has more than a 50-50 chance of regaining average hearing with medical attention. If the child becomes an "old case," because of delayed medical attention, his chances of regaining average hearing with medical attention drop to about one in eight. Thus, the need for *early* detection and treatment of defective hearing is essential. Yet, one national survey suggests that only 11 per cent of school age children receive auditory

---

[41] Albert J. Harris, *op. cit.*, p. 148.
[42] Robert M. Cameron, "An Audiologist Looks at Hearing in the High School," *Journal of Health, Physical Education, and Recreation,* Vol. XXIX, No. 2 (February 1958), p. 45.

tests; [43] in another report, [44] this figure was placed at over one-half the school population of the United States.

Simple Hearing Tests

Two simple tests of hearing have been used extensively in the schools for the purpose of screening out those in need of further examinations by otologists. These are the *watch-tick* test and the *forced-whisper* test.

Watch-tick test. The watch is a convenient instrument for testing hearing. The use of the stop-watch is best, as consistent sounds may be obtained and the watch can be stopped and started as desired. The subject should close his eyes, so as not to observe the location of the watch, and stop one ear with a finger. The hearing distance of the normal ear is 36 inches. The hearing score may be recorded by using this 36 inches as the denominator and the distance at which the subject hears the watch tick as the numerator. Thus, $36/36$ would be a normal score. However, since the intensity of watch ticks vary, the distance at which that of a particular watch should be heard may be determined by finding out the distance at which most children hear it.

Forced-whisper test. In this test, the subject's head should be turned sideward with the ear being tested turned toward the examiner (although some authorities prefer that the back be turned) and the ear not being tested closed by pressure with the forefinger. The examiner should stand 20 feet from the pupil and either ask questions or speak numbers or words in an unaccentuated whisper. If the subject cannot hear the voice at this distance, the examiner moves to a 15-foot distance, and so on, until he is heard. The distance at which the subject hears the whispered voice is placed as the denominator, the numerator of the fraction remaining constant at 20. Thus, normal hearing would be recorded as $20/20$; if the subject can hear the examiner only at 15 feet, his score would be recorded as $20/15$. Another way of scoring this test is merely to check a child as having a hearing impairment if he must be four or more

---

[43] W. G. Hardy, "Clinical Audiology in Public Health and School Health," *American Journal of Public Health*, Vol. XL, No. 5 (May 1950), p. 575.

[44] W. H. Gardiner, "Report of Committee on Hard of Hearing Children, American Hearing Society," *Hearing News*, Vol. XVIII (February-May 1950).

feet nearer than other children in order to hear whispered words or numbers.

Although the watch-tick test is superior to the forced-whisper test, both are but crude measures of auditory acuity, as the testing conditions are not sufficiently standardized. While they may serve to disclose marked hearing losses, they are unsatisfactory when compared with more adequate testing methods.

The Audiometer

By far the most satisfactory way of measuring hearing in the schools is to use the *audiometer*. This instrument has raised hearing tests to the level of a highly effective and economical measure. In general, two types of audiometers are available for school screening use. These are the pure-tone audiometer and the phonograph or group audiometer. In using either of these instruments, the testing room must be quiet, free from interruptions, and removed from the disturbing sounds of music rooms, gymnasiums, typewriters, telephones, and traffic noises.

Pure-Tone Audiometer.[45] Both the intensity and pitch of sounds may be controlled with the pure-tone audiometer. Intensity of sound is regulated by a knob and can be varied from zero or normal hearing upward to maximum intensity. Variations are in steps of five decibels, the decibel being a unit of sound intensity. The pitch of sounds may be varied by turning another knob, in octave steps from 128 to 8192 vibrations a second. However, the newer audiometers are calibrated in even numbers. This instrument has a set of earphones and is equipped with a switch which permits sounds to reach either ear as desired by the tester. An "interrupter switch" enables the tester to prevent any sound from reaching either ear, so may be used to check children suspected of giving incorrect responses.

In using the pure-tone audiometer, the sweep-check method is usually employed first. The intensity dial is set at the 15 decibel loss position. The tone dial is changed rather quickly from 250 to 4000 vibrations per second. In the interest of rapid screening the extremes of low and high frequencies may be omitted. A child who hears each tone with the intensity dial set at 15 decibels is con-

---

[45] Wilson, *op. cit.*, pp. 93-95.

sidered to have normal hearing. Those who fail to hear two or more tones should be recalled for a retest. For retests, the sound at each pitch level is increased in intensity until the child can hear it, or the maximum intensity is reached. A loss of 15 decibels or more in two or more tones on a retest indicates a significant hearing impairment.

In administering pure-tone audiometer tests, the tester should explain to the children the purposes of the test and the procedures to be followed. The child should be seated so that he cannot see the dials of the audiometer. He is asked to nod or give a hand signal when he hears each new tone. The tester should be seated in order to watch carefully the child's face; he should use the interrupter switch at intervals as a check on the subject's responses.

Group Audiometer. The group audiometer is similar to a phonograph, and is equipped with earphones for the testing of as many as 40 subjects at one time. An instrument for testing one individual at a time is also available, and is superior for use when careful examining is required. The test consists in playing a record on which are recorded the voices of a man and a woman speaking a series of numbers in a lower and lower tone. Each subject, listening through the earphones, writes down the numbers he hears on a special form provided for this purpose. Each ear is tested separately. One side of the disk is for the right ear, the other for the left.

Normal hearing is represented by the "zero line" on the record. Hearing loss is recorded in terms of "decibels." A decibel is one-tenth of a "bel," which in turn is the unit of energy for the transmission of sound by electricity. A loss of six decibels is considered within the normal hearing range, but pupils with a loss of nine decibels or more should be referred to a specialist for further examination.

Audiometer Standards. There are a number of excellent audiometers on the market which are especially designed for school use. Reliable information concerning them may be secured from the following agencies, which have set up standards and specifications for testing instruments of this type:

Council on Physical Therapy, American Medical Association, 535 North Dearborn Street, Chicago, Illinois.

American Standards Association, 29 West 39th Street, New York City.

The National Bureau of Standards, U. S. Department of Commerce, Washington, D.C.

The National Bureau of Standards will test any privately or publicly owned audiometer to determine whether or not the individual instrument meets the specifications of its make and type.

Evaluation of Audiometer Testing. The desired screening program for the detection of children with hearing losses would select from a group of apparently well individuals the maximum number with a significant or potentially significant disability and the minimum number without such disability. The pure tone audiometer is generally conceded as the most effective method presently available.[46]

Yankower and associates compared the case-finding effectiveness of the group phonograph fading numbers test, the group pure tone test, and the individual pure tone check test. The subjects were 2,404 pupils in the third through seventh grades of the Rochester, N. Y., public schools. Approximately five per cent of these children were found to have a verified hearing loss by otological examination. Not one of the three screening devices was able to select all of these cases: 33 per cent were selected by the group phonograph screening procedure, 69 per cent by the group pure tone method, and 95 per cent by the individual sweep check process. Although the individual pure tone sweep check was the best case finder, it also selected more children with no hearing loss than did either of the two group tests.

In the Cleveland public schools, Kinney [47] found that the percentage of suspected cases selected by the sweep check method was very little higher than by the group phonograph screening process. Both methods were used to screen 2,068 children; each child was tested by both methods on the same day. There were 118 suspected cases (5.75 per cent) by the phonograph method; the sweep check method identified the same 118 cases plus five additional ones.

The time required to administer the various hearing screening tests may frequently be a factor in selecting the device to use. Obviously, the group methods require much less time per pupil than do the individual methods. Also, the skill required of the tester is

---

[46] A. Yankower, M. L. Geyer, and H. C. Chase, "Comparative Evaluation of Three Screening Methods for Detection of Hearing Loss in Children," *American Journal of Public Health*, Vol. XLIV, No. 1 (January 1954), p. 77.

[47] Charles E. Kinney, "Cleveland Hearing Conservation Program," *Transactions of American Academy of Ophthalmology and Otolaryngology*, Vol. L (November-December 1945), p. 94.

less for the group phonograph process than for the pure tone procedures.

Symptoms of Ear Disorders

In addition to testing periodically the auditory acuity of the ears, all teaching personnel in the schools should be alert to signs of ear diseases and disorders. Fowler [48] has listed a large number of these symptoms, the following, among others, being included in his list:

1. Deafness, dullness, heaviness, or blocking sensations in the ear persisting for more than a few minutes, especially after exposure to cold, swimming, head colds, chronic or recurrent sinusitis, shock or other causes of lowered resistance; after trauma and severe or prolonged acoustic shocks.

2. Asking for the repetition of words or phrases.

3. Failure to respond when called or to locate properly the source or direction of a sound.

4. Distortion of speech out of proportion to age.

5. Buzzing in the ears, dizziness (these symptoms may also be caused by a number of other conditions, such as head colds, sinus infection, anemia, and certain circulatory, neurologic, and gastrointestinal upsets).

6. Headache, fever, sweats, acidosis, nausea, vomiting, coma, otherwise unexplained.

7. Tenderness, itching, heat; or pain, deformity, or swelling in or about the ear.

8. Facial spasm or facial paralysis.

Any or all of these conditions may occur without ear disease, and some of them without any disease being present. However, when observed, they should be reported to the physician for investigation.

Selected References

Dukelow, Donald A., and Fred V. Hein, eds., *Health Appraisal of School Children*. Chicago: American Medical Association, 1957.

Health Services for the School-Age Child in Oregon. Salem: State Department of Education; Portland: State Board of Health, 1951.

---

[48] Edmund P. Fowler, "Prevention of Disease and Disorders of the Ears between the Ages of Three and Twelve Years," *Preventive Medicine*, Vol. VIII, No. 6 (June 1938), p. 55.

Oberteuffer, Delbert, *School Health Education*, rev. ed. New York: Harper & Brothers, 1954.

Smiley, Dean F., and Fred V. Hein, eds., *Physicians and Schools*. Chicago: American Medical Association, 1947.

Wilson, Charles E., ed., *School Health Services*. Washington: National Education Association, 1953.

CHAPTER FIVE

Physiological Fitness

Physiological tests, especially of cardiovascular-respiratory nature, have been experimented with in this country since 1884, when Angelo Mosso, an Italian physiologist, invented the ergograph. Mosso's original premise was that the ability of a muscle to perform was dependent upon the efficiency of the circulatory system—the efficiency with which fuel is supplied to the muscles and waste materials are carried away. Since then, many other experimenters have worked in this field, claiming that tests based upon the cardiovascular function measured qualities variously described by such terms as *functional health, physiological efficiency, organic condition, athletic condition, physical fitness,* and *endurance.*

THE CARDIOVASCULAR FUNCTION

During vigorous exercise, the blood circulation quickens—blood and lymph stream through the muscles, supplying the cells with oxygen and nutrition and removing waste products. The heart's activity is accelerated, exercising and strengthening its own fibers, as well as pumping the blood and stimulating its circulation. Muscles are enlarged and their endurance is increased through strenuous exercise. The gain in the endurance of a muscle, however, is out of all proportion to its size. Therefore, the quality of contractions must be improved through such factors as: fuel is made available in greater amount; oxygen is more abundant, owing to improved circulation of blood through the muscle; better coordination of the individual muscle fibers and more complete use of all muscle fibers are realized. Thus, the cardiovascular system performs a vital service in the performance of sustained muscular activity.

Physical educators have long been concerned with the measurement of *cardio-respiratory endurance*. This form of endurance involves the continued activity of the entire organism, during which major adjustments of the circulatory and respiratory systems are necessary, as in running, swimming, climbing, and the like. This form of endurance is not only dependent upon the strength of the muscles involved in the activity but must rely greatly on the effective functioning of the circulatory system. Examples are: the resting body consumes approximately 250 cc. of oxygen per minute; in championship performances, the oxygen consumption may increase 1600 per cent, to four liters per minute, when the individual is engaged in continued vigorous exercise. In order to transfer four liters of oxygen from the lungs to the muscles, 34 liters of blood are required; inasmuch as the volume of blood in the body is approximately five liters, the effort means that the blood must circulate through the body seven times a minute.[1]

Roger Bannister, the great miler, reported the performance of four subjects on a severe treadmill run while breathing controlled mixtures of air and oxygen. In atmospheric air, the subjects stopped exercising from exhaustion after eight minutes. When breathing 33 per cent oxygen, their performance was much improved; while with 66 per cent oxygen, they appeared able to continue running indefinitely.[2]

It is not the intent of this discussion to present a complete exposition of the physiology of endurance activity. It is the intent to stress the significance of the essential reliance of such activity on the circulatory-respiratory system. As a consequence of this well recognized relationship, many cardiovascular tests have been proposed as measures of cardio-respiratory endurance.

THE ACCURACY OF CARDIOVASCULAR TESTS

The elements most frequently measured in cardiovascular testing include pulse rate at rest, after exercise, and after rest following

---

[1] Khalil G. Wakim, "Physiological Aspects of Therapeutic Exercise," *Journal of the American Medical Association*, Vol. CXLII (January 14, 1950), p. 100.

[2] R. G. Bannister, "The Control of Breathing during Exercises," *FEIP Bulletin*, Vol. II (1950), p. 47.

exercise; systolic and diastolic blood pressures; and venous pressures. These may be taken reclining, sitting, or standing; and the changes that take place after activity or after various shifts of position may be recorded, as well as the direct readings themselves.

In 1928, Schwartz, Britton, and Thompson,[3] published reliability coefficients of blood-pressure measurements that were so low as to be valueless for accurate testing. Believing that these low reliability coefficients obtained by Schwartz and his associates were due to experimental conditions under which their study was conducted, McCurdy and Larson,[4] in 1935, conducted a study to determine the reliability and objectivity of blood-pressure measurement under controlled experimental conditions. Larson [5] subsequently determined the reliability and objectivity of three organic efficiency tests and of all test items of which they were composed. The reliability coefficients were determined by Larson using 21 subjects; the objectivity coefficients, by students with 180 subjects. Satisfactory reliability was obtained for most of the items. The objectivity coefficients, for the most part, however, were low, but with two exceptions, sitting systolic pressure and vital capacity, being below .75. Larson explains the latter situation by stating that the student examiners were not experienced and were constantly being hurried in their measurements.

It is generally agreed by experimenters that many factors influence the elements included in the cardiovascular-type test. Larson, in his review of the cardiovascular-respiratory function,[6] pointed out that both heart rate and blood pressure are affected by the following: exercise, age, sex, diurnal changes, season and climate, altitude, changes in body posture, digestion, air and water movements, loss of sleep, respiration, metabolism, and emotional and nervous conditions. These factors increase considerably the complexity of cardiovascular measurement. Emotional and nervous states, such as worry, fear, and anger, are particularly difficult to control, as also

---

[3] L. Schwartz, R. H. Britton, and L. R. Thompson, *Studies in Physical Development and Posture*, Public Health Bulletin No. 179 (Washington: United States Public Health Service, 1928).

[4] J. H. McCurdy and L. A. Larson, "The Reliability and Objectivity of Blood-Pressure Measurements," *Supplement to the Research Quarterly*, Vol. VI, No. 2 (May 1935), p. 3.

[5] Leonard A. Larson, "A Study of the Validity of Some Cardiovascular Tests," *Journal of Experimental Education*, Vol. VII, No. 3 (March 1939), p. 214.

[6] Leonard A. Larson, "Cardiovascular-Respiratory Function," *Supplement to the Research Quarterly*, Vol. XII, No. 2 (May 1941), p. 456.

is the amount of physical exercise engaged in by the subject immediately preceding the taking of the tests. Even slight nervousness or muscular tension will increase the individual's score.

The objectivity of cardiovascular tests is definitely uncertain, and reliability can be secured only under the most favorable circumstances. It is necessary, too, to require a rest period for the subject just prior to taking the test. Even under these conditions, Larson states that the average of two or three repeated measurements under identical conditions should be made if such tests are to be used for individual diagnosis.

CRAMPTON BLOOD-PTOSIS TEST [7]

The Crampton Blood-Ptosis Test was one of the earliest of the cardiovascular tests proposed to evaluate the general condition of the individual. The principle of the test is based on changes in heart rate and systolic blood pressure upon standing from a reclining position. Directions for administering this test are as follows:

1. The subject reclines until his pulse rate reaches a constant rate. A constant rate is reached when two repeated 15-second counts are the same.
2. While still in the reclining position, his heart rate is taken for one minute; then, his systolic blood pressure is taken.
3. The subject stands. When his pulse rate has reached a steady state, and while standing, heart rate and systolic blood pressure tests are again taken.

A norm chart for this test, which may be used for both men and women, appears in Table XVI, Appendix B. This is a double-entry table, which must be entered with the differences between the reclining and standing heart rates and systolic blood pressures. Thus, if a person's increase in heart rate is five and his systolic pressure increases 8 mm. Hg., his cardiovascular rating is 90. Or, the individual, who has a heart rate increase of 20 and a systolic blood pressure decrease of 6 mm. Hg., his cardiovascular rating is 40. Crampton maintains that most people in good to fair condition will score between 60 and 100; scores below zero are evidence of impaired circulation, a toxic state, or acute severe physical disturbance.

McCloy [8] points out that the Crampton Test seems to reflect

---

[7] C. Ward Crampton, "A Test of Condition: Preliminary Report," *Medical News,* Vol. LXXXVII (September 1905), p. 529.

[8] Charles H. McCloy and Norma D. Young, *Tests and Measurements in Health and Physical Education,* 3rd ed. (New York: Appleton-Century-Crofts, Inc., 1954), p. 291.

changes in relative sickness, but does not reflect adequately the more positive changes in health; furthermore, it does not appear to differentiate differences in athletic condition. The test, therefore, may have special value to determine the readiness of patients for bed exercises in convalescent care.

BARACH ENERGY INDEX [9]

Another early cardiovascular test is the Barach Energy Index. This test purports to measure the energy expended by the heart: the systole gives the energy factor in the work of the heart itself; the diastole provides the energy factor in the peripheral resistance; the pulse rate indicates the number of systoles and diastoles occurring in a minute. The test items utilized, then, are systolic and diastolic blood pressures and pulse rate per minute. All measures are obtained with the subject in a sitting position. Before taking the tests, a constant pulse rate should be reached.

Scoring for the Barach Index is as follows:

$$\text{Energy Index} = \frac{\text{pulse rate (systolic pressure + diastolic pressure)}}{100}$$

Thus, if an individual has a systolic blood pressure of 120, a diastolic pressure of 82, and a pulse rate of 70:

$$\text{Energy Index} = \frac{70(120 + 80)}{100} = 140$$

Dividing by 100 has the effect of dropping the last two numbers from the product in the numerator of the index.

According to Barach's early studies, a robust person will have an Energy Index varying from 110 to 160. The upper normal limit is considered to be 200; the lower limit, 90. Those scoring above 200 may be hypertensed; those below 90 may be hypotensed. With 200 University of Illinois men, Cureton [10] obtained a mean Energy Index of 141; the range was 70 to 220.

In a validation of cardiovascular tests, Hunsicker [11] utilized a

---

[9] J. H. Barach, "The Energy Index," *Journal of American Medical Association,* Vol. LXII (February 14, 1914), p. 525.

[10] Thomas K. Cureton, *Physical Fitness Appraisal and Guidance* (St. Louis: C. V. Mosby Co., 1947), p. 285.

[11] Paul A. Hunsicker, "A Validation of Cardiovascular Tests by Cardiac Output Measurements," Microcarded Doctor of Philosophy Dissertation, University of Illinois, 1950.

criterion of cardiac output, consisting of heart stroke volume for an all-out treadmill run divided by body surface area. The Barach Energy Index correlated —.50 with this criterion. This correlation exceeded those with such other cardiovascular tests as the Harvard Step Test and the Schneider Test.

SCHNEIDER TEST [12]

The Schneider Test was the earliest of the more comprehensive cardiovascular tests. It was devised during World War I to test whether or not aviators were functionally fit to fly. The six items comprising the test, with directions for their administration, are as follows:

1. *Reclining pulse rate:* After the subject has reclined quietly for five minutes, count his heart rate for 20 seconds every 20 seconds until two consecutive counts are the same; multiply this count by three to obtain the rate for one minute, and record.

2. Before the subject stands, take the systolic pressure. This reading should be checked two or three times before recording.

3. *Standing pulse rate:* After the subject has stood for two minutes to allow the pulse to reach its normal rate, count the heart rate until two 15-second counts agree; multiply this count by four, and record.

4. *Increase in pulse rate on standing:* Calculate the difference between the standing and reclining pulse rate, and record.

5. *Increase in systolic blood pressure standing compared with reclining:* Take the systolic pressure; calculate the difference between standing and reclining; and record.

6. *Pulse rate increase immediately after exercise:* Timing him with a stop watch, have the subject step up on a chair 18½ inches high five times in 15 seconds; count the pulse for 15 seconds immediately at the cessation of exercise; multiply this count by four; and record. In the stepping procedure, the subject should stand with one foot on the chair at the first count; keeping this foot on

---

[12] E. C. Schneider, "A Cardiovascular Rating as a Measure of Physical Fitness and Efficiency," *Journal of the American Medical Association,* Vol. LXXIV, No. 5 (May 29, 1920), p. 1507.

the chair, he should continue to step up and down with the other foot; both feet should be on the floor at the end of the 15 seconds.

7. *Return of pulse rate to standing normal after exercise:* Continue taking the pulse in 15-second counts until the rate has returned to the normal standing rate; record the number of seconds it takes for this return. This time is taken from the end of the exercise bout to the beginning of the first normal 15-second pulse count. If the pulse has not returned to normal at the end of two minutes, record the number of beats above normal.

Norm charts for this test appear in Table XVII, Appendix B. The scores for each test item range between +3 and −3. A perfect record, the sum of the values for all six tests, is a score of +18; deficiency is rated as 9 or less. In using the scoring table, parts A and B and parts C and D must be used together. For example, if an individual's pulse increase on standing is 13 (see Part B) and his reclining rate is 75 (see Part A), he is graded 2 on his standing increase.

Reliability for the Schneider Test by the test-retest method is variously reported, but, when the test is given with extreme care, it is as high as .86 [13] and .89.[14] Recent research indicates that the test is related to endurance criteria; however, there are conflicting reports of the degree of this relationship. McCloy [15] obtained a correlation of .43 between the Schneider Test and a measure of the present status of the health of his subjects. Using this test with college men, Cureton [16] obtained the following correlations: mile run, −.65; two-mile run, −.63; three and one-half mile steeplechase, −.50; composite of four endurance runs, −.81. In Cureton's study, however, the subjects were highly selected. Taylor and Howe [17] reported a correlation of .68 between Schneider's scores and instructor's ratings of "physical fitness" of 60 college women.

---

[13] R. A. McFarland and J. H. Huddleston, "Neurocirculatory Reactions in Psychoneuroses Studied by the Schneider Method," *American Journal of Psychiatry*, No. 93, 1936, p. 567.

[14] Thomas K. Cureton and others, *Endurance of Young Men.* Washington: Society for Research in Child Development, Vol. X, No. 1, Serial No. 40, 1945, p. 214.

[15] C. H. McCloy and Norma D. Young, *Tests and Measurements in Health and Physical Education,* 3rd ed. (New York: Appleton-Century-Crofts, Inc., 1954), p. 292.

[16] Thomas K. Cureton, *op. cit.,* Chap. 9.

[17] M. W. Taylor and E. C. Howe, "Alkali Reserve and Physical Fitness," *American Physical Education Review,* Vol. XXXIV, 1929, p. 570.

Henry and Herbig [18] obtained a correlation of .44 between scores on this test and improvement in time on the 800-yard run.

The evidence pertaining to this test is conflicting. One variable that may account for these differences is the degree of care required to obtain proper test scores on the test. Also, there is evidence that a revised weighting of the items may result in an improvement in the predictive value of the index. The test has value as one physiological fitness item to supplement the findings on the medical examination. In its present state, evidence is not sufficient to justify its use in physical education to evaluate circulatory-respiratory endurance.

McCurdy-Larson Test of Organic Efficiency [19]

In constructing their Organic Efficiency Test, McCurdy and Larson selected five items (from a total of 26 with which they experimented), by the bi-serial correlation method, and combined them into a test battery. An Organic Efficiency Index was established by combining the weighted scores of the five tests. Scoring tables were prepared and standards set up enabling the examiner to classify the subjects tested, although norm tables were not originally constructed. Subsequently, however, McCurdy and Larson [20] found that age-to-age variations may be significant when a number of years, considered as one period, is compared with another group of years, considered as a second period, and prepared scales for three age groups, as follows: 18 to 34, 35 to 49, and 50 to 80. The five test elements are as follows:

1. Sitting diastolic blood pressure.
2. Breath-holding 20 seconds after standard stair-climbing exercise.
3. Difference between standing normal pulse rate and pulse rate two minutes after exercise.

---

[18] Franklin Henry and W. Herbig, "The Correlation of Various Functional Tests of Cardio-circulatory System with Changes in Athletic Condition of Distance Runners." Mimeographed report presented at Research Section, A.A.H.P.E.R., San Francisco, 1939.

[19] J. H. McCurdy and L. A. Larson, "Measurement of Organic Efficiency for the Prediction of Physical Condition," Supplement to the Research Quarterly, Vol. VI, No. 2 (May 1935), p. 11.

[20] J. H. McCurdy and L. A. Larson, "Age and Organic Efficiency," The Military Surgeon, Vol. LXXXV, No. 2 (August 1939), p. 93.

4. Sitting pulse pressure.

5. Standing pulse pressure.

As a result of further research, Larson [21] devised a short test which has a validity coefficient nearly as high as the complete battery, consisting of the following three items: sitting diastolic pressure, breath-holding after exercise, and standing pulse pressure.

McCurdy and Larson maintain that endurance is basic in measuring organic capacity, believing that, if one is able to run or swim more than a normal distance without undue fatigue, he is in good physical condition. The criteria used for the validation of their Organic Efficiency Test were: the "good" physiological group, represented by 60 Springfield College varsity swimmers in mid-season condition and 40 American Olympic swimmers in the peak of condition before the start of the Olympic games in 1936; and the "poor" physiological group, represented by 138 infirmary patients examined immediately after confinement in the infirmary for two or more days with respiratory infections. The bi-serial correlation obtained between the test and the criterion groups was .70; and between the test items and "time" for the 440-yard swim was .68.[22]

TUTTLE PULSE-RATIO TEST [23]

The fact has been well demonstrated that the physical condition of an individual has a definite effect upon both the rate of the heart beat and the time required for the rate to return to normal after the cessation of exercise. It has also been shown that the individual who is physically conditioned will be less affected by a given amount of exercise than when in poor condition. It is on the basis of these factors that pulse-ratio tests have been mostly justified. These tests are based on the ability of the heart to compensate for exercise. The first pulse-ratio test was developed in the physiology laboratory of Guy's Hospital, London, England.[24] Subsequently

---

[21] Leonard A. Larson, "A Study of the Validity of Some Cardiovascular Tests," *Journal of Experimental Education*, Vol. III, No. 3 (March 1939), p. 214.

[22] J. H. McCurdy and L. A. Larson, "The Validity of Circulatory-Respiratory Measures as an Index of Endurance Condition in Swimming," *Research Quarterly*, Vol. XI, No. 3 (October 1940), p. 3.

[23] W. W. Tuttle, "The Use of the Pulse-Ratio Test for Rating Physical Efficiency," *Research Quarterly*, Vol. II, No. 2 (May 1931), p. 5.

[24] G. H. Hunt and M. S. Pembrey, "Tests of Physical Efficiency," *Guy's Hospital Reports*, Vol. LXXI, 1921, p. 415.

several tests of this sort were reported in this country, particularly the Tuttle Pulse-Ratio Test and the Harvard Step Test.

Tuttle's Pulse-Ratio Test was announced in 1931; there has been considerable research related to the test since that time. Directions for administering the test are as follows:

1. The amount of exercise is standardized by requiring the subject to step on and off a stool or bench, 13 inches high and of such dimensions that it may be mounted and dismounted satisfactorily.
2. The subject is seated in close proximity to the bench, so that when he rises, he is in position to start the test. The subject sits quietly until the pulse rate becomes constant, i.e., until repeated counts are the same. Then, the pulse is counted for 30 seconds and the amount is doubled; the result is recorded as the normal pulse for one minute.
3. The subject stands and steps up and down on the bench for one minute at a rate of 20 steps for boys and 15 steps for girls. The stepping process is performed in four counts, as follows: one, left foot is placed on bench; two, right foot is placed on bench; three, left foot is placed on floor; four, right foot is placed on floor. (Left-footed persons should start with left foot). The subject should come to an erect position on the bench each time. The steps may be timed with a metronome. If a metronome is not available, any number of steps which approximate the specified cadence may be used; the tester counts these for one minute and records the number (S_1 in the formula).
4. Immediately after the cessation of exercise, the subject is seated and his pulse counted for two minutes. The pulse count is begun at the instant he places both feet on the floor at the end of the exercise session. This beginning of the count is important, since compensation begins very soon after exercise and delay in starting the count leads to considerable error. The total pulse rate for two minutes after exercise is divided by the normal pulse for one minute; this is the first pulse ratio (R_1 in the formula).
5. After the pulse has returned to normal, a second pulse-ratio is obtained. The stepping exercise again is for one minute; the rate is 40 steps for boys and 35 for girls. Actually, any rapid cadence may be used and the number of steps recorded (S_2 in the formula).
6. As before, the pulse rate for two minutes is recorded and a second pulse-ratio is computed (R_2 in the formula).
7. Compute the number of steps needed for a 2.5 ratio (S_0), utilizing the following formula:

$$S_0 = S_1 + \frac{(S_2 - S_1)\ (2.5 - R_1)}{R_2 - R_1}$$

To illustrate: Sitting normal pulse = 75
Pulse two minutes after first stepping = 165
First pulse-ratio (R_1) = 2.20 (165 ÷ 75 = 2.20)
Pulse two minutes after second stepping = 210
Second pulse-ratio (R_2) = 2.80 (210 ÷ 75 = 2.80)
Number of steps: First exercise (S_1) = 20;
Second exercise (S_2) = 40

$$S_0 = 20 + \frac{(40 - 20)\ (2.5 - 2.20)}{2.80 - 2.20} = 30 \text{ steps}$$

The means for this test are: 33 steps for boys ten to twelve years; 30 steps for boys over twelve and male adults; 25 steps for adult females. An *efficiency rating* is also proposed, which places results on a percentage basis. Inasmuch as 50 steps per minute was found to produce a ratio of 2.5 in well-conditioned athletes, the formula for this rating is as follows:

$$EF = \frac{100\ (\text{No. steps required for 2.5 pulse ratio})}{50}$$

Subsequently, Tuttle and Dickinson [25] found that the ratio from a single stepping performance of 30 to 40 steps of exercise is nearly as satisfactory as the ratio obtained from the two stepping exercises. A correlation of .957 was obtained between the original test and the single pulse-ratio with 40 steps per minute; with 30 steps per minute, this correlation was .930.

Some evidence exists which relates Tuttle pulse ratios with physical condition. Tuttle and Skien [26] reported that the Efficiency Ratings (EF) of athletes during their competitive season are materially increased; a common occurrence is a decrease in the EF after athletic competition. Flanagan [27] obtained a significant correlation between EF's and endurance in sprint running. However, Henry and Kleeberger [28] found lower correlations and concluded that general muscular endurance is not a determining factor in the pulse-ratio test.

Results of the Pulse-Ratio Test agree well with the findings of physicians concerning the status of the cardiovascular system. Sev-

---

[25] W. W. Tuttle and R. E. Dickinson, "A Simplification of the Pulse-Ratio Technique for Rating Physical Efficiency and Present Condition," *Research Quarterly*, Vol. X, No. 2 (May 1939), p. 73.

[26] W. W. Tuttle and J. S. Skien, "The Efficiency Rating of High School Boys as Shown by the Pulse-Ratio Test," *Research Quarterly*, Vol. I, No. 3 (October 1930), p. 27.

[27] Kenneth Flanagan, "The Pulse-Ratio Test as a Measure of Athletic Endurance in Sprint Running," *Supplement to the Research Quarterly*, Vol. VI (October 1935), p. 50.

[28] F. M. Henry and F. L. Kleeberger, "The Validity of the Pulse-Ratio Test of Cardiac Efficiency," *Research Quarterly*, Vol. IX (March 1938), p. 32.

eral investigators, Sievers,[29] Lee,[30] and Carpenter,[31] have found that the pulse-ratio was in agreement with the reports of physicians in respect to functional heart murmurs, organic lesions with definite evidence of decompensation, and neurogenic hearts. Little evidence is available, however, to support the use of the test as a measure of general physical condition. The test, therefore, has a special relationship to the medical examination, as a supplementary aid in detecting heart disturbances.

The procedure for checking the condition of the heart by use of the Pulse-Ratio Test is as follows: after the number of steps necessary for a subject to obtain a 2.5 ratio, have him perform the stepping test at this number of steps and compute his pulse-ratio in the usual manner. If this ratio is more than .07 above or below 2.5, and the same result is obtained upon subsequent testing, the heart may be defective in some way and the subject should be referred to a physician.[32] As McCloy [33] aptly points out, however, it should be strongly emphasized that under no circumstances should a test of this type be considered an adequate substitute for a thorough medical examination of the heart.

HARVARD STEP TEST [34,35]

The Harvard Step Test is another test of the same general type as the Tuttle Pulse-Ratio Test. This test was originally constructed for college men. Following are instructions for its administration:

1. The subject steps up and down 30 times a minute on a bench 20 inches high. Each time, the subject should step all the way up on the bench with the body erect. Stepping is done in four counts, as for the Tuttle Pulse-

---

[29] Henry Sievers, "A Simple Method of Detecting Abnormal Hearts by the Use of the Pulse-Ratio Test," *Research Quarterly*, Vol. VI, No. 2 (May 1935), p. 36.

[30] Ethard N. Lee, "A Further Study of Tuttle's Test as a Means of Detecting Non-Compensated Organic Heart Lesions," *Research Quarterly*, Vol. VIII, No. 1 (March 1937), p. 123.

[31] Eileen Carpenter, "Further Observations on Tuttle's Test for Non-Compensated Heart Lesions," *Research Quarterly*, Vol. VIII, No. 1 (March 1937), p. 130.

[32] Sievers, *op. cit.*

[33] McCloy and Young, *op. cit.*

[34] Lucien Brouha, "The Step Test: A Simple Method of Measuring Physical Fitness for Muscular Work in Young Men," *Research Quarterly*, Vol. XIV, No. 1 (March 1943), p. 31.

[35] Lucien Brouha, Norman W. Fradd, and Beatrice M. Savage, "Studies in Physical Efficiency of College Students," *Research Quarterly*, Vol. XV, No. 3 (October 1944), p. 211.

Ratio Test; however, he may lead off with the same foot each time or change feet as he desires, so long as the four-count step is maintained.

2. The stepping exercise continues for exactly five minutes, unless the subject is forced to stop sooner due to exhaustion. In either case, the duration of the exercise in seconds is recorded; the maximum number of seconds is 300 for the full five-minute period.

3. Immediately after completing the exercise, the subject sits on a chair. The pulse is counted 1 to 1½, 2 to 2½, and 3 to 3½ minutes after the stepping ceases.

4. A Physical Efficiency Index (PEI) is computed, utilizing the following formula:

$$\text{PEI} = \frac{\text{Duration of Exercise in Seconds} \times 100}{2 \times \text{Sum of Pulse Counts in Recovery}}$$

To illustrate: The subject completed the exercise period, 300 seconds; his recovery-period pulse counts were: 75 for 1 to 1½ minutes, 50 for 2 to 2½ minutes, and 35 for 3 to 3½ minutes (the sum is 160).

Substituting in the formula,

$$\text{PEI} = \frac{30,000}{2 \times 160} = 94$$

On the basis of about 8,000 tests carried out on college students, the following norms were prepared:

> Below 55 = Poor physical condition
> From 55 to 64 = Low average
> From 65 to 79 = High average
> From 80 to 89 = Good
> Above 90 = Excellent

A *short form* of the Harvard Step Test was proposed by Johnson and Robinson at the Harvard Fatigue Laboratory.[36] The exercise phase is the same as for the regular test; however, the pulse is counted once from one minute to one minute thirty seconds. The score is obtained from the formula:

$$\text{PEI} = \frac{\text{Duration of Exercise in Seconds} \times 100}{5.5 \times \text{Pulse Count}}$$

---

[36] Reported by Edward C. Schneider and Peter V. Karpovich, *Physiology of Muscular Activity*, 4th ed. (Philadelphia: W. B. Saunders Company, 1953), p. 270.

The norms for the rapid form are: Below 50, Poor; 50-80, Average; Above 80, Good.

In the original validation of the Harvard Step Test, Brouha tested 2200 Harvard male students. The following means were obtained: 75 for all students, 93 for all athletes, 88 for the freshman track team, 90 for the varsity baseball team, 95 for the varsity track team, and 109 for the varsity crew. The freshman class before training averaged 69; after training, their average was 76. Using the short form, Taddonio and Karpovich obtained the following means: 62, sedentary individuals; 86, sprinters and hurdlers; 99, marathon runners; 105, freshman cross-country runners; and 111, varsity cross-country runners.

Attempts to validate the Step Test as a measure of physical strength and endurance, however, have mostly failed. With 117 male students, Cureton and his associates,[37] using a 15-inch bench, obtained correlations between .002 and .31 with 27 different tests of muscular strength, muscular endurance, and running endurance. Bookwalter,[38] utilizing 1,269 A.S.T.P. cadets as subjects, reported no relationship between this test and the Army Physical Fitness Test, nor between it and age, height, weight, 100-yard pick-a-back, and 300-yard dash criteria. Neff and Steitz[39] also obtained low correlations between the test and strength and endurance items and batteries. On the positive side, Taddonio and Karpovich[40] obtained a rank-difference correlation of .63 between the short form of the Harvard test and the order in which Springfield College men finished an intramural cross-country race.

MODIFICATIONS OF THE HARVARD STEP TEST

A number of modifications of the Harvard Step Test have been proposed so as to adapt the test to groups other than normal college men. The stepping process is the same as for the original test; unless otherwise indicated below, the three after-exercise pulse counts are also the same.

---

[37] Thomas K. Cureton, et al., op. cit., Chap. 7.

[38] Karl W. Bookwalter, "A Study of the Brouha Step Test," The Physical Educator, Vol. V, No. 3 (May 1948), p. 55.

[39] Charles B. Neff and Edward S. Steitz, "A Study to Determine Physical Fitness Test Items against Criteria of Composite Scores of PFI, Army, and Harvard Step-Up Tests." Unpublished master's thesis, Springfield College, Springfield, Mass., 1948.

[40] Taddonio and Karpovich, op. cit.

College Women and High School Girls

Clarke [41] studied the use of the step test with 296 Radcliffe College women. She used a bench 18 inches high; the exercise consisted of 30 steps per minute for four minutes. Based on the Harvard men's norms, the distribution of these women was as follows: excellent, 2 percent; good, 15 percent; high average, 31 percent; low average, 9 percent; poor, 43 percent.

Brouha and Gallagher [42] used a bench 16 inches high for high school girls; the exercise was the same as for college women.

Secondary School Boys

In preliminary trials of the step test, Gallagher and Brouha [43] found a wide range of size in boys between the ages of 12 and 18 years. As a consequence, two heights of benches were used for the small and large boys. The division of the boys was made on the basis of body surface area, as follows:

Less than 1.85 square meters: 18-inch bench

1.85 square meters and above: 20-inch bench

Surface area may be easily determined from the nomographic chart in Figure 5.1.

The stepping rate is 30 steps a minute for four minutes, unless, of course, the subject stops sooner because of exhaustion. The investigators presented the following distribution of scores after testing 600 private school boys:

Score of 50 or less:	Very poor physical condition	2 per cent
51–60:	Poor physical condition	18 per cent
61–70:	Fair physical condition	50 per cent
71–80:	Good physical condition	25 per cent
81–90:	Excellent physical condition	4 per cent
91 or more:	Superior physical condition	1 per cent

---

[41] Harriet L. Clarke, "A Functional Physical Fitness Test for College Women," *Journal of Health and Physical Education*, Vol. XIV, No. 7 (September 1943), p. 358.

[42] Lucien Brouha and J. Roswell Gallagher, "A Functional Test for High School Girls," *Journal of Health and Physical Education*, Vol. XIV, No. 10 (December 1943), p. 517.

[43] J. Roswell Gallagher and Lucien Brouha, "A Simple Method of Testing the Physical Fitness of Boys," *Research Quarterly*, Vol. XIV, No. 1 (March 1943), p. 23.

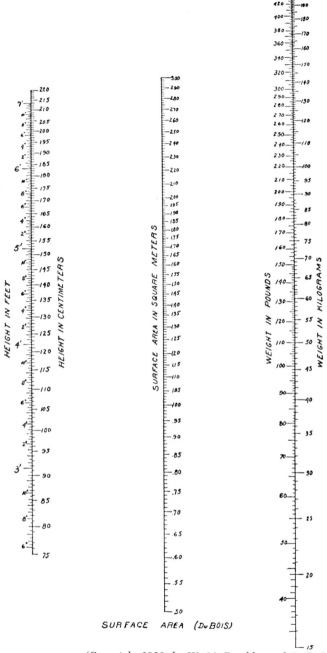

Figure 5.1.   DuBois Body Surface Chart: Nomograph.

109

Convalescent Patients

Karpovich, Starr, and Weiss [44] used the 20-inch bench and a cadence of 24 steps per minute over a period of 30 seconds for evaluating the condition of patients in army hospitals for participation in mild physical activity. As the condition of the patient improved at the direction of the ward medical officer, his readiness for more strenuous exercise was measured by his ability to perform the same exercise for longer periods, until he reached five minutes. His physical condition was evaluated both by the pulse response and by ability to endure exercise.

APPLICATION OF CARDIOVASCULAR TESTS

The evidence supporting the use of cardiovascular tests in health and physical education programs is still inconclusive. This fact is shown by the relationship between various cardiovascular tests themselves, between cardiovascular tests and general endurance, and between cardiovascular tests and bodily strength.

Relationships Between Cardiovascular Tests

The correlation between certain cardiovascular tests is low. In a carefully conducted experiment, Sambolin [45] correlated the results of the following tests applied to the same subjects: (a) Schneider's Physical Efficiency Index, (b) McCurdy-Larson's Organic Efficiency Index, (c) Crampton's Blood-Ptosis Fitness, and (d) McCloy's Efficiency Index. A fairly high correlation (.68) was obtained between McCloy's and Schneider's tests. The other correlations were low, the highest being .29 between the Schneider test and Crampton's test. The McCurdy-Larson correlations with the other tests were so low as to be insignificant.

Cook and Wherry [46] also obtained low correlations between tests based on cardiovascular manifestations. They obtained a coefficient of —.28 between the Harvard Step Test and the cardiovascular phase of the Behnke Step-Up Test and between the Schneider Test

---

44 Peter V. Karpovich, Merritt P. Starr, and Raymond A. Weiss, "Physical Fitness Test for Convalescents," *Journal of the American Medical Association,* Vol. CXXVI (December 2, 1944), p. 873.

45 Luis F. Sambolin, "Extent of Relationship Between Several Selected Strength and Cardiovascular Tests." Unpublished master's thesis, Syracuse University, 1943.

46 Ellsworth Cook and Robert J. Wherry, "A Statistical Evaluation of Physical Fitness Tests," *Research Quarterly,* Vol. 21, No. 2 (May, 1950), p. 94.

and the endurance phase of the Behnke Step-Up Test; the Harvard test correlated .23 with the endurance phase of the Behnke test. The correlation between the Harvard and Schneider tests for their Navy submarine personnel was .08.

Supposedly, the various cardiovascular-type tests are designed to measure much the same thing. With one exception, however, the tests utilized in Sambolin's study are not. The test items in the McCloy and Schneider tests, which had the highest correlation, although not identical are comparable, both being based upon changes in heart rate and blood pressure from reclining to standing positions and upon changes in these elements following a standard amount of exercise.

Relationship Between Cardiovascular Tests and General Endurance

As reported above, McCurdy and Larson obtained correlations of .68 and .70 between their test and their endurance criteria of 440-yard swimmers and infirmary patients. These coefficients are not high enough to assure educators of their consistent accuracy. Nevertheless, these studies show that circulatory-respiratory condition is significant if exercise, at least when applied to 440-yard swimmers, reaches the endurance stage—when it is vigorous and of long duration. Whether this conclusion can also be applied to other types of physical activities is not clear.

Using the Tuttle Pulse-Ratio Test, Flanagan [47] reported a correlation of —.89 with a ratio index of endurance, based upon the ability to maintain on a 220-yard run the speed a subject has established on a 60-yard run (where endurance is not the dominant factor). The correlation of .63 obtained between the short form of the Harvard Step Test and the order of finish of a college intramural cross-country run was mentioned above. However, Henry and Kleeberger [48] in a similar experiment reported a correlation of but —.46, and pointed out that Flanagan's correlation is spuriously high owing to the omission of 9 of his 56 subjects who were found to be away from the general distribution (regression line).

---

[47] Kenneth Flanagan, "The Pulse-Ratio Test as a Measure of Athletic Endurance in Sprint Running," *Supplement to the Research Quarterly*, Vol. VI, No. 3 (October 1935), p. 46.

[48] Franklin M. Henry and Frank L. Kleeberger, "The Validity of the Pulse-Ratio Test of Cardiac Efficiency," *Research Quarterly*, Vol. IX, No. 1 (March 1938), p. 32.

Relationship Between Cardiovascular Tests and Strength

Conflicting reports have also been made on the relationship between cardiovascular tests and strength. Rifenberick [49] obtained the following correlations between the Tuttle Pulse-Ratio Test and the Physical Fitness Index (PFI): [50] (1) With 28 eighth-grade boys in fall tests, .80; (2) in spring tests, .83; (3) with 32 seventh-grade boys in fall tests, .94; and (4) in spring tests, .90. Cureton and Wickens [51] conclude contrarily that muscular strength is not correlated with "organic endurance condition" as measured by the McCurdy-Larson test. However, in the latter experiment, present PFI testing techniques were not followed; particularly, the belt was not used in the leg-strength test. Neff and Steitz [52] also obtained insignificant correlations between the Harvard Step Test and the PFI.

Experimentation by Sambolin,[53] where most recent testing procedures were carefully observed, resulted in insignificant correlations between all strength items in the PFI battery and the cardiovascular-type tests devised by Schneider, Crampton, and McCloy, as shown in Table I. The correlations between the McCurdy-Larson and the various strength tests, however, indicated some relationship between this test and *total strength:* low correlations of .35 to .41 with individual items and a jump to .55 with the Strength Index (SI), which is the total score of all tests in the battery. At the same time, the insignificant correlation of .20 with the PFI indicates slight relationship with *gross strength related to relative size.*

In the strength tests, the large boy (unless his size is due to fat) has the advantage in securing a high SI. With strength norms based upon age and weight, all boys regardless of size have a comparable opportunity to obtain a high PFI. However, body size is not an essential element in physical fitness: a small man can be as fit as a large one. The tendency of the McCurdy-Larson test to be posi-

---

[49] Robert H. Rifenberick, "A Comparison of Physical Fitness Ratings as Determined by the Pulse-Ratio and Rogers' Test of Physical Fitness," *Research Quarterly*, Vol. XIII, No. 1 (March 1942), p. 95.

[50] A strength test with norms based upon weight and age.

[51] Thomas K. Cureton and J. Stuart Wickens, "The Center of Gravity Test and Its Relation to Posture, Physical Fitness and Athletic Ability," *Supplement to the Research Quarterly*, Vol. VI, No. 2 (May 1935), p. 93.

[52] Neff and Steitz, *op. cit.*

[53] Luis F. Sambolin, *op. cit.*

PHYSIOLOGICAL FITNESS

TABLE I

RELATIONSHIP BETWEEN STRENGTH TESTS AND CARDIOVASCULAR
TESTS IN TERMS OF COEFFICIENTS OF CORRELATION

Strength Tests	Cardiovascular Tests			
	Schneider	McCurdy-Larson	McCloy	Crampton
Physical Fitness Index	.003	.20	.004	.07
Strength Index	− .03	.55	.10	.07
Arm Strength	− .04	.41	.12	.12
Right plus Left Grips	.04	.35	.17	.08
Lung Capacity	.02	.31	− .001	.06
Leg Strength	− .03	.39	.13	.11
Back Strength	− .01	.39	− .002	− .04

tively related to gross strength, therefore, would tend to reduce its value to physical educators as a measure of the basic fitness of the individual.

Usefulness of Cardiovascular Tests

The relationship of cardiovascular tests to various aspects of body condition is not sufficiently well known; furthermore, the tests themselves are composed of elements many of which must be given with extreme care and repeated several times in order to obtain accurate results. However, certain of these tests hold promise for limited use in physical education. For example, the McCurdy-Larson test is useful in determining the physical condition of endurance swimmers, but is not so valuable in appraising stamina and endurance. The Harvard-type step test certainly is differential of athletes and non-athletes, but generally has not correlated well with endurance criteria; a modified form of this test has been used successfully in determining the exercise tolerance of convalescents. In several different studies, the use of the Tuttle pulse-ratio test has led to the detection of defective hearts; the ultimate diagnosis, of course, should only be done by a physician and such testing should not be substituted for a thorough medical examination of the heart.

Certain studies point to possible modifications or substitutes for the present forms of the step tests. Russell [54] experimented with the length of time college men could continue stepping up and down on a 17-inch bench at a rate of 40 steps per minute; each subject continued stepping until unable to do so because of exhaustion. He obtained the following correlations between the length of time this all-out step test was performed, and various motor fitness tests: .70 with the Illinois test, .64 with the Army Air Forces test, .64 with the Navy test, and .61 with the Indiana test. He also obtained the high correlation of .85 between the length of time the step test was continued and the gross oxygen intake on a treadmill run to exhaustion. A second possibility is revealed by Davis, [55] who obtained a correlation of .66 between Leighton workmeter performance [56] and increase in pulse rate from a stepping exercise.

Neither of these studies used pulse-beat recovery after strenuous exercise as the basis for evaluation, as is true for the usual step test. Rather, Russell's evaluation was based on the length of time an individual can continue a vigorous exercise; Davis' evaluation was based on the amount of increase in pulse rate as a result of vigorous exercise. Quite possibly, physical educators may find one of these measures useful for evaluating cardiorespiratory endurance.

CARDIOVASCULAR TESTING AIDS

In this section, a number of aids for those who wish to use cardiovascular testing in their physical education programs will be presented.

Benches for Step Tests

Four different heights of benches are necessary for the various step tests described in this chapter. These are as follows: 13 inches

---

[54] Walter L. Russell, "A Study of the Relationship of Performance in Certain Generally Accepted Tests of Physical Fitness to Circulatory-Respiratory Capacity of Normal College Men," Microcarded Doctor of Education Dissertation, Louisiana State University, 1948.

[55] John S. Davis, "A Study of Physical Fitness by Analyzing Military Physical Efficiency Tests and Leighton Workmeter," Doctor of Education Dissertation, University of Oregon, 1948.

[56] The Leighton Workmeter is an apparatus designed to measure the number of feet of rope a subject can pull in one minute against a constant breaking pressure (20 pounds in this study).

for the Tuttle Pulse-Ratio Test; 20 inches for the Harvard Step Test and the larger secondary school boys; 18 inches for college women, high school girls, and the smaller secondary school boys; 18½ inches for the Schneider Test. Depending on the test utilized, a sturdy bench of the proper height can easily be constructed; the surface on the step should be ample in size so that the subject feels secure when mounting it.

Where it is desirable to test a number of subjects simultaneously, a long bench can be used so that several boys or girls can mount it at the same time. A number of assistants will be needed, each to count the pulse rate of a single subject. These assistants should be well trained so that they perform the pulse counts correctly and alike. The tester can then supervise the entire operation, count the cadence, signal the end of the test (preceded by a warning signal), and indicate the start and stop of pulse-count periods. The timer needs to call out the elapsed time for any subject who quits before the termination of the stepping time. Gallagher and Brouha [57] have reported that 600 boys have been given this test in a little more than three hours with the assistance of 30 helpers.

In the Schneider and Tuttle Pulse-Ratio tests, the pulse counts must start immediately upon the cessation of exercise. The timer should give a warning signal 15 seconds before the end of testing time. The pulse counter should grasp the subject's wrist, being careful not to interfere with his stepping, and find his pulse before the exercise is completed in order to start the count promptly.

Where individual testing is done and where the physical educator is using more than one test with different bench heights, a combination bench may be constructed. Such a bench is illustrated in Figure 5.2. The step heights of this bench are 13, 18, and 20 inches. The surface area for each bench is 18 by 18 inches.

Cadence and Pulse Count

Stepping counts may best be regulated by a metronome. These may be set for the proper cadence for the test to be administered. As stepping is usually a four-count movement, the metronome may be set for any one of these movements. For example, in the 30-step-

---

[57] Gallagher and Brouha, op. cit.

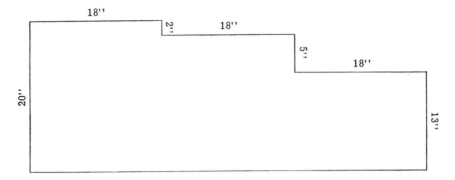

Figure 5.2. Combination Step-Up Bench.

per-minute Harvard Step Test, the metronome may be set at "30", in which case the subject completes the four-count step each time; or, the metronome may be set at "60", in which case the subject mounts the bench on one beat and returns to the floor on the next; or, the metronome may be set at "120", in which case the subject completes each part of the step at each beat. The first situation is a bit too slow to follow smoothly; the latter situation is too fast and may result in some confusion. Thus, the 60 cadence is recommended. The tester also helps as needed by calling out the cadence.

If several subjects are taking the test simultaneously, it may be difficult for all to hear the count. The tester may help by calling out the count: UP, UP, DOWN, DOWN. It is also possible to connect the metronome to an amplifier; the amplifier can then be adjusted to a degree of sound which can be clearly heard by all. Another device which has proven effective is to make a tape recording of the metronome cadence; by turning up the sound on the player, the cadence can be heard easily.

Pulse counts can be made in various ways. The most reliable pulse is taken with a stethoscope placed on the chest below the left nipple at a point halfway between the sternum and the left nipple. Lacking a stethoscope, either the carotid or radial pulse may be utilized. For the carotid pulse, place three fingers on the carotid artery below the ear at the base of the neck. For the radial pulse, place three fingers on the radial artery on the thumb side of the wrist.

Blood Pressure Measurement

The systolic blood pressure is needed for the Crampton Blood-Ptosis Test, the Barach Energy Index, and the Schneider Test; the diastolic blood pressure is necessary for the Barach Energy Index. Blood pressure measurements are made with a mercury sphygmomanometer; a stethoscope is also needed. The cuff is wrapped snugly around the upper part of the left arm just above the elbow joint. The stethoscope earphone is placed in the tester's ears; the stethoscope bell is placed firmly over the brachial artery just above the elbow slightly toward the inside of the arm. The cuff is pumped up with the instrument bulb until no pulse beat can be heard. The tester, then, slowly releases the pressure, watching the mercury column as he does so. When the first pulse sound is heard, the mercury column is read. This is the *systolic pressure,* recorded in millimeters of mercury (mm. Hg.). The tester continues slowly to release the pressure in the cuff. When a dull, forceless beat is heard, the pressure on the mercury column is again read. This is the *diastolic pressure.* Blood pressure is usually recorded with the systolic reading first. Thus, a recording of 122/72 means a systolic pressure of 122 mm. Hg. and a diastolic pressure of 72 mm. Hg. A great deal of practice is necessary in order to take blood pressure measurements accurately.

Endurance Measures

Considerable difficulty has been encountered in developing tests to measure the distinctive quality of general endurance found in prolonged running and swimming. Various approaches to this problem have been made, as follows:

1. *Straight runs:* Such runs as the 220-yard, the 300-yard, and the mile have been used. For example, the 300-yard shuttle run was used extensively by the Army and the Army Air Forces during World War II and since in their motor-fitness batteries. A disadvantage in using the shorter runs as measures of endurance is that they are dependent in large part upon speed; they are really sprint races, albeit endurance is needed. The longer runs, such as the mile, require a knowledge of pace for best results.

2. *Endurance ratio:* The endurance ratio is the proportion between times in short and long runs. This technique is intended to

account for the individual's basic speed in the short event; the ratio indicates how well this speed is carried over the longer distance. McCloy [58] computed a factor analysis on 12 athletic events, administered to 400 well-conditioned soldiers. Four factors were found, identified as follows: circulo-respiratory endurance, velocity, muscular endurance, and mesomorphic body build (tentatively identified). An endurance ratio, obtained as the ratio between the 300-yard and six-seconds runs, had a high factor weighting with circulo-respiratory endurance (.88).

3. *Drop-off index:* In the drop-off index the slowing up in seconds for various parts of a long run is recorded. Cureton [59] utilized this technique in the 100-yard swim by recording the slowing up cumulatively from lap to lap throughout the distance. Another form of the drop-off index is the difference between the time required for a relatively long run and the time that would have been made had the runner maintained the speed he established in the sprint.

4. *Residual index:* Henry and Kleeberger [60] objected to such indices as the above because the index scores of their subjects showed a considerable correlation with times on the short distance, indicating that the indices did not achieve their purpose. As a result of their experimentation, a residual index was proposed consisting of the ratio between time on the 70-yard dash, less the time for the first 10 yards (to eliminate variability in starting time) and time in the 220-yard sprint. These investigators also proposed a variation of the residual index in which the effect of speed was partialed out by statistical procedure.

Some difficulty has been encountered in establishing the various running indices as measures of circulatory-respiratory endurance. However, these tests, especially the endurance ratio, appear to have considerable potentiality for this purpose in physical education. In addition to limitations indicated in the above discussion, Henry and Farmer [61] found the test-retest reliabilities of the various in-

---

[58] C. H. McCloy, "A Factor Analysis of Tests of Endurance," *Research Quarterly,* Vol. XXVII, No. 2 (May 1956), p. 213.

[59] Thomas K. Cureton, "A Test for Endurance in Speed Swimming," *Supplement to the Research Quarterly,* Vol. VI, No. 2 (May 1935), p. 106.

[60] Franklin M. Henry and F. L. Kleeberger, "The Validity of the Pulse-Ratio Test of Cardiac Efficiency," *Research Quarterly,* Vol. IX, No. 1 (March 1938), p. 32.

[61] Franklin M. Henry and Daniel S. Farmer, "Condition Ratings and Endurance Measures," *Research Quarterly,* Vol. XX, No. 2 (May 1949), p. 126.

dices with which they experimented were between .48 and .58. Although reliabilities for the runs were fairly satisfactory (.73 for the 300-yard; and .87 for the 220-yard), the individual speed patterns varied considerably from test to test.

Among the reasons for low reliability and validity of these tests are: lack of knowledge of pace and of skill in running on the part of unskilled subjects; psychological limits of poorly conditioned and unskilled runners when breathlessness and fatigue are experienced; and, the fear of an all-out effort over such exhausting distances as the 220- and 300-yard runs. Furthermore, adequate criteria have not been available for validation of endurance tests. Such criteria are extremely difficult to apply, as they infer an all-out effort terminating in complete exhaustion. Few subjects are willing to punish themselves to this extent.

SELECTED REFERENCES

Cureton, Thomas K., *et al.*, *Endurance of Young Men.* Washington: Society for Research in Child Development, Vol. X, No. 1, Serial No. 40, 1945.

Larson, Leonard A., "A Study of the Validity of Some Cardiovascular Tests," *Journal of Experimental Education,* Vol. VII, No. 3 (March 1939), p. 214.

————, "Cardiovascular-Respiratory Function," *Supplement to the Research Quarterly,* Vol. XII, No. 2 (May 1941), p. 456.

McCloy, C. H., "A Factor Analysis of Tests of Endurance," *Research Quarterly,* Vol. XXVII, No. 2 (May 1956), p. 213.

Schneider, Edward C., and Peter V. Karpovich, *Physiology of Muscular Activity,* 4th ed. Philadelphia: W. B. Saunders Company, 1953.

Wakim, Khalil G., "Physiological Aspects of Therapeutic Exercise," *Journal of American Medical Association,* Vol. CXLII (January 14, 1950), p. 100.

CHAPTER SIX

Nutrition and Body Build

The use of tests to measure the nutritional status of children in school has been common for a good many years. The purpose of this measurement is primarily to discover those who are malnourished and those who are obese so that appropriate remedial procedures may be applied. Efforts in this direction should continue, constituting a major phase of the physical measurement program.

Malnutrition is particularly serious and a threat to health among children and young adults; it is most apt to develop during the period of rapid growth in children's lives. A normal amount of fatty tissue is necessary to the body: to act as reserve fuel, to furnish padding about the nerve endings, and to buoy up the visceral organs and keep them in place. Accordingly, the very thin person is apt to be high-strung and nervous; the abdominal organs commonly sag out of normal position; and the poorly nourished muscle tissues, including the muscles of the abdominal wall and the muscle layers of the intestines, become relaxed and flabby. Such persons suffer from nervous indigestion, constipation, and a wide variety of ill-defined ailments. Furthermore, malnourished individuals are usually listless and fatigue easily, or else keep going under strain, which results in a dangerous accumulation of fatigue products. They also show diminished resistance to fatigue and general lowered vitality. Tuberculosis and other respiratory infections are especially apt to develop in young people if they are undernourished. Life insurance figures show that in the early twenties mortality increases about one per cent for every pound below average weight for height.

Obesity is a problem that chiefly concerns adults, although many obese children are found in school. Although a well-filled body and a moderate store of fat are advantageous for children and young adults, nevertheless, definite obesity whenever found is disadvantageous. It results in disfigurement and inefficiency of physical movement. It is also so dangerous that obese persons are poor risks in operations. Moreover, their resistance to infectious diseases is lowered; and excessive weight places an additional burden upon the circulatory system and the kidneys, so that such persons are prone to develop functional disorders of the heart, high blood pressure, nephritis, and so forth.

Life insurance figures show that at the age of thirty-five, mortality increases about 1 per cent for every pound over normal weight for height; at the age period forty to forty-four years, an excess of 20 per cent in weight increases mortality 30–40 per cent above the normal for these ages; and a 40 per cent excess weight for the latter period involves an 80–100 per cent increase in mortality. Moreover, when abdominal girth is more than two inches greater than the chest girth at full expansion, the extra mortality is 50 per cent above the excess mortality associated with the overweight stage.[1]

Armstrong and associates[2] contrasted the mortality rate of overweight persons, limited to substandard life insurance, with persons accepted for standard insurance. The mortality rates were 79 per cent for men markedly overweight and 42 per cent for men moderately overweight above the standard risk group; comparable percentages for women were 61 and 42 respectively. The excess mortality rate was due to the greater number of deaths from degenerative diseases. Joslin and associates[3] found from an analysis of 3,000 clinical records that 63 per cent of males and 67 per cent of females showed evidence of overweight at the outset of diabetes. From a survey of 74,000 industrial workers, Master and associates[4] found at every age and for both sexes that average

[1] Metropolitan Life Insurance Company, *Statistical Bulletin*, Vol. XVIII (May 1937), p. 5.

[2] D. B. Armstrong, *et al.*, "Obesity and Its Relation to Health and Disease," *Journal of American Medical Association*, Vol. CXLVII, 1951, p. 1007.

[3] E. P. Joslin, *et al.*, *Treatment of Diabetes Mellitus* (Philadelphia: Lea and Febiger, 1952).

[4] A. M. Master, *et al.*, "The Normal Blood Pressure Range and Its Clinical Implications," *Journal of American Medical Association*, Vol. CXLIII, 1950, p. 1464.

blood pressure increased with body weight for a given height.

The departure from a height-weight standard may in some instances be due to body components other than fat. Welham and Behnke,[5] for example, concluded that "according to standard height-weight tables, the majority of football players could be classified as unfit for military service, and as not qualified for first class insurance by reason of overweight." Obviously, overweight in these men is due largely to non-fat components. Evidence exists that the over-all pattern of overweight, rather than excess fat alone, is the underlying factor in the above mortality figures. Spain and others[6] and Gertler and his associates[7] found many more deaths from coronary heart disease among mesomorphs than among endomorphs, which thus relates causation more to body build than to obesity. Kurlander and his group[8] reported no relationship between heart disease and obesity; however, there was a pronounced relationship when obesity was included with other body components producing overweight conditions.

Overweight is especially prone to develop between the ages of thirty-five and forty-five years, and becomes more and more dangerous with advancing age. Although obesity at these advanced ages is not specifically a school problem, nevertheless, the dangers should be understood and proper steps adopted early for those children portraying signs of excessive weight.

CHARACTERISTICS OF MALNUTRITION

Bogert describes malnutrition as "a state in which either the *food intake is inadequate in some respect* to meet body needs, or in which physiological and environmental *conditions are such that the body is unable to utilize sufficient food materials* to provide for its proper growth, maintenance, and repair."[9] Thus, food inadequate in

---

[5] W. C. Welham and A. R. Behnke, "The Specific Gravity of Healthy Men," *Journal of American Medical Association*, Vol. CXVIII, 1942, p. 498.

[6] D. M. Spain, *et al.*, "Observations on Atherosclerosis of the Coronary Arteries in Males under Age 46," *Annals of Internal Medicine*, Vol. XXXVIII, 1953, p. 254.

[7] M. M. Gertler, *et al.*, "Young Candidates for Coronary Heart Disease," *Journal of American Medical Association*, Vol. CXLVII, 1951, p. 621.

[8] Arnold B. Kurlander, "Obesity and Disease," in Josef Bnzek, ed., *Body Measurements and Human Nutrition* (Detroit: Wayne University Press, 1956), p. 93.

[9] L. Jean Bogert, *Nutrition and Physical Fitness*, 6th ed. (Philadelphia: W. B. Saunders Company, 1954).

amount or deficient in essential materials, or internal or external conditions that interfere with the normal processes by which the food is utilized in the body, will tend to produce a malnourished condition. This condition will, of course, be more or less severe, depending upon the extent of the deficiency thus brought about.

Naturally, signs of malnutrition are produced upon the body in various degrees depending upon the extent of the nutritional disturbance. To assist health and physical education teachers in becoming familiar with these signs, in Table II the more striking characteristics of the well-nourished individual are contrasted with those frequently found among individuals who are malnourished.

The physical educator has an especially good opportunity to note the nutritional characteristics of children, as they may be observed informally without clothes in locker rooms and showers and in abbreviated attire in the gymnasium and on the athletic field. Thorough acquaintance with the characteristics of good nutrition and malnutrition will enable the physical educator to screen out boys and girls in need of help in developing a properly nourished body.

In making judgments of the nutritional status of school-age children, however, it should be remembered that they have a high degree of subjectivity. Consequently, they are open to the inaccuracies and differences of opinion between judges which are typical of other ratings of this sort. Franzen [10] studied the agreement between physicians' judgments of nutritional status. The children in five different groups were examined by a number of physicians, using an adaptation of the Dunfermline Scale, and their judgments of the same children were intercorrelated. The median correlation between any two physicians was .60; correlations occurred as low as .18 and as high as .82. When the physicians used 46 items, each of which was credited as satisfactory or debited as unsatisfactory for each child, the correlation between physicians was raised only five points to .65.

Although the objectivity of physicians' ratings of nutritional status is low, the reliability of the analytic rating scheme of 46 items is high. Correlations by the split-half method, any 23 items correlated with the other 23, are as follows for five physicians using 61 cases: .99, .97, .96, .95, and .90. These correlations indicate that

---

[10] Raymond Franzen, *Physical Measures of Growth and Nutrition* (New York: American Child Health Association, 1929).

TABLE II

COMPARISON OF THE CHARACTERISTICS OF GOOD NUTRITION
AND MALNUTRITION [*]

Item	Good Nutrition	Malnutrition
1. Body	Well developed	Undersized, poorly developed; presence of physical defects
2. Weight	About average for height	Usually thin, but may be normal or overweight
3. Muscles	Well developed and firm	Small and flabby
4. Skin	Healthy color	Loose, pale, waxy, or sallow
5. Subcutaneous fat	Good layer	Usually lacking
6. Mucous membrane (eyelids and mouth)	Reddish pink	Pale
7. Hair	Smooth and glossy	Often rough and without luster
8. Eyes	Clear and without dark circles under them	Dark hollows or blue circles under eyes
9. Facial expression	Alert, but without strain	Drawn, worried, old—or animated but strained
10. Posture	Good: head erect, chest up, shoulders flat, abdomen in	Fatigue posture: head thrust forward, chest flat and narrow, shoulders rounded, abdomen protruding
11. Disposition	Good-natured and full of life	Irritable, overactive—or phlegmatic, listless
12. Sleep	Sound and restful	Difficult to get to sleep; sleep restless
13. Digestion and elimination	Good	Subject to nervous indigestion and constipation
14. Appetite	Good	"Finicky" about food
15. General health	Excellent	Lacks endurance and vigor

[*] Adapted from L. Jean Bogert, *Nutrition and Physical Fitness,* 6th ed. (Philadelphia: W. B. Saunders Company, 1954).

when a physician judges a child to be malnourished, he is consistent in rating the child high or low on most items.

Judgments upon which important decisions concerning the child are reached should be reasonably accurate and certain, and not relative to the individual who happens to make the judgments. If a child is malnourished, he should be consistently recognized as malnourished, regardless of who examines him. Consequently, other testing procedures for measuring nutritional status should be sought and utilized in conjunction with physicians' examinations.

AGE-HEIGHT-WEIGHT

For years, age-height-weight tables have been used in the schools as indices of nutritional status, while monthly weighing of children and the plotting of their weight curves have been common practices.[11] The usual policy has been to consider as malnourished all children who were 10 per cent below the average for their sex, age, and height; as obese, those who were 20 per cent above the average. The advantages of this practice are the universal appeal and understanding of weight, the simplicity and economy of the measurement, and the opportunity to center health lessons in the classroom around the numerous and varied reasons for losing and gaining weight. Excellent health programs have been developed in this way, the periodic weighing effectively motivating the child.

Recent research, however, has cast considerable doubt, not on the health programs so developed, but on the reliance that can be placed upon age-height-weight tables as a measure of nutritional status. A number of conflicting statements have been made. Certain authorities on nutrition, such as Bogert, maintain that the use of these tables results largely in omissions rather than commissions: that children who are from 7 to 10 per cent below average weight are definitely malnourished and exhibit signs of lowered vitality and lowered physical efficiency, while to be more than 10 per cent underweight usually means a dangerous reduction in fitness and stamina; but also that malnourished children are not necessarily underweight, since frequently individuals may be up to or may exceed the average weight for their type and yet have low vitality or be in poor health, with soft, flabby flesh, poor color, and often poor bones and teeth.

The weight of the body is undoubtedly an excellent index of body nutrition when related to several other conditions. However, the

---

[11] See L. Jean Bogert, *op. cit.*, for age-height-weight tables.

most serious faults in applying age-height-weight tables to determine nutritional status are the complete neglect of body build, or skeletal dimensions, and of the gross proportion of bone, muscle, and fat in considering the standard weight that one should equal. For example, two individuals may be of the same age, height, and weight, and yet be totally different in their nutritional status: one may be of tall, slender build with good muscle development and adequate subcutaneous flesh; the other may be tall, big-boned, of stocky build, with poor muscle development and little subcutaneous flesh. Furthermore, two individuals may be of the same skeletal size, may weigh the same, and still be vastly different in the proportions of muscle and fat, as well as the size and density of the internal organs. Yet, in both of these situations, the individuals are classified alike. Actually, one's weight cannot be completely understood unless differentiated according to body build and the components of the various tissue types.

The latter conclusions are verified somewhat by Franzen's studies.[12] Individual differences in chest dimensions and hips are much more important than height as determiners of variations in weight. Actually, however, weights appearing on the height-weight tables are largely based on individuals with small chest and hip dimensions. The following correlations were reported:

1. Zero: Height with girth of upper arm and girth of calf.
2. Negative: Height with amount of subcutaneous tissue.
3. Low: Weight for a given height with girth residuals and with subcutaneous tissue.

Thus, the reasons for underweight, as determined by age-height-weight tables, are mainly other than the condition of muscles and subcutaneous tissue; in fact, tall children are actually penalized.

WEIGHT AND BODY BUILD

Recognizing the inadequacy of height as a basis for predicting body weight, several experimenters have proposed methods of assaying weight upon various skeletal dimensions. In the early days of physical education, during the time of Hitchcock, Seaver, and Sargent, measurement was very largely based upon anthropometric

---

[12] Raymond Franzen, *op. cit.*

tests of this type. It fell into disrepute, however, largely because it attempted to define a uniform type of body proportions that all should attain; hereditary individual differences, except that of height, were ignored. Present anthropometry recognizes individual differences and attempts to appraise the subject in terms of his structural differences and to determine his potentialities in terms of those structural characteristics. To measure nutritional status, the percentage by which an individual is overweight or underweight is compared with that of others of his own skeletal build. Several researches of this sort have been conducted.

Pryor's Width-Weight Tables [13]

After studying various anthropometric measures, Pryor proposed a "Width-Length" Index, computed by the following formula:

$$\text{Width-Length Index} = \frac{\text{Bi-iliac Diameter}}{\text{Standing Height}} \times 1000.$$

Pryor concluded that the bi-iliac diameter, or width of the pelvic crest measured from the widest points of the iliac crest, was the most important and least variable of any of the measures with which she experimented. This measure, also, does not change with shifts in posture and with respiration. Furthermore, the Width-Length Index remains proportionately identical for the same children at different ages, as shown by the calculation of the indices every six months for a four-year period on 100 boys and 100 girls during adolescence. For example, a child found to be 8 per cent broader than the average for his age-sex group at age 10 years remained approximately 8 per cent broader than average at 14 years of age. The converse is also true. However, the relationship between the Width-Length Index and body weight, although slightly superior, still suffers from the gross defects of other measures of this general type mentioned above.

The Pryor weight tables are based on sex and age and the following three anthropometric tests: chest width, hip width, and standing height. The equipment required to administer these tests are: a stadiometer, or other method for measuring height; weight scales; a straight arm sliding caliper, calibrated in centimeters. Directions for administering the tests are as follows:

---

[13] Helen B. Pryor, *Width-Weight Tables* (Stanford University, California: Stanford University Press, 1940).

Age: Age is recorded to the nearest birthday.

Weight: For most accurate results, weight should be taken without clothes; recorded to the nearest pound. If measured with clothes, a deduction equal to approximately the weight of the clothes worn should be made.

Height: Standing height is measured without shoes, with the pupil standing as tall as he can; the record is made to the nearest inch.

Chest width: The subject stands relaxed, breathing normally, with arms at the side of the body. The tester stands facing the subject with the sliding caliper held horizontal at nipple level and with the arms of the caliper resting, without pressure, on the sides of the thoracic cage. The measurement is taken at the end of a normal expiration; and recorded to the nearest tenth of a centimeter.

Hip width: This measurement is made from the front with the two arms of the caliper pressed firmly against the widest point of the iliac crest. In testing girls, tilt the caliper slightly upward; in testing boys, tilt it slightly downward. The measurement should be taken without intervening clothes; record to the nearest tenth of a centimeter.

Pryor has constructed Width-Weight Tables [14] for each age and sex from one year to forty years and over. Seven normal weights are given for each age and height, based upon the Width-Length Index. The central column of figures in each instance represents the average weight for age and height, medico-actuarial tables [15] being used, except for the ages of 6 to 16, where Baldwin-Wood weights are used instead. Starting from the central column in each table, the three columns to the right represent 5, 7, and 10 per cent heavier weights than the central column; those to the left represent similar percentages which are lighter. For ages 6 to 16, however, since there is a greater variability in physical measurement during this period of rapid growth, the percentages are 7, 10, and 15, respectively.

---

[14] The Pryor Width-Weight Tables are too extensive for duplication in this text. They may, however, be secured from the Stanford University Press, Stanford University, California, as well as 20-inch maple calipers for measuring chest and hip widths.

[15] *Medico-Actuarial Investigation,* Vol. I, Association of Life Insurance Medical Directors and the Actuarial Society of America, 1912.

Wellesley Weight Prediction Method [16]

In studying methods of weight prediction for college women, Ludlum and Powell found that height, chest depth, and chest width were the most effective of the items studied. The following regression equation was obtained between these tests and the weights of 1,580 women from nineteen colleges throughout the United States:

$$\text{Weight} = 2.6 \text{ (Sum of Measurements)} - 154.3.$$

The coefficient of correlation between actual and the predicted weights was .71, with a predictive index of .30. Height correlated with actual weights was .57, with a predictive index of .17. Thus, the new formula is approximately twice as effective in predicting weight as in height alone.

Measurements for the Wellesley weight prediction method are taken in the following manner:

1. *Height:* standing; readings taken to the nearest ½ inch.

2. *Chest depth:* horizontal distance between the midsternal and midspinal lines at the level of the lower end of sternum; readings taken to the nearest ½ centimeter.

3. *Chest width:* horizontal midaxillary distance at the same level as for chest depth; readings taken to the nearest ½ centimeter.

In measuring chest depth and chest width, readings are taken at the end of a normal expiration. A straight arm sliding caliper, similar to that used in the Pryor test described above, calibrated in centimeters, is used for measuring these chest diameters. Table XVIII, Appendix B, is provided, from which weight in pounds may be read directly from the sum of the three measurements.

The Wetzel Grid [17]

The Wetzel Grid is devised as a direct reading control chart on the quality of growth and development in individual boys and girls. It is divided into seven channels: the three center channels are for good to fair physiques; the two flanking channels on the right indicate thin children; the two flanking channels on the left, fat children. The child's position on the grid is plotted from his height,

---

[16] F. E. Ludlum and Elizabeth Powell, "Chest-Height-Weight Tables for College Women," *Research Quarterly*, Vol. XI, No. 3 (October 1940), p. 55.

[17] Norman C. Wetzel, *The Treatment of Growth Failure in Children* (Cleveland: NEA Service, Inc., 1948).

weight, and age. From this plotting, his developmental level and his age schedule of development are determined; repeated plottings indicate the direction of his growth and development. If the child's growth is normal, even though he has a thin build, he will stay in the same channel as time goes on, moving upward progressively. But, if malnutrition, fatigue, or illness hampers growth, the child slips out of his accustomed channel. Two grids are available: a baby grid and the regular grid for school children.[18]

A copy of the Wetzel Grid appears in Figure 6.1. Directions for its use are as follows:

1. At the time of the first testing, record the pupil's name and date of birth in the upper left-hand corner of the grid. Below the name are spaces for recording the date, age, weight, height, and developmental level for the initial and subsequent tests. The illustration on the chart is for a boy, 10 years of age, with a weight of 55¼ pounds and a height of 50 inches, at the time of initial testing.

2. The pupil's height and weight are plotted on the physique channels. For this boy, the plot fell in channel M; from the Physical Status Chart on the left, he is classified as "good." (Individuals in channels A_1 and A_2 are classified as stocky; in A_3 and beyond, obese; in B_2, fair; in B_3, borderline; in B_4 and beyond, poor.) The subject's developmental level is 66, as shown by the diagonal lines crossing the channels. At each subsequent testing, this plot is made again; this indicates the individual's growth pattern.

3. The pupil's Age Schedule of Development is next plotted; the panel for this purpose is on the right side of the grid. Thus, with our boy of 10 years and developmental level of 66, the age schedule falls between the 82 per cent and 98 per cent lines or about 90 per cent; this age-level relation becomes a point on a child's schedule of development, known as an auxodrome.

The auxodrome is a curve representing the age at which a child arrives at any developmental level in the channel. Five such time tables of development are included in the panel; these have been standardized to give the percentage of children on or ahead of these respective schedules. Thus, with our subject, 90 per cent of boys have reached the 66th level in the channel as early as 10 years, as

---

[18] Wetzel Grids and other information pertaining to them may be secured from NEA Service, Inc., 1200 West Third Street, Cleveland 13, Ohio.

far as rate of development is concerned. The 67 per cent auxodrome is taken as the standard of reference for determining whether a child is advanced, normal, or retarded.

4. Several methods employing the auxodrome may be used to determine a child's physical advancement, as follows:

a. *Position of auxodrome relative to the standard:* This position was explained above with our subject falling on the 90 per cent line. In this case, the boy would be considered retarded, as he is below the 67 per cent line.

b. *Developmental age:* This is determined by reading the age at which the 67 per cent norm crosses a given developmental level. For the boy in the illustration, the level of 66 crosses the 67 per cent line at age 8⅓ years, which, thus, becomes his developmental age.

c. *Developmental ratio:* This ratio is as follows:

$$\text{Developmental Ratio} = \frac{\text{Developmental Age}}{\text{Actual Age}}$$

Hence, in the example: D.R. = 8.33/10, or .833.

In his original work, Wetzel compared Grid ratings of 2,093 school children, kindergarten through the twelfth grade, with physicians' estimates. Agreement was reported for 94 per cent, except for those children rated as fair, and upon whom physicians themselves had difficulty in agreeing. Moreover, the Grid caught 95 per cent of those children classified as poor or borderline by the doctors. Kahn and associates [19] found growth failures by Wetzel Grid methods in 157 children with acute rheumatic fever; the follow-up position determination of 130 of the children revealed a shift toward marked improvement in growth and development. Bruch [20] confirmed the usefulness of the Grid technique in the early recognition of abnormal changes in the height-weight relationship. However, he obtained no agreement between developmental age, as assessed by the grid, and skeletal age, as appraised from hand and wrist X-rays. Hall [21] obtained consistently low correlations between

[19] Lawrence Kahn, George Brown, and David Goldring, "Wetzel Grid Analysis of Rheumatic Children," *Journal of Pediatrics*, Vol. XLI, No. 1 (July 1952), p. 47.

[20] Hilde Bruch, "The Grid for Evaluating Physical Fitness (Wetzel)," *Journal of American Medical Association*, Vol. LCXVI, No. 15 (April 11, 1942), p. 1289.

[21] Sue M. Hall, "A Comparative Study of the Carlson Fatigue Curve Test, the Brouha Step Test, the Wetzel Grid, and the Medical Examination," Microcarded Doctoral Dissertation, Ohio State University, 1948.

GRID for Evaluating PHYSICAL FITNESS
in Terms of PHYSIQUE (Body Build), DEVELOPMENTAL LEVEL and BASAL METABOLISM
— A Guide to Individual Progress from Infancy to Maturity —

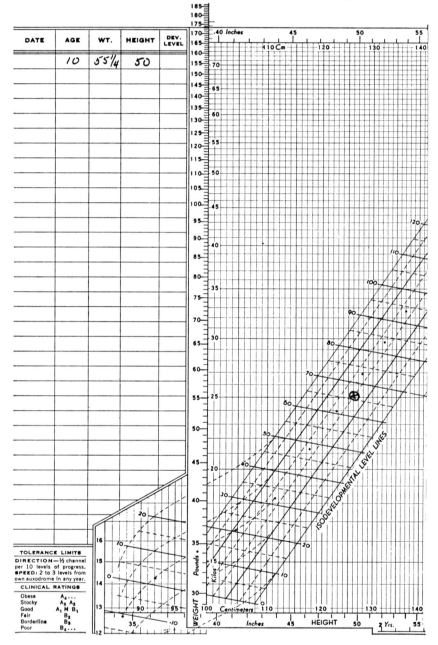

DATE	AGE	WT.	HEIGHT	DEV. LEVEL
	10	55¼	50	

TOLERANCE LIMITS

DIRECTION—½ channel per 10 levels of progress.
SPEED: 2 to 3 levels from own auxodrome in any year.

CLINICAL RATINGS

Obese	A₄...
Stocky	A₃ A₂
Good	A₁ M B₁
Fair	B₂
Borderline	B₃
Poor	B₄...

Figure 6.1.

132

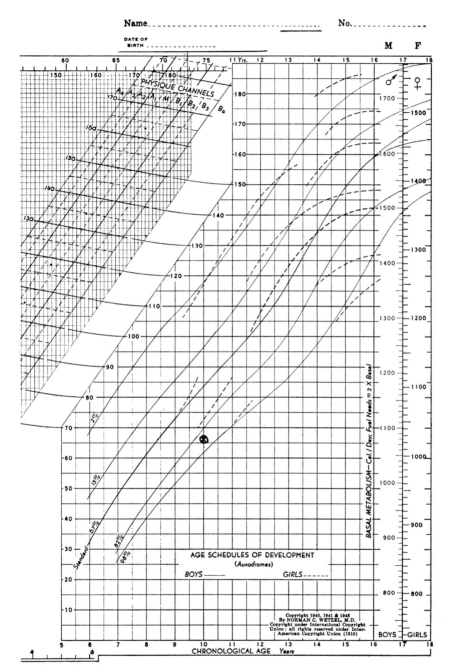

Figure 6.1. (Continued)

Grid measures and the Carlson Fatigue Test, the Brouha Step Test, and the results of the medical examination.

The Wetzel Grid has been studied by several investigators for application to physical education activities. Grueninger [22] reported that maximum performance on twelve motor fitness test items was found in channels A_1 and A_2 with a regular decline in channels removed from these classes; in the case of developmental levels, performance improved steadily up to 170, after which it dropped. Re-analyzing the original Grueninger data, Miller [23] found no situations in which performance differences between adjacent channel means were statistically significant. Miller concluded that the use of the grid channels for performance classification is a dubious procedure.

Bookwalter and associates,[24] with 1,977 elementary school boys, found that large boys, classified as thin and medium by the Grid, perform equally well on the Indiana Motor Fitness Test; for average size, thin boys performed better than medium physique boys; the very obese were the poorest physical performers. Bartell [25] reported that medium build high school boys by Wetzel classification were generally superior to slender and obese groups at the same developmental level on the following McCloy tests: General Motor Capacity, General Motor Ability, and Motor Quotient. There was also a tendency for the medium group to be better socially adjusted.

Rousey [26] obtained a critical ratio of 7.05 when the mean performance on the Indiana Motor Fitness Test of 429 secondary school boys classified on the Grid as growth successes was compared with 233 boys who were classified as growth failures; his correlations between fitness items and physique channels, however, were low (.29 to .47). According to Rains,[27] outstanding secondary school

22 Robert M. Grueninger, "Physical Performance of High School Boys and College Men Classified by the Grid Technique," Microfilmed Doctoral Dissertation, University of Michigan, 1949.

23 Kenneth D. Miller, "The Wetzel Grid as a Performance Classifier with College Men," *Research Quarterly*, Vol. XXII, No. 1 (March 1951), p. 63.

24 Karl W. Bookwalter, *et al.*, "The Relationship of Body Size and Shape to Physical Performance," *Research Quarterly*, Vol. XXIII, No. 3 (October 1952), p. 271.

25 Joseph A. Bartell, "A Comparison Between Body Build and Body Size with Respect to Certain Sociophysical Factors Among High School Boys," Microcarded Doctoral Dissertation, University of Pittsburgh, 1952.

26 Merle A. Rousey, "The Physical Performance of Secondary School Boys Classified by the Grid Techniques," Microcarded Doctoral Dissertation, Indiana University, 1949.

27 David D. Rains, "Growth of Athletes and Non-Athletes in Selected Secondary Schools as Assessed by the Grid Technique," Microcarded Doctoral Dissertation, Indiana University, 1951.

athletes are classified in physique channels M through A_5, with channel A_2 as the most satisfactory; over 75 per cent of the athletes had developmental levels over 150, while less than 50 per cent of the non-athletes exceeded this level. Solley [28] obtained no significant differences on eight co-ordination test items for boys, 10 to 14 years of age, classified as accelerated, average, and retarded by use of the Wetzel developmental ratio.

It appears that the Wetzel Grid has definite possibilities for use in detecting nutritional and growth disturbances in children. The main weakness of the Grid technique is in the degree of assurance that the child is actually placed in the appropriate channel at the time his initial measurements are made. If the child is wrongly placed at this time, the teacher may help perpetuate an improper growth pattern. Considerable doubt is expressed as to the effectiveness of any of the Grid measures in classifying children for physical education activities.

Other Measures

Meredith [29] constructed Height-Weight Interpretation Charts for boys and girls extending from early childhood through adolescence.[30] These charts provide for plotting by age each child's height in zones designated as heavy, moderately heavy, average, moderately light, and light. Whenever a child's height and weight plots do not lie in corresponding zones (i.e., tall and heavy, short and light, etc.), the discrepancy may either denote normal slenderness or stockiness of build, or reflect an undesirable state of health.

The Fels Composite Sheet [31] is designed for recording and interpreting various kinds of growth and development measurements. Height, weight, ossification, body measurements, age of walking, and other growth characteristics may be simultaneously recorded in comparable units. Values entered on the Composite Sheet are plotted in terms of how much the child differs, in standard deviation

---

[28] William H. Solley, "Ratio of Physical Development as a Factor in Motor Co-ordination of Boys Ages 10 to 14," *Research Quarterly*, Vol. XXVIII, No. 3 (October 1957), p. 295.

[29] Howard V. Meredith, "Interpreting Growth: Ways to Use Height and Weight Measures of School Children," *Saskatchewan Recreation*, Fall 1947, p. 1.

[30] These forms may be obtained from the American Medical Association, 535 North Dearborn Street, Chicago, Illinois.

[31] Lester W. Sontag and Earle L. Reynolds, "The Fels Composite Sheet: A Practical Method for Analyzing Growth Progress," *Journal of Pediatrics*, Vol. XXVI, 1945, p. 327.

units, from the average group tendency. This difference is called the child's *standard score* for the item being considered. Thus, the tests plotted may be viewed not only for their own relationship to the group tendency for each item, but also for their relation to each other.[32]

MUSCLE DEVELOPMENT AND SUBCUTANEOUS TISSUE

Although indices of body build have been found superior to height alone as measures of nutritional status, they still indicate only the percentage by which an individual is overweight or underweight for his own skeletal dimensions. This information has been shown to be inadequate, as it does not show the direct body condition causing malnutrition. For example, it is quite possible for two individuals to weigh the same and have comparable skeletal proportions, but have greatly different proportions of fat and muscle: one individual may have a large amount of fat and poor musculature; the other may have little subcutaneous tissue but be well developed physically.

Both a normal amount of fat and good musculature are necessary. The amount of fat just under the skin, especially in certain select body areas, such as the upper arm, chest, abdomen, back, and side, bears a high relationship to the total amount of fat of the body, and the total amount of fat on the body is closely related to the general nutritive condition of the individual.[33] From measures of subcutaneous tissue, therefore, one may determine to what extent underweight may be due to undernutrition. Likewise, the development of the muscular system varies with different skeletal proportions, and should be considered if underweight or poor nutrition is due to poor muscular development. Various experimenters have taken these additional factors into account when proposing measures of nutritional status. The latter tests, although complicated and difficult to administer, are superior to other measures of this sort.

The ACH Index

In a careful analysis of various combinations of anthropometric

---

[32] The Fels Composite Sheet may be obtained from the Samual S. Fels Research Institute, Antioch College, Yellow Springs, Ohio.

[33] C. H. McCloy, "Anthropometry in the Service of the Individual," *Journal of Health and Physical Education*, Vol. V, No. 7 (September 1934), p. 7.

measures made on over 10,000 school children in 75 cities in the United States, Franzen [34] selected the following seven measures as having the greatest significance in determining the amount and quality of soft tissue in relation to skeletal build: (1) hip width, (2) chest depth, (3) chest width, (4) height, (5) weight, (6) upper arm girth, and (7) subcutaneous tissue over the biceps muscle. Using these measures, it is possible to discover children who are lowest in three respects, namely, arm girth for skeletal build, amount of fat for skeletal build, and weight for skeletal build. Therefore, these measures were proposed to measure nutritional status, taking into account the four essential elements to which reference was made above: weight, skeletal dimensions, muscle development, and amount of subcutaneous tissue.

However, the application of these seven measures requires considerable skill and takes much more time than can routinely be given in school situations. Consequently, a simpler combination of these elements, known as the ACH Index,[35] was developed to serve as a screening device for selecting those in need of further examination. The ACH Index is composed of the following three measures: (A) upper arm girth; (C) chest depth; and (H) width of hips.

The ACH Index can be used in two distinctly different ways, depending upon the degree of discrimination desired, as follows: (1) Set the scoring standards to select a fourth of the children measured, if nearly all the extreme nutrition cases are to be selected. This procedure identifies 90 per cent of the children who would have been selected if all seven measures had been applied to the entire group in the first place. However, this selection also includes an appreciable number of other cases who do not have extreme defects, and would, therefore, necessitate the application of the balance of the seven measures to this group in order finally to determine those in need of nutritional attention. (2) Set the scoring standards to select only a tenth of the group instead of a quarter. With these standards, about 60 per cent of the selection would be extreme nutrition cases, and an additional 20 per cent would border on extreme defects. This procedure, however, does miss some extreme cases, but these omissions are deliberately sacrificed in the interest of speed and simplicity of the measurements.

---

[34] Raymond Franzen, *op. cit.*
[35] Raymond Franzen and George Palmer, *The ACH Index of Nutritional Status.* New York: American Child Health Association, 1934.

Tissue Symmetry Analysis [36]

Cureton maintains that it is not enough to show the relative proportion of skeletal build, muscular development, muscle strength, and adipose tissue, and suggests instead a profile comparison of the various measures of bone, muscle, strength, and fat. He proposes a procedure for tissue symmetry appraisal which serves as a screen test to select those markedly asymmetrical for follow-up with the physician and health and physical education teachers.

A profile chart is presented, based upon a percentile scale, so that one's deviation in any important element from his own established standard is obvious at a glance. For example, the individual who has normal weight but excess adipose tissue and insufficient muscle may be readily discovered, as may also the individual with great development of bone and insufficient muscle or fat to meet ordinary health and performance needs. The amount of fat and the measured strength give important clues to fitness. In young men, it may be demonstrated that strength tends to diminish as fat increases. In Cureton's conception, the "fit" state coincides with high strength and moderate adipose tissue for the body-type classification.

Four indices are used in making the symmetry analysis. Complete directions for giving the tests involved, together with photographs of the testing techniques, appear in the reference. The indices are as follows:

1. Skeletal Index: chest breadth, ankle girth, chest depth, hip width, and height.

2. Muscle Girth Index: gluteal girth, calf girth, biceps girth, and thigh girth.

3. Adipose Index: cheeks, abdomen, hips, gluteals, front thigh, and rear thigh.

4. Weight Prediction: skeletal index, muscle girth index, and adipose index.

NUTRITION TEST CONFUSION

A number of studies have compared various tests for identifying the nutritional status of individuals. The results have added an ele-

---

[36] Thomas K. Cureton, *Physical Fitness Appraisal and Guidance* (St. Louis: C. V. Mosby Company, 1947), Chap. 5.

ment of confusion to the selection of such measures, as fairly extensive disagreements were found to exist.

Marshall,[37] using a group of 77 boys aged seven to twelve years, compared four methods of appraising physical status: the Baldwin-Wood age-height-weight tables, the Pryor-Stolz age-height-hip-weight standards, the Franzen-Palmer ACH Index, and the McCloy age-height-weight-chest-knee-weight tables. The frequencies of underweight for the four methods presented marked disagreement, varying from 72 per cent by Pryor-Stolz, through 23 per cent by Baldwin-Wood and McCloy, to five per cent by Franzen-Palmer. A study by Allman,[38] in which the Baldwin-Wood age-height-weight tables, the Pelidisi Formula and the ACH Index were related to an experienced physician's estimates of nutritional status, resulted in similar disagreement among the tests. In the case of girls, the Baldwin-Wood Tables agreed very closely with the physician's ratings; in the case of boys, the Pelidisi more nearly approximated the doctor's ratings.

Craig[39] determined the expected weight of 101 Wellesley College women between the ages of 17 and 22 by the Medico-Actuarial Mortality Investigation age-height-weight tables, the revised Pryor width-weight tables, the Boillin weight expectancy regression equation, the McCloy method for appraising physical status, and the Ludlum (Wellesley) method of weight prediction for college women. The five methods were found to disagree on the classification of college women as underweight, normal weight, or overweight to such an extent that the methods should not be used interchangeably. The Ludlum method is recommended for use with college women.

Somatotypes

The concept that an individual's body type is related to his health, immunity from disease, physical performance, and personality char-

---

[37] Everett L. Marshall, "Comparison of Four Current Methods of Estimating Physical Status," *Child Development*, Vol. VIII (1937), p. 89.

[38] Delmar I. Allman, "A Comparison of Nutritional Indices," *Research Quarterly*, Vol. VIII, No. 2 (May 1937), p. 79.

[39] Margaret B. Craig, "A Comparison of Five Methods Designed to Predict the 'Normal' Weight of College Women," *Research Quarterly*, Vol. XV, No. 1 (March 1944), p. 64.

acteristics has developed from ancient times.[40] Hippocrates designated two fundamental physical types, the *phthisic habitus* and the *apopletic habitus*. The *phthisic* had a long, thin body, which was considered particularly subject to tuberculosis. The apoplectic was a short, thick individual with a predisposition toward diseases of the vascular system leading to apoplexy. Rostan defined three essentially different types: the *type digestif, type musculaire* and *type cérébral*. Kretschmer's three types, *pyknic, athletic,* and *asthenic,* received considerable attention. The concept of body types, as shown in numerous studies, proved inadequate in many respects. However, there remained considerable evidence that the physique pattern is significant and is related to an understanding of the individual, physically, mentally, emotionally, and socially.

Primary Components

Sheldon, assisted by Stevens and Tucker,[41] after extensive research, came to the belief that human beings could not be classified into just three physique types, but that nearly all individuals were mixtures. However, they did designate three primary components of body build that provide first-order criteria for differentiating among individuals. The names of the three components were derived from the three layers of the embryo, as follows: (a) First component, *endomorph,* named after the endoderm from which the functional elements of the digestive system emanate; (b) second component, *mesomorph,* named after the mesoderm from which come the muscles and bones; (3) third component, *ectomorph,* named after the ectoderm from which develops the sensory organs. Brief descriptions of these components follow.

Endomorphy. In *endomorphy,* the digestive viscera dominate the body economy. A predominance of soft roundness throughout the various regions of the body is evident, with mass concentration in the center. Other characteristics are: large, round head; short, thick neck; broad, thick chest, with fatty breasts; short arms, with "hammy" appearance; large abdomen, full above the navel and pendulous; heavy, fat buttocks; and short, heavy legs.

---

[40] W. B. Tucker and W. A. Lessa, "Man: A Constitutional Investigation," *Quarterly Review of Biology,* Vol. XV (September 1940), pp. 265, 411.

[41] W. H. Sheldon, S. S. Stevens, and W. B. Tucker, *The Varieties of Human Physique* (New York: Harper & Brothers, 1940).

Mesomorphy. In *mesomorphy*, muscle, bone, and connective tissue are dominant. The mesomorphic physique is heavy, hard, and rectangular in outline, with rugged, massive muscles and large, prominent bones. Other characteristics are: prominent facial bones; fairly long, strong neck; thoracic trunk dominant over abdominal volume; broad shoulders, with heavy, prominent clavicles; muscular upperarm and massive forearms, wrists, hands, and fingers; large, heavily muscled abdomen; slender, low waist; heavy buttocks; and massive forelegs.

Ectomorphy. Linearity and fragility predominate in the *ectomorph*. The dominant ectomorph has a frail, delicate body structure, with thin segments, anteroposteriorly. Other characteristics are: relatively large cranium, with bulbous forehead; small face, pointed chin, and sharp nose; long, slender neck; long, narrow thorax; winged scapula and forward shoulders; long arms, muscles not marked; flat abdomen, with hollow above navel; inconspicuous buttocks; and long, thin legs.

Determination of Somatotypes

Sheldon's designation of somatotypes was originally in terms of a rating scale from 1 to 7 for each component; later, half numbers were also used. In each instance, the first numeral in the sequence refers to endomorphy; the second, to mesomorphy; the third, to ectomorphy. Thus, a somatotype with the greatest endomorphic dominance is 7-1-1; with the greatest mesomorphic dominance, 1-7-1; with the greatest ectomorphic dominance, 1-1-7. Based on a 7-point scale, 88 somatotypes have been described; these are illustrated in Sheldon's Atlas of Men.[42] An atlas of women and a children's atlas of somatotypes are in preparation.

While a description of the many somatotypes goes beyond the scope of this text, a presentation of four examples may aid the physical educator in forming a rough concept of this form of body assessment. The illustrations [43] are drawn from junior high school boys serving as subjects in the Medford, Oregon, Growth Study conducted by the author. The illustrations are as follows:

Dominant endomorph (Figure 6.2). This boy is 11 years of age;

---

[42] William H. Sheldon, *Atlas of Men* (New York: Harper & Brothers, 1954).

[43] Acknowledgments are made to Barbara Honeyman Heath, Monterey, California, for making these somatotype assessments.

his ponderal index is 12.15; his somatotype designation is 6-3-2. Note the over-all endomorphic characteristics, especially the high waist and the double chin.

Dominant mesomorph (Figure 6.3). This boy is 14 years of age and is an outstanding junior high school athlete. His ponderal index is 13.00; his somatotype designation is 2-6-3. He has an excellent muscular physique.

Dominant ectomorph (Figure 6.4). This boy's somatotype designation is 2-2-7. He is 15 years of age; his ponderal index is 14.40. The linearity of this physique type is obvious.

Medium type (Figure 6.5). The somatotype of this boy is quite evenly divided among the three components; the designation is 4-4-4. He is 14 years of age; his ponderal index is 13.30.

The entire somatotyping process is described in Sheldon's Atlas. These materials include specifications for the camera needed in photographing the subjects, the type of film and its development and printing for making the photographs, and various aids in making somatotype assessments. A brief enumeration of the steps in somatotyping are as follows:

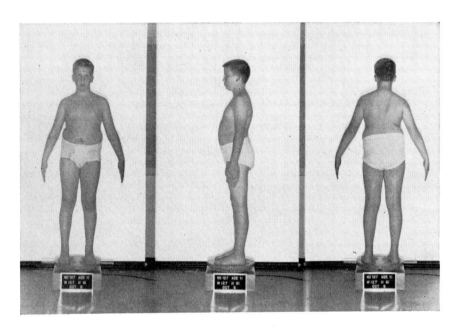

Figure 6.2. Dominant Endomorph Somatotype.

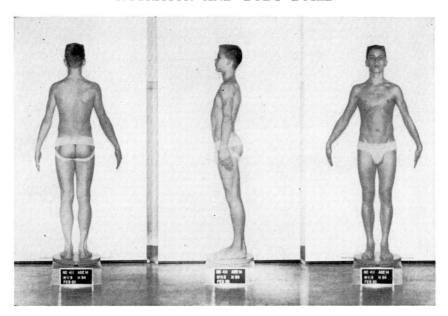

Figure 6.3.   Dominant Mesomorph Somatotype.

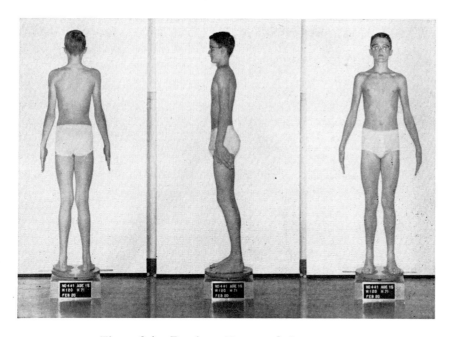

Figure 6.4.   Dominant Ectomorph Somatotype.

143

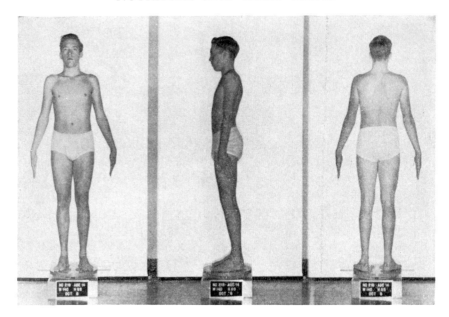

Figure 6.5.   Mid-Type Somatotype.

1. The subject is photographed in three planes on one film: frontal, lateral, and dorsal. A data board with the individual's age, height, and weight is recorded in the photograph.

2. The ponderal index $\dfrac{\text{height}}{\sqrt[3]{\text{weight}}}$ is determined as an aid in locating the somatotype. This index may be obtained without computation from a nomograph available in the Atlas.

3. A table in the Atlas is next consulted, which shows the location of somatotypes for various intervals of height-over-cube-root-of-weight (ponderal index).

4. Through anthroposcopy and inspection of the Atlas, the final somatotype assessment is made.

The combination of the above objective measures and experienced inspection yields a reliable somatotype rating. Tanner [44] reported objectivity coefficients among three well trained somatotype evaluators from .82 to .93 for the three components. He indicated further that trained observers agree to within half a rating on a 7-

[44] J. M. Tanner, "Reliability of Anthroposcopic Somatotyping," *American Journal of Physical Anthropology*, Vol. XII n.s., No. 2 (June 1954), p. 257.

point scale in 90 per cent of the instances. Hawthorne [45] reported similar objectivity coefficients; his coefficients ranged from .87 to .91.

Application

The individual's somatotype should become increasingly important to physical education. In the realm of measurement, it should be considered more and more in the establishment of norms for many types of physical education tests, if the results of tests are to be properly interpreted. This is true, for example, with the determination of nutritional status previously discussed in this chapter, a problem that has already become an area of study for recent experimenters in this field. In considering somatotypes as related to age-height-weight tables, the endomorph is normally overweight, the mesomorph is nearer average, and the ectomorph is well below these standards. Yet, if based upon weight tables alone, they are all judged alike. In Sheldon's Atlas, however, an age-height-weight table is presented for each of his 88 somatotype designations. Likewise, tests of posture, strength, flexibility, endurance, or circulatory-respiratory functions may be understood more clearly in terms of their biological and social significance when reviewed against the general background of constitutional potentialities and limitations.

Certain somatotypes are also related to specific types of athletic performance. Findings by Cureton,[46] after experimenting with Springfield College men made up largely of athletes and with practically no endomorphs in the group were as follows: (a) mesomorphs received the highest scores in athletic performance involving strength and power; (b) ectomorphs were favored in the Brace test, a test which requires body balance, flexibility, and agility; (c) mesomorphs and meso-endomorphs do better in aquatic events; (d) ectomorphs received the lowest scores in the McCurdy-Larson Organic Efficiency Test. In a factor analysis study, Sills [47] obtained

[45] Jesse J. Hawthorne, "Somatotyping and Its Relationship to Selected Motor Performance of College Men," Microcarded Doctoral Dissertation, University of Texas, 1954.

[46] Thomas K. Cureton, "Body Build as a Framework of Reference for Interpreting Physical Fitness and Athletic Performance," Supplement to the Research Quarterly, Vol. XII, No. 2 (May 1941), p. 301.

[47] Frank D. Sills, "A Factor Analysis of Somatotypes and Their Relationship to Achievement in Motor Skills," Research Quarterly, Vol. XXI, No. 4 (December 1950), p. 424.

145

motor ability positive loadings with mesomorphy; the motor ability loadings were negative with endomorphy. Hawthorne [48] found mesomorphs to have superior strength and agility to the other somatotype components; endomorphs were generally poorest in strength, agility, power, reaction time, motor ability, and hand and arm dexterity.

Irving [49] compared various anthropometric and strength tests of boys 9 to 15 years of age classified as primary endomorphs, primary mesomorphs, primary ectomorphs, and mid-types. Endomorphs were found to be generally higher in such anthropometric measures as upper arm girth, chest girth, calf girth, and hip width; they also reached a much higher Wetzel developmental level, and, of course, were located primarily in the upper physique channels. The mesomorphs had a greater mean upper arm girth than did the ectomorphs or the mid-types; the ectomorphs were taller than the other groups. The mesomorphs were definitely superior in mean arm strength, as scored by Rogers' method, although there were no significant differences when arm strength was scored by McCloy's formula. The mesomorphs also had the highest mean Physical Fitness Index, although the mean of the ectomorph was nearly as high. The ectomorph had a higher mean back lift than did the other classifications.

Cureton [50] made extensive studies of the body build of Olympic men and women athletes of the 1932, 1936, and 1948 Olympiads. The results of these and other analyses of athletic groups are as follows: heavy athletes are relatively more mesomorphic (solid, dense muscle) types; track athletes run to slim body build with considerable ectomorphy (frail, linear) types but with well developed musculature; swimmers are more frequently meso-endomorphic (muscular and fat) types; weight lifters and weight throwers are frequently meso-endomorphics; and gymnasts, tumblers, and agile athletes are often meso-ectomorphic. Very seldom do men and women low in mesomorphy succeed in athletics. The dynamic athletic type has an above-average component of muscular fitness.

In addition, Sheldon has shown that body build is related to en-

---

[48] Hawthorne, *op. cit.*

[49] Robert N. Irving, "Somatotype Relationships Among Pre-Adolescent and Adolescent Boys," Microcarded Doctor of Education Dissertation, University of Oregon, 1959.

[50] Thomas K. Cureton, *Physical Fitness Appraisal and Guidance,* p. 108.

docrine function. From somatotyping several groups of clinical patients on whom endocrine data were available, it was found that mesomorphic ectomorphs are almost uniformly endowed with active thyroids, that mesomorphic endomorphs have sluggish thyroids, that in acromegalics and other mesomorphs there is relatively active secretion by the anterior lobe of the pituitary and by the adrenal cortex, and that the ectomorphic endomorphs and the endomorphic ectomorphs tend to lack secretions from the posterior lobe of the pituitary, and the males lack gonadal secretion. It appears certain, from these studies, that different standards of normality are needed for the interpretation of basal metabolic rates. Normal persons who are mesomorphic ectomorphs show an average BMR reading at least twenty points higher than normal individuals of the same age who are predominantly mesomorphic endomorphs.

The rate of physiological sexual maturation, at least in females, can be better understood in relation to the individual's somatotype. From studies so far conducted, it seems apparent that dominance of the ectomorphic component tends to postpone sexual maturation, as indicated by appearance of the menses, and a modest predominance of either of the endomorphic or mesomorphic components tends to hasten it. On the other hand, a strong predominance of either of the latter components alone tends, in the female, to suppress sexual development.

SELECTED REFERENCES

Baldwin, Bird T., "The Use and Abuse of Height-Weight Tables," *Journal of the American Medical Association,* Vol. LXXXII (January 5, 1942), p. 1.
Bogert, L. Jean, *Nutrition and Physical Fitness,* 5th ed. Philadelphia: W. B. Saunders Company, 1949.
Cureton, Thomas K., *Physical Fitness Appraisal and Guidance.* St. Louis: C. V. Mosby Company, 1947.
Meredith, Howard V., "Interpreting Growth: Ways to Use Height and Weight Measures of School Children," *Saskatchewan Recreation,* Fall 1957, p. 1.
McCloy, C. H., "Anthropometry in the Service of the Individual," *Journal of Health and Physical Education,* Vol. V, No. 7 (September 1934), p. 7.
Sheldon, William H., *Atlas of Men.* New York: Harper & Brothers, 1954.
Sheldon, W. H., S. S. Stevens, and W. B. Tucker, *The Varieties of Human Physique.* New York: Harper & Brothers, 1940.

CHAPTER SEVEN

Measurement in
Remedial Work

In this chapter, tests especially related to remedial physical education will be considered. Remedial programs have been instituted in many schools and colleges throughout the country in the belief that the correction of certain types of defects and deficiencies is conducive to the well-being of the individual. Thus, tests designed to evaluate the following conditions will be presented: anteroposterior posture, lateral spinal deviations, foot condition, bodily flexibility, strength of individual muscle groups, and muscular fatigue.

POSTURE VALUES

The physical educator, in considering the place of posture in his program, is faced with two fundamental questions of validity: first, what is the significance of posture and foot condition in relation to the physical fitness of the individual; and second, what tests are available for measuring posture status with satisfactory precision?

Many extravagant claims have been made concerning the value of correct posture and posture training. Deaver [1] has compiled from published reports widely divergent statements, not only on the dire effects of poor posture, but on the great mental and physical rewards for those who maintain good posture, such as: "Posture expresses

---

[1] G. G. Deaver, "Posture and Its Relation to Mental and Physical Health," *Research Quarterly*, Vol. IV, No. 1 (March 1933), p. 221.

mental as well as physical states." "Posture is an index of personality." "Erect posture is an expression of intelligence." "The posture often proclaims the man." "Posture shows the rise and fall of nations." Cureton [2] lists a series of popular titles in which the relationship of posture to health and physical fitness is repeatedly implied, such as: "You're Only as Young as Your Back!" "How You May be Making Yourself a Cripple!" "He Stoops to Conquer and Loses!" "How Man is Penalizing Himself in the Race for Good Health and Long Life by Incorrect Posture!" "Slouching at Work and Play!" "Breathing Incorrectly and Cramping Vital Organs Until the Capacity to Resist Disease is Impaired." Cowell [3] states that one's mental attitude toward life, comrades, work, and self is strongly colored by his state of health, and that bodily posture is of importance, since it is one of the determining factors of the physiological state; he maintains that physical poise is related to mental poise.

Posture is defined by the Subcommittee on Orthopedics and Body Mechanics of the Hoover White House Conference on Child Health and Correction [4] as "the mechanical correlation of the various systems of the body with reference to the skeletal, muscular and visceral systems and their neurological associations." Ideal posture may be said to be obtained when this mechanical correlation is most favorable to the proper functioning of these systems. From a theoretical standpoint, therefore, it seems reasonable to believe that poor posture, with the resulting pressure upon and displacement of visceral and other internal organs, nerves, and blood vessels, must impair their functioning, thus reducing the physical fitness of the individual. Many critical thinkers have carefully considered this relationship, although many of the data are based on extreme case studies; but adequate proof of the relationship itself does not exist. A brief summary of present information on the subject follows.

Goldthwaite [5] suggests a strong relationship between posture and circulation, and indicates that good circulation in the vital organs is impossible with a slumped chest because of resultant poor breath-

[2] Thomas K. Cureton, "Bodily Posture as an Indicator of Fitness," *Supplement to the Research Quarterly*, Vol. XII, No. 2 (May 1941), p. 348.

[3] C. C. Cowell, "Bodily Posture as a Mental Attitude," *Journal of Health and Physical Education*, Vol. I, No. 5 (May 1930), p. 14.

[4] Robert B. Osgood, *Body Mechanics: Education and Practice* (New York: Appleton-Century-Crofts, Inc., 1932), p. 166.

[5] J. E. Goldthwaite, *Body Mechanics* (Philadelphia: J. B. Lippincott Company, 1934).

ing and mechanical blockage. He maintains further that ulcered stomach, postural diabetes, gasteroptosis and enteroptosis are traceable to poor posture. Many older students of this problem describe the harmful effects on health of visceroptosis, the abnormal falling downward of the abdominal viscera. Extreme cases of this sort show lack of endurance and are usually afflicted with constipation, headaches, and offensive breath.

Fox[6] reports that dysmenorrhea occurs with greater severity among college women with a sway-back postural condition. Karpovich[7] indicates that lordosis may be associated with orthostatic albuminuria. Ringo[8] obtained a low but definite relationship among college women between posture and trunk strength imbalance. Moriarity and Irwin[9] concluded from a study of school children that there is a significant association between poor posture and physical and emotional factors, including disease, fatigue, self-consciousness, fidgeting, hearing defects, restlessness, timidity, underweight, and asthma. The Baruch Committee on Physical Medicine[10] maintains that many individuals with severe ailments and disabilities may have abnormal posture as a causative factor.

Clinical research has indicated postural involvement in many organic abnormalities found in the body. Experiments conducted in physical education on the relationship between posture and physical and mental efficiency, however, reveal very little or no relationship. Deaver[11] reports a slight tendency for physical fitness, motor ability, and health to be related to posture, but no relationship so far as vital capacity, intelligence, scholarship, personality integration, or leadership is concerned. Alden and Top[12] found practically no re-

---

[6] Margaret G. Fox, "The Relationship of Abdominal Strength to Selected Postural Faults," *Research Quarterly*, Vol. XXII, No. 2 (May 1951), p. 141.

[7] Peter V. Karpovich, *Physiology of Muscular Activity*, 4th ed. (Philadelphia: W. B. Saunders Company, 1953).

[8] Mildred B. Ringo, "An Investigation of Some Aspects of Abdominal Strength, Trunk Extensor Strength, and Anteroposterior Erectness in College Women," Microcarded Doctoral Dissertation, University of Oregon, 1956.

[9] Mary J. Moriarity and Leslie W. Irwin, "A Study of the Relationship of Certain Physical and Emotional Factors to Habitual Poor Posture Among School Children," *Research Quarterly*, Vol. XXIII, No. 2 (May 1952), p. 221.

[10] *Report of the Baruch Committee on Physical Medicine.* New York: 597 Madison Avenue, April 1, 1945.

[11] G. G. Deaver, *op. cit.*

[12] Florence D. Alden and Hilda Top, "Experiment on the Relation of Posture to Weight, Vital Capacity, and Intelligence," *Research Quarterly*, Vol. II, No. 3 (October 1931), p. 38.

lationship between posture and weight, vital capacity, and intelligence; DiGiovanna [13] concludes that there seems to be a fairly definite tendency for posture to be positively related to athletic achievement only; Dunbar [14] found a positive correlation between posture and athletic ability, but it was not high; and Rawles [15] concluded, after experimenting with 300 young adult women, that "it appears there is much current exaggeration of the connection in the adult between posture and performance efficiency, physical or intellectual." With college women as subjects, Davies [16] found very little, if any, relationship between postural divergencies and performance on Scott's motor ability test.

Klein and Thomas,[17] on the other hand, reported that: Improvement in nutritional condition was more frequent among children who received posture training than among those who did not (*especially among those who actually improved their posture*); the rate of absence due to sickness for those receiving posture training was 38 per cent lower in the spring quarter than it had been in the fall, while, for those not receiving posture training, the rate for the spring quarter showed an increase of two per cent over the rate in the fall. The unique feature of this study was that a fairly well controlled experiment was conducted over a period of two years; thus, the effects of posture training over a period of time were evaluated.

Lack of Posture Standards

A common handicap faced by all the experimenters investigating the benefits of posture is that they have lacked precise testing instruments and methods for measuring posture, all these investigators having used either the silhouette or some form of general inspection. Deaver took silhouettes of his subjects and judged them according to the Harvard Posture Charts. Alden and Top used Bancroft's "Straight Line Test" as applied to silhouettes. DiGiovanna

---

[13] Vincent G. DiGiovanna, "A Study of the Relation of Athletic Skills and Strength to Those of Posture," *Research Quarterly*, Vol. II, No. 2 (May 1931), p. 67.

[14] Ruth O. Dunbar, "A Study of Posture and Its Relationship," *American Physical Education Review*, Vol. XXXII, No. 2 (February 1927), p. 75.

[15] H. P. Rawles, "Objective Evaluation of Standards and Types of Posture." Unpublished master's thesis, Wellesley College, Wellesley, Mass., 1925.

[16] Evelyn A. Davies, "Relationship Between Selected Postural Divergencies and Motor Ability," *Research Quarterly*, Vol. LXXVIII, No. 1 (May 1957), p. 1.

[17] Armin Klein and Leah C. Thomas, *Posture and Physical Fitness* (Washington: U. S. Department of Labor, Children's Bureau, 1931).

gave each individual a segmental posture examination and a final check-up of general posture by a process of careful inspection, a mental comparison being made between the findings in the examination and the standards illustrated in the posture charts of the Children's Bureau, United States Department of Labor. Klein and Thomas compared silhouettes with the posture charts of the Children's Bureau. Dunbar used the Bancroft Triple Posture Test. Davies used subjective postural screening by three judges.

There is ample proof to substantiate the statement that posture standards based upon the measures mentioned are decidedly lacking in precision and accuracy, a condition that lowers greatly the validity of the experiments conducted on the relationship between posture and the mental and physical traits of individuals. Cureton found that the profile silhouette alone is valueless *for quantitative measurement or evaluation,* as it is misleading and does not represent accurately the true spinal curvatures, showing instead the muscular contours of the back, the scapulae, and frequently the elbows. Other errors found in the silhouetteograph method were: difficulty in measuring the silhouettes exactly due to lack of sharply defined edges, caused by improper adjustment of the camera lens or improper lighting; the smallness of the silhouette, causing likelihood of an error in determining the multiplier for the particular picture to enlarge the measurement to full size; and the photographic errors due to improper adjustment of the lens or improper location of the subject.

The unreliability of the subjective judgment of certain physical and mental traits is a well-established fact. In a subsequent study, Cureton [18] found that the subjective inspectional scheme for measuring posture, as carried out by three trained and experienced examiners, who had worked intimately with each other for at least three years, gave results only 13.4 per cent better than pure chance guesses as an average in ranking pupils, the mean correlation being .51. This study corroborates the findings of Franzen,[19] that subjective judgments of the type made on posture, nutrition, and various physical defects included in the medical examination are "in a fair

---

18 T. K. Cureton, J. S. Wickens, and H. P. Elder, "Reliability and Objectivity of the Springfield Postural Measurements," *Supplement to the Research Quarterly,* Vol. VI, No. 2 (May 1935), p. 81.

19 Raymond Franzen, *Physical Defects: The Pathway to Correction* (New York: American Child Health Association, 1934).

percentage of cases unreliable enough to throw considerable doubt on their usefulness."

Phelps and Kiphuth [20] question the "Straight Line Test" as proposed by Bancroft, when they state that "the position of the mastoid with regard to the acromion of the shoulder is valueless because of the mobility of the shoulders."

Thus there may be seen in the inability of previous experimenters to measure posture a fundamental reason why attempts to correlate posture with health, scholarship, intelligence, athletic activity, organic condition, and similar criteria have mostly failed. When measures of any one of these are correlated with posture, the result will never be higher than the reliability of the posture test. Therefore, until the value or lack of value of posture can be definitely established, the conscientious physical educator must decide for himself whether the results derived from good posture are beneficial to the physical well-being of the individual and whether or not he will continue with posture training.

Tests of Anteroposterior Posture

Posture measurement has attracted the attention of physical educators for many years. A number of special instruments were brought forward in the nineties to measure anatomical and physiological relationships. These included instruments for measuring the amount of the pelvic tilt, for showing the exact contour of the chest, for tracing the anteroposterior depth at all points of the trunk, and for recording outlines of the body and abnormalities of spinal curvature. Other approximate schemes for measuring posture have considerable value as motivating devices in teaching posture, such as Bancroft's Triple Posture Test, Denniston's Double-Pole Posture Test, and Crampton's Work-a-Day Tests. There are also a number of postural scales based largely upon the opinions of experts in the field, such as the Brownell scale of silhouettes for ninth-grade boys, and a similar scale by Crook for measuring the anteroposterior posture of preschool children. Buhl has presented a "posturemeter" which is based upon the principle that, as the posture of the thoracic region improves, the chest moves forward and upward and the head

---

[20] W. W. Phelps, R. J. H. Kiphuth, and C. W. Goff, *The Diagnosis and Treatment of Postural Defects*, 2nd ed. (Springfield, Mass.: Charles C Thomas, 1956).

moves backward, thus improving the general posture of the individual.

All of the tests so far mentioned consist of "over-all" postural measurement; that is, a general posture grade is assigned. In these instances no attempt has been made to break up posture into its component parts. Thus, it is not possible to tell from a posture score what parts of the body are weak, or the exact areas wherein the individual is defective. No basis is presented upon which specific postural exercises may be prescribed. Posture tests constructed recently break with this procedure and consider each of the parts of posture separately, such as the position of the head, the shoulders, the abdomen, and so on. This is a step in the right direction, since "composite" posture scores are usually misleading and do not give an adequate description of the individual situation.

Subjective Posture Appraisals

Phelps, Kiphuth, and Goff appraisal.[21] Phelps, Kiphuth, and Goff in their subjective examination procedures for measuring posture, painstakingly and effectively describe, with excellent illustrations, each of the various items included in a complete posture appraisal, including the position or alignment of the neck, shoulders, thoracic spine, lumbar spine, pelvic tilt, overcarriage, chest, abdomen, lateral spinal deviation, knees, and feet. This is the best subjective system yet proposed. It is subject, however, to all the errors common to other types of subjective measurement, as is shown by the results of Cureton's experiments given below.

Iowa Posture Test.[22] The posture test developed by the Women's Department of the Division of Physical Education, State University of Iowa, has been used with considerable success. This test provides a three-point rating scale for each of the following five functional conditions: foot mechanics, standing position, walking, sitting, and stooping to pick up a light object. Foot mechanics appraisal will be described later in this chapter; criteria for evaluating the other postural conditions are presented here.

---

[21] Phelps, Kiphuth, and Goff, *op. cit.,* Chap. 6.
[22] Mimeographed form by Women's Department, Division of Physical Education, State University of Iowa.

Standing Position: Correct alignment of body segments

3 points   Axis through head, neck, trunk and legs approximately a straight line.

2 points   Slight general deviation, or moderate deviation of one part.

1 point   Marked general deviation.

Walking: A. Correct alignment of body segments

Rate as above, checking particularly for any changes from the standing position.

Walking: B. Weight distribution

3 points   Weight carried only slightly farther forward than in the standing position.

2 points   Weight carried in a perpendicular position.

1 point   Weight carried backward or too far forward. Note backward carriage with B; too far forward with F.

Sitting Position

3 points   Upper trunk well balanced over pelvis, head erect, chest high, shoulders back (not stiff), abdomen controlled, normal upper-back curve.

2 points   Slight to moderate deviation from above sitting standard.

1 point   Marked deviation from correct standard.

Rising from Sitting Position

3 points   One foot slightly under chair with other foot slightly forward, trunk bent slightly from hips, push-up from feet; arms relaxed, hips kept well under body, no stiffness.

2 points   Fair performance.

1 point   Poor performance.

Stooping to Pick Up Light Object

3 points   One foot slightly ahead of the other, feet and hips well under body; bend at knees, slight bend at hips; relatively straight line of trunk, back controlled; arms relaxed, smooth movement, balance maintained throughout; object picked up slightly ahead of foot.

2 points   Very slight deviation from good standard in several items listed or moderate deviation in no more than three.

1 point   Markedly incorrect performance, especially bending from hips with knees straight.

In the original Iowa Posture Test, an additional category, ascending and descending stairs, is included. If desired, the physical educator could easily add items involving running, jumping, carrying objects and the like.

This test has the following to commend it: inexpensive; easy to administer; functional application, not being limited to the static standing posture; individual testing requires about five minutes, although Lee and Wagner claim that 40 children have been examined in as many minutes through group testing methods.[23] A reliability coefficient of .97 for this posture scoring scheme was obtained by Moriarity.[24]

Woodruff body alignment posture test.[25] A body alignment frame was designed by Woodruff to avoid the time consuming and expensive photographic techniques of posture examination while providing a more reliable procedure than subjective appraisal alone. The construction of this frame is shown in Figure 7.1. The nine strings running lengthwise of the frame are three-fourths of an inch apart. The center string is a different color for easy identification.

In using the frame, as shown in Figure 7.1, a base line six feet

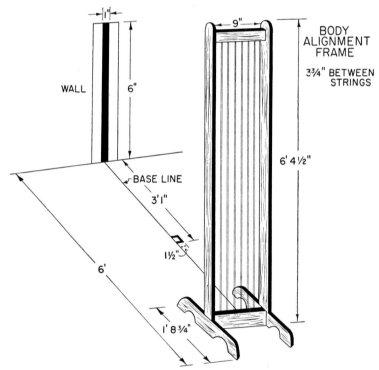

Courtesy of Janet Woodruff, School of Health and Physical Education, University of Oregon

Figure 7.1. Woodruff Posture Frame: Equipment and Measurements.

---

[23] Mabel Lee and Miriam M. Wagner, *Fundamental Body Mechanics and Conditioning* (Philadelphia: W. B. Saunders Company, 1949), p. 283.

[24] Moriarity and Irwin, *op. cit.*

[25] Janet Woodruff, School of Health and Physical Education, University of Oregon.

long is drawn on the floor at right angles to a wall; the frame is centered at the end of this line and at right angles to it. Another line, one inch wide, is drawn on the wall perpendicular to the floor and intersecting the line on the floor. A one and one-half inch line is drawn perpendicular to the base line, three feet one inch (inclusive of the line) from the wall.

The subject stands between the body alignment frame and the wall with the left side toward the tester. The left foot is placed in such a position that the ankle bone is opposite the free end of the one and one-half inch line; the right foot is placed parallel to the left foot. The subject should then adjust the foot position so that the base line runs under the top of the instep. A natural standing position, looking straight ahead, is assumed by the subject. The examiner takes a position ten feet in front of the frame.

In giving the test, the examiner looks through the frame and lines the center string of the frame with the wall line. For perfectly balanced posture, the "plumb-line" test applies, in which the center string, if the posture is "perfect," passes in front of the ankle joint, just in front of the dimple behind the knee cap, through the center of the hip and shoulder joints, and through the mastoid process. Posture scoring is accomplished by judging the deviation, either forward or backward, for the number of strings for each of the following segments from the one directly below (therefore, not necessarily the deviation from the center string each time): ankle, knee, hip, shoulder, head. A score of 25 shows no deviations from this line; one point is deducted for each string deviation. For the first test given college women, the mean posture score is around 20; the range of scores is from 16 to 25.

By the test-retest method, 80 per cent agreement was obtained in scoring "overhang," which denotes the distance the shoulders are carried posterior to the center of the hip joint.

Objective Posture Tests

A number of objective posture tests have been proposed, most of which require either special apparatus or some form of photography or both.

Cureton's posture measurement. One of the first thorough analyses of objective posture measurement was made by Cureton, who studied the validity of various posture-testing devices and attempted

157

to measure objectively many of the separate items included in the Phelps and Kiphuth posture appraisal.

Cureton's first task was to determine the validity of various instruments proposed for posture measurement, including the conformateur, the spinograph (a spine-tracing device), and the silhouetteograph.[26] Preliminary measurements utilizing all three devices were taken on 15 subjects, the conformateur and spinograph giving comparable results, but the silhouetteograph being greatly in error. A manikin was next measured with the various devices, in order to eliminate the errors resulting from the inconstancy of the subject in assuming the same position exactly in a series of trials. A metal conformateur with measurements taken directly from the rods was found to be superior to other measurements taken separately in order to record conveniently the posture picture. A recommended procedure, proposed after additional research, called for a combination of the conformateur, as perfected by Cureton and Gunby, and the silhouetteograph. Details for the improvement of the conformateur will be found in the reference. This conformateur lends itself readily to use in combination with the silhouetteograph, allowing a double check upon gross errors and the opportunity of obtaining quantitative results. It also provides a personal picture, which may have value in motivating the subject to improve his posture.

In a subsequent experiment, Cureton, Wickens, and Elder [27] studied the reliability and objectivity of four postural areas, as follows: (1) the position of the head and neck; (2) the alignment of the chest and abdomen; (3) the position of the shoulders; and (4) the alignment of the spine. A comparison between subjective judgments by experts and an objective measurement of each of the posture items included in the study was worked out for reliability and objectivity, the comparison being made by converting reliability and objectivity coefficients into a rough per cent estimate by using the *predictive index.* The objective measurement schemes were shown to be from two to five times as reliable as the subjective inspectional method, depending on the part measured; and from three to fifteen times as objective.

Cureton did not attempt to define either good or bad posture, nor

[26] Thomas K. Cureton, "The Validity of Antero-Posterior Spinal Measurements," *Research Quarterly,* Vol. II, No. 3 (October 1931), p. 101.

[27] T. K. Cureton, J. S. Wickens, and N. P. Elder, *op. cit.*

did he present norms for evaluating postural status. In a subsequent study, however, he stated that postural measurements do not correlate highly with each other, most of the relations of distinctly different items being below .30, a fact that supports the belief that each aspect of posture is due to specific mechanical forces and neural learnings, and that each must therefore be dealt with specifically.[28]

Wellesley posture measurements. MacEwan and Howe,[29] in studying the posture of girls and women, recognized what Cureton subsequently proved, that in photographs and silhouettes the profile picture alone does not accurately represent the true spinal curvatures. In an attempt to locate the actual position of the spine from a photograph of the subject, aluminum pointers, 9 cm. long by 4 mm. wide and ¼ gm. in weight, were attached at the end of the sternum, on the prominence of the first piece of the sacrum, and on the spinous processes of every second vertebra beginning with the 7th cervical. By measuring inward the proper distance from the tips of the pointers, the real position of the chest and spine is located and drawn on the picture regardles of the musculature of the back or projecting scapulae, arms, or other protuberances.

The following postural measurements may be made by the technique developed by MacEwan and Howe: (1) the amount of anteroposterior curvature in the dorsal and lumbar areas of the spine; (2) the amount of segmental angulation and body tilt; and (3) the position of the head and neck. The sum of these three measurements gives the individual's posture grade on a numerical scale of 1 to 25. This numerical scale may be translated into a letter grade: A+ to E— inclusive.

Validity for this posture test was claimed on the grounds that the battery of measurements was in reasonable agreement with the composite judgment of a group of physical educators who were outstanding authorities on the posture of girls and women. With 243 subjects used for intensive study, the correlation between the criterion posture grade (five judges) and thoracic depth was .47; and between the criterion posture grade and lumbar depth, .56.

---

[28] Thomas K. Cureton, "Bodily Posture as an Indicator of Fitness," *Supplement to the Research Quarterly,* Vol. XII, No. 2 (May 1941), p. 348.

[29] C. G. MacEwan and E. C. Howe, "An Objective Method of Grading Posture," *Research Quarterly,* Vol. III, No. 3 (October 1932), p. 144.

Wickens and Kiphuth posture test. Wickens and Kiphuth [30] designed a posture test for use with men at Yale University. This test
utilized certain of the Cureton measurement procedures; instead
of the conformateur, the Wellesley aluminum pointers were employed to locate the actual position of the spine; photography was
used to record the image. Before the student was photographed
the following specific points on the left side of the body were
marked with a black flesh pencil to serve as landmarks for determining segmental alignment on the picture: tragus of the ear, front
tip of the shoulder, acromion, greater trochanter of the femur, styloid process of the fibula, and center of the external malleolus. In
order to determine the amount of anteroposterior spinal curvature,
five aluminum pointers were attached to the back, located at the

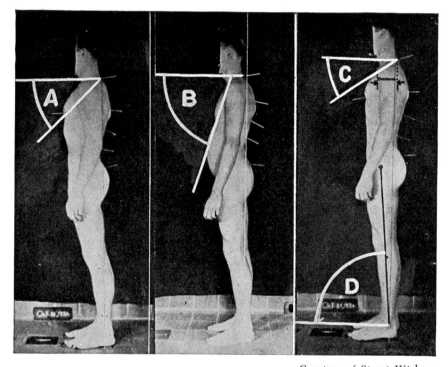

Courtesy of Stuart Wickens

Figure 7.2. Wickens-Kiphuth Posture Test.

[30] Stuart Wickens and Oscar W. Kiphuth, "Body Mechanics Analysis of Yale University Freshmen," *Research Quarterly,* Vol. VIII, No. 4 (December 1937), p. 38.

spinous process of the 7th cervical vertebra, the greatest convexity backward of the dorsal curve, the point of inflection between dorsal and lumbar curves (the point where the curve reverses its direction), the greatest convexity backward of the lumbar curve, and the most prominent part of the sacrum. One pointer was placed at the lower end of the sternum to determine the carriage of the chest. The feet were adjusted so that a plumb bob fell through the external malleolus, and the anteroposterior photograph was taken.

After the negative had been developed and the picture printed, small perforations were made at the proximal ends of each of the pointers, through the flesh pencil marks, and at the flesh line of the most protuberant part of the abdomen. The glossy side of the picture was placed face down on the frosted-glass surface of a mimeoscope illuminated from underneath, thus making the picture transparent; measurements were made on the back of the photograph. The following measurements were taken, as illustrated in Figures 7.2 and 7.3:

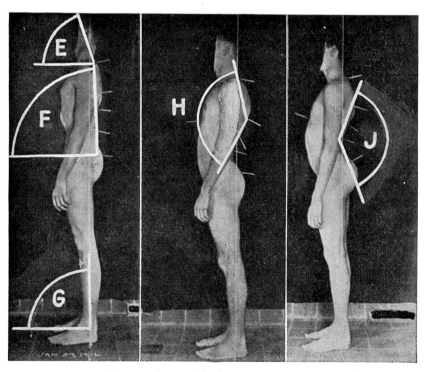

Figure 7.3. Wickens-Kiphuth Posture Test (continued).

1. *Head and Trunk:* The position of the head and neck was determined by scaling the angle made by a horizontal line through the 7th cervical and a line from the 7th cervical through the tragus of the ear. (Angle E)
2. *Kyphosis:* The amount of kyphosis was determined by scaling the angle made by a line from the greatest convexity backward of the dorsal curve through the 7th cervical and a line from the greatest convexity backward through the inflection point. (Angle H)
3. *Lordosis:* The lordosis angle was formed by a line from the greatest concavity backward of the lumbar curve through the inflection point and a line from the greatest concavity backward through the most prominent part of the sacrum. (Angle J)
4. *Chest:* The angle formed by a horizontal line through the 7th cervical and a line from the 7th cervical through the end of the sternum gave a measure of the carriage of the chest. Men carrying their chests in an elevated position showing a smaller angle than those having a flat chest. (Angle A)
5. *Abdomen:* If the abdominal line is straight and does not extend beyond the sternum, then the angle formed by a line from the most prominent part of the abdomen through the end of the sternum and a horizontal line through the 7th cervical will be 90 degrees or greater. On the other hand, if the abdomen extends beyond the sternum, the angle will read less than 90 degrees. (Angle B)
6. *Shoulders:* The shoulder angle was determined by scaling the angle made by a horizontal line through the 7th cervical and a line from the 7th cervical through the front tip of the shoulder. (Angle C) Measuring with vernier calipers the horizontal distance between two vertical lines erected through these points gives a linear rating of the shoulder's position.
7. *Trunk:* An important item in segmental alignment is the lean of the trunk forward or backward as it is balanced on the hip joint. The term *overcarriage* is applied to faulty carriage of the trunk where its weight is carried backward so that a vertical through the 7th cervical falls outside the most prominent part of the sacrum. This may be objectively measured by using the angle formed by a horizontal line through the sacral point and a line from the sacral point to the 7th cervical. As the trunk leans forward, the angle becomes less than 90 degrees, while in overcarriage it increases beyond 90 degrees. (Angle F)
8. *Hips:* The position of the hips was measured by the degree that the greater trochanter of the femur was carried forward or backward relative to the external malleolus. (Angle D)
9. *Knees:* Although "bow-legs" or "knock-knees" cannot be determined from a picture taken in the anteroposterior plane, an idea of knee posture with regard to "flexed knees" or "hyper-extended knees" may be obtained by scaling the angle formed by a horizontal line through the external malleolus and a line from the external malleolus through the styloid process of the fibula. In case of flexed or "easy" knees, the angle will be less than 90 degrees; with hyper-extended knees, greater than 90 degrees. (Angle G)

Objectivity coefficients were determined for the different measurements by photographing and rephotographing 30 subjects after the points were affixed by two different examiners independent of each other. The following coefficients show the precision of affixing the pointers and scaling the pictures: .72 for head and neck, .85 for kyphosis, and .73 for lordosis. Duplicate sets of 100 pictures were graded by two different examiners with correlations of .96 and .97 for the same three measurements. Thus, the application of the measurement procedures to the photographs has a high degree of consistency; when the whole process of preparing and photographing the subject is repeated, the objectivity coefficients are only slightly better than those obtained by Cureton with his conformateur procedure.

Subsequently, a method of taking PhotoMetric posture pictures for use with the Wickens and Kiphuth posture measurements was developed at Yale University.[31] By a system of mirrors placed in specific positions, four images of the individual from the following four angles are produced in a single exposure: left side, front, rear, and overhead. Before taking the picture, the subject is prepared with aluminum pointers and body markings, as for the Wickens and Kiphuth method. From slides of the photographs, images of one-half life size are projected on a screen, from which measurements within a tolerance of 1/16th inch in 72 inches may be made. In addition to the Wickens and Kiphuth posture measurements, the PhotoMetric picture permits an assessment of shoulder displacement.

A distinct advantage of the Wickens and Kiphuth technique is that it can be applied without the use of a conformateur. Silhouettes could be used instead of photographs by utilizing Cureton's scheme of lights over essential points on the body, such as the tragus of the ear, the acromion, and so forth.

Massey's posture technique.[32] In selecting the combination of body adjustments which best reflect the total posture of the body, Massey developed a criterion composed of the combined ratings of three qualified judges. The Cureton-Gunby conformateur technique was utilized to record posture, with small angle-iron pointers instead of lights being used to designate such landmarks as would be

---

[31] Phelps, Kiphuth, and Goff, *op. cit.,* Chap. 6.

[32] Wayne W. Massey, "A Critical Study of Objective Methods for Measuring Anterior Posterior Posture with a Simplified Technique," *Research Quarterly*, Vol. XIV, No. 1 (March 1943), p. 3.

invisible in the silhouette. From the resultant silhouette, 30 angles and seven linear deviations representing segmental alignments were made. The Kellogg, Goldthwaite, and MacEwan-Howe posture tests were also investigated in relation to the criterion.

As a result of the study, the following angles proved to be of greatest significance in over-all posture evaluated: Angle I, head and neck-trunk alignment; Angle II, trunk-hip alignment; Angle III, hip-thigh alignment; and Angle IV, thigh-leg alignment. This combination of angles resulted in a multiple correlation of .985 with the criterion. It was also found that the Kellogg measurements of "head angle," "chest ratio," and "pelvic obliquity" were fairly satisfactory as a measure of posture. The multiple correlation with the criterion was .855.

Center of gravity test. Before leaving anteroposterior posture measurement, it might be well to review briefly the center of gravity test reported upon by Cureton and Wickens,[33] together with its relationship to posture, physical fitness, and athletic ability. The "gravity line" is frequently referred to in posture and corrective physical education books; its significance in indicating the stance and alignment of the body is repeatedly implied. The apparatus used by Cureton and Wickens consisted of a balance board, supported at both ends from the center of a weight scale, such as the Toledo dial scales or the lever-arm type, with a vertical pin located in the exact center of the board. The subject stands on the balance board in a normal postural position, facing in the direction of the length of board and with his internal malleoli lined up even with the vertical pin. The examiner balances the scales, first the forward one and then the rear scale, until both scales have their lever arms swinging freely between the guide stops, or reads the weights directly, if the Toledo dial scales are used. The scales are read and both readings recorded. One-half of the weight of the board is deducted from each reading. The individual's score from the weights, showing how far the center of gravity is being balanced in front of the internal malleoli, may be read directly from a prepared

[33] T. K. Cureton and J. Stuart Wickens, "The Center of Gravity Test of the Human Body in the Antero-Posterior Plane and Its Relation to Posture, Physical Fitness and Athletic Ability," *Supplement to the Research Quarterly*, Vol. VI, No. 2 (May 1935), p. 93.

table, and the percentile score determined from a percentile rating scale.

A satisfactory degree of precision was found for the test, objectivity and reliability coefficients being in the .90's. The administration of the test takes approximately one minute per subject. The relationships of this test to posture, strength and physical fitness, endurance, condition, body build, and athletic ability have the following correlations, several of which are highly significant:

Center of Gravity and:	r	Remarks
1. Body lean	.86	Weight toward toes.
2. Kyphosis	−.36	Shifts gravity to compensate.
3. Strength index	.50	Back flattens with forward position of body.
4. Physical fitness index	.75	Physical fitness
5. McCurdy-Larson Test of Organic Condition	.06	
6. Body build	No relationship found	
7. Sargent Vertical Jump	.49	

Evidence is thus presented to show that men in better physical condition muscularly with better aptitude for athletics have flatter upper backs.

Conclusion

Excellent work has been done in the development of postural measurements. Certain of these measures, however, have objectivity coefficients which, while much superior to subjective judgment, are still below the accepted standard of .80, and all are below the preferred standard of .90. That this seeming lack of precision is due not entirely to the measurement itself, but to the inability of the subject to assume exactly the same position on each repetition of the test, may be deduced.

Another weakness of research in postural measurement is that norms have not been developed for any of the tests, with the exception of the arbitrary scale established by MacEwan and Howe for over-all posture positions. Average posture and the ideal toward which physical educators should work in their posture instruction need to be defined objectively.

The question of practicability may also be raised in connection with the posture measures, as the administration of any one of the objective tests requires expensive equipment and necessitates the expenditure of considerable time. This drawback is also true of other good tests in physical education and is not being accepted as an insurmountable obstacle. Such a question should be answered by physical educators after a careful consideration of the values to be obtained from the subsequent program. If major emphasis on posture training is to be a part of the physical education program, then the expenditure may be justified.

LATERAL DEVIATION OF THE SPINE

Fitz [34] described a "scoliometer" for measuring and graphically plotting lateral curvatures of the spine, which consisted of transparent celluloid, 2/100 in. in thickness, 52 cm. in length, and 16 cm. in width, ruled with longitudinal gradations 1 cm. apart and horizontal gradations 4 cm. apart. Two small level glasses, the tubes of which were bent to the curve of a circle of 12-inch radius, were attached to the celluloid; one of these was fastened at a right angle to the longitudinal lines (A) and the other was fastened at a right angle to the horizontal lines (B). The subject was prepared by marking with a skin pencil the tops of the spinous processes of the vertebrae, the posterior-superior spines, and the spines and lower angles of the scapulae. The major purposes of this device are as follows:

1. To determine lateral curvature of the spine: the scoliometer was placed upon the back in such a way as to bring the zero point of the longitudinal scale to the tip of the 7th cervical vertebra and to bring the end of the mid-vertical line to the cleft of the buttocks, after which the deviation was read through the transparent celluloid and the point of greatest convexity determined from the horizontal lines. The entire curve may be plotted by designating the deviation at each successive horizontal line.
2. To determine lateral deviation of the spine with reference to a true vertical midline (lateral tilt): the scoliometer was placed upon the back with the zero upon the 7th cervical process and the bubble of level "A" upon its index. The lines of the scoliometer are then vertical and the measurement can be made.
3. To determine lateral tilt of the pelvis: after spotting the anterior-superior iliac spines with the skin pencil, the scoliometer was applied so that the longitudinal lines were horizontal as determined by level "B," and

[34] George W. Fitz, "A Simple Method of Measuring and Graphically Plotting Spinal Curvature and Other Assymetrics by Means of a New Direct Reading Scoliometer," *American Physical Education Review*, Vol. XI, No. 1 (March 1906), p. 18.

the zero line was adjusted to one of the antero-superior spines, after which any unevenness in the level of the pelvis was discovered and measured.

4. To determine the shoulder levels: with the scoliometer in a horizontal position, as determined by level "B," the difference in the levels of the shoulders was detected and measured.

Believing that the scoliometer had definite possibilities for objective measurement of lateral deviations of the spine, Clarke and Shay conducted a study of its use as a precision instrument.[35] A scoliometer was constructed after the manner described by Fitz, except that the prescribed levels were omitted. Thus, the experiment was limited to the measurement of lateral curvatures only. The use of the Clarke-Shay Scoliometer is shown in Figure 7.4.

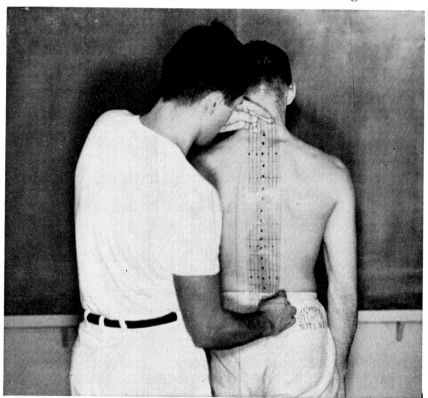

Figure 7.4. The Clarke-Shay Scoliometer in Use.

---

[35] H. Harrison Clarke and Clayton T. Shay, "Measurement of Lateral Spinal Deviations," *Black and Gold of Phi Epsilon Kappa*, Vol. XVII, No. 2 (March 1940), p. 38.

167

An objectivity coefficient of .89 was obtained for the Scoliometer Test, when successive measurements were taken within a short time (the back markings not being repeated). It was not entirely satisfactory when the measurements were made after the lapse of several days, the correlations being approximately .60 for both reliability and objectivity. Considerable doubt, however, exists concerning the subject's ability to assume the same position each time he is measured. Marking the entire back proved most exact.

The following criticisms may be made of the scoliometer as a precision instrument in measuring lateral curvatures of the spine:

1. The main difficulty encountered in the use of the scoliometer is in keeping the celluloid from twisting, especially when projecting scapulae tend to displace it.

2. The scoliometer is too short for the taller individuals.

3. If only lateral deviations are measured, the scoliometer may advantageously be made smaller, reducing its width by one-half.

Another method of objectively measuring lateral curvatures, the Taut-String Test, was also tried. This test consists of stretching a string from the 7th cervical to the 5th lumbar vertebrae, and noting the amount of lateral deviation from the string. In conducting this experiment, inside calipers were used for measuring the curvature and a steel metric rule for determining the amount of deviation.

The Taut-String Test as administered was found to be slightly superior to the scoliometer. Criticisms concerning its use are as follows:

1. Difficulty is encountered in keeping the string straight between the 7th cervical and the 5th lumbar vertebrae, especially when a pronounced kyphosis is present and bows the string posteriorly, and when the lateral curvature is of such a nature that the erector spinae muscles of the back tend to deflect the string sideward.

2. Difficulty is also encountered in measuring the deviation when the convexity is in the lumbar area and the individual has a pronounced lordosis. The string is then two to three inches from the back, and sighting the calipers through this distance is not easy.

3. The point of greatest convexity of the curvature is occasionally found to be in error when only one mark on the back is used, as contrasted with measures where the entire back is marked.

4. An assistant is required in giving the test in order to hold the string while the calipers are being applied.

FOOT MEASUREMENT

Examinations of the feet have generally consisted of subjective checkings of certain foot characteristics considered indicative of the status of the foot. Among these have been such characteristics as the following: angle of stance, ankle overhang, height of the longitudinal arch, bowing of the Achilles tendon, pronation or supination, foot flexibility, presence of callouses on bottom of foot, and the like. Pronation, or inward rolling of the ankles with resulting disalignment of the feet and legs, is the most widely accepted criterion of foot weakness and strain. Kelly [36] reported that 50 to 60 per cent of the child population shows pronation to a greater or lesser degree. However, she points out, functional foot complaints are relatively uncommon among children and very common among adults. To identify and correct potential foot disturbances is a logical purpose of remedial physical education.

Pain on Pressure

Kelly [37] studied 35 anthropometric and X-ray variables with three groups of children, eight to fourteen years of age, to determine their relative effectiveness in identifying criteria of potentially painful feet. The three groups of children were as follows: (1) 75 children judged to have symptomless, normal, or well aligned feet and legs; (2) 52 children were symptomless, but with markedly weak or pronated alignment; (3) 51 children reported persistent symptoms typical of functional foot strain. Both pronated and painful groups showed greater flexibility than the normal group with regard to the arch, the ankle, and the trunk and hamstrings, and similar but less significant greater flexibility in ten of eleven additional variables studied. Pain on pressure to the sole of the foot differentiated the normal from the painful feet, and the pronated from the painful feet.

---

[36] Ellen D. Kelly, "A Comparative Study of Structure and Function of Normal, Pronated, and Painful Feet Among Children," *Research Quarterly*, Vol. XVIII, No. 4 (December 1947), p. 291.
[37] *Loc. cit.*

The following three pressure points were used to determine the presence of pain in the foot: (1) under the junction of the first and second metatarsals with the first cuneform bone, (2) under the insertion of the tibialis anterior muscle, and (3) under the posterior insertion of the plantar-calcaneo-navicular ligament into the calcaneus bone. As shown in Figure 7.5, the subject lowers the weight of the leg and foot onto a half-inch diameter padded nailhead, which is resting on the platform of a bathroom-type scale. With the foot relaxed, the minimum pounds pressure required to elicit a pain response is the score used. If no pain is recorded at 12 pounds, the pressure is automatically discontinued.

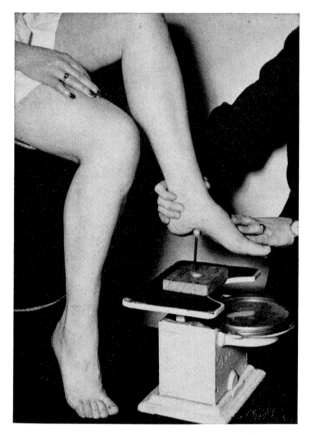

Courtesy of Ellen Kelly

Figure 7.5. Kelly Test for Foot Pain Systems.

Iowa Foot-Mechanics Test

As indicated above, a foot mechanics test was included as a part of the Iowa posture battery for college women.[38] In taking this test, each subject walks ten steps forward and then back, while the tester observes heel-toe walking from the side. This short walk is repeated while the tester checks on toeing straight ahead from in front. The test is scored as follows:

A. *Heel-toe walking*
    3 points   Heel in contact with ground first; weight transferred through outside of foot to ball of foot; toes used in gripping action; spring in walk.
    2 points   Fair performance.
    1 point   Poor performance.

B. *Absence of pronation*
    3 points   No bony bulge in front of and below medial malleolus; no marked protrusion inward of navicular; no inward bowing of heel cord.
    2 points   Some pronation.
    1 point   Marked pronation.

C. *Feet parallel*
    3 points   Feet parallel: a very slight angle of toeing out is permissible.
    2 points   Moderate toeing out.
    1 point   Marked toeing out.

The Footprint Angle

The use of footprints as measures of foot condition, especially of the height of the arch, has been the subject of several studies. Footprints have become popular, as they are easily taken and yield pictures easily comprehended by the subject. They also lend themselves to objective measurement. Footprints may be made with a pedograph or with homemade devices. One homemade device for taking footprints consists of an ordinary picture frame across which is stretched light rubber sheeting. Fingerprint ink is rolled on the underside of this sheeting and the print taken on ordinary paper. This device is inexpensive, takes an excellent footprint, and in addition shows the callouses and other growths on the underside of the foot. Its main disadvantage is the necessity of constantly re-applying the fingerprint ink to the rubber sheeting.

---

[38] State University of Iowa, *op. cit.*

The first attempt to measure footprints was made by Schwartz,[39] who originated the footprint angle. This angle is based on the theory that as arches become higher, arch-angles increase steadily. Both Schwartz and Rogers [40] obtained high reliability coefficients for this angle but failed to indicate objectivity for the measurement. Clarke,[41] however, by refining the method of determining the arch-angle, was able to obtain a reliability coefficient of .97 and an objectivity coefficient of .95. Cureton subsequently verified Clarke's results.

The procedures used in scoring the footprints, as illustrated in Figure 7.6, follow:

1. Draw a line to represent the medial border of the foot between the points of the imprint at the base of the first metatarsal bone (base of the big toe) and the calcaneous or heel bone.

2. Locate a point where this line touches the imprint on the inner side of the big toe.
3. Then, with a ruler held on this point, swing it down from the toes until it just touches the edge of the print on the inside of the arch, and draw a line from the point across the print.

Figure 7.6.   The Clarke Footprint Angle.

No white paper should show between this line and the print.
4. Measure the angle at the junction of the two lines with a protractor.

The average or normal footprint angle for adult males is placed at about 42 degrees. Some question has been raised, however, as to whether the footprint angle actually measures the height of the arch. Cureton [42] pointed out that the footprint shows the fleshy pads and musculature of the plantar surface of the foot rather than the bony alignment of the arch. He did, however, definitely prove that the footprint angle does measure the external height of the

[39] L. Schwartz, R. H. Britton, and J. R. Thompson, *Studies in Physical Development and Posture*, U. S. Public Health Bulletin No. 179 (Washington: Government Printing Office, 1928).

[40] Frederick Rand Rogers, *Fundamental Administrative Measures in Physical Education* (Newton, Mass.: Pleiades Company, 1932), p. 99.

[41] H. Harrison Clarke, "An Objective Method of Measuring the Height of the Longitudinal Arch of the Foot," *Research Quarterly*, Vol. IV, No. 3 (October 1933), p. 99.

[42] Thomas K. Cureton, "The Validity of Footprints as a Measure of Vertical Height of the Arch and Functional Efficiency of the Foot," *Research Quarterly*, Vol. VI, No. 2 (May 1935), p. 70.

arch, when he obtained correlations of .86 and .96 between it and the height of imprints made in moist sand (sandbox method).

Cureton further found that the height of the arch, as measured by either the footprint or the sandbox method, was not a significant factor in the functional efficiency of the foot. These data explode the popular theory that a measure of the external height of the arch may be used as a diagnostic device in the selection of individuals needing foot correction. Apparently, therefore, the principal value of the footprint angle is to measure the increase in arch height in those cases selected by other means for treatment, and then only where arch height is one of the factors involved. The footprint, however, is a motivating device, which, like the silhouette in posture training, portrays to the individual obvious facts concerning the condition of his feet, thus emphasizing in his mind the need for correction.

FLEXIBILITY TESTS

The Goniometer

In a literature review, Moore [43] has shown that goniometry, or the use of instruments for measuring the range of motion in joints of the body, has been discussed since the turn of the century. The medical needs of both World Wars intensified its use in evaluating the rate of improvement of patients recovering from orthopedic disabilities. Many types of goniometers have been devised; generally, measurement is based on degrees of a circle.

One form of the goniometer is illustrated in Figure 7.7. This device consists of a 180-degree protractor with extended arms, constructed from plexiglas. The two arms are 15 inches long; the one at the zero line is fixed, the other movable. A winged nut at the center point where the two arms meet may be tightened to hold the movable arm in position once the measurement is made.

The application of the goniometer is simple. For example, if the range of motion of the elbow joint is to be tested, the arms of the goniometer are placed parallel with the upper and lower arms of the body, with the center of motion at the elbow joint; readings are taken with the elbow flexed as fully as the disability permits, and

---

[43] Margaret L. Moore, "The Measurement of Joint Motion: Introductory Review of the Literature," *Physical Therapy Review*, Vol. XXIX, No. 6 (June 1949), p. 1.

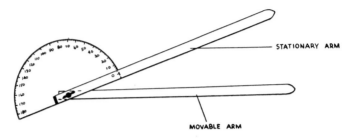

Figure 7.7. The Goniometer.

again with as full extension as possible; the difference between the two readings represents the range of motion.

Leighton Flexometer

Another device for measuring the range of motion of several joints is the "flexometer," developed by Jack Leighton,[44] illustrated in Figure 7.8. This instrument is equipped with a rotating flat circular dial, marked off in degrees of a circle, and a movable pointer. Both the dial and the pointer always point upward and coincide when the

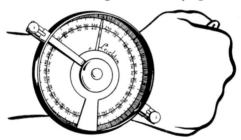

Figure 7.8. Leighton Flexometer.

instrument is placed in operating position. A locking device is provided for the dial and another for the pointer. In use, the instrument is strapped on the moving part being tested. The dial is locked at one extreme position (*i.e.,* full flexion of the elbow); the movement is made and the pointer is locked at the other extreme position (*i.e.,* full extension of the elbow). Thus, the direct reading of the pointer on the dial is the range of motion which takes place. Twenty-one flexibility tests have been devised, involving movements of both trunk and extremities. Reliability coefficients for the various tests range from .889 to .997. Average range of motion for the tests are given in the reference.

[44] Jack R. Leighton, "A Simple Objective and Reliable Measure of Flexibility," *Research Quarterly,* Vol XIII, No. 2 (May 1942), pp. 205-216. (Description of improved instruments: correspondence with author.)

Trunk-Hip Flexibility Tests

General body flexibility, represented by hip and back flexion, has long been of interest to physical educators, as body suppleness has been considered advantageous in physical performances. A number of tests have been proposed to test this trait. The Leighton flexometer and the Cureton test may be used for this purpose. Several others are described below.

Scott and French bobbing test.[45] A 20-inch scale, marked in half-inch units, is attached to a stable bench or chair, so that half the scale is above and below the level of the bench. An alternative method is to arrange the scale so that the bench level is zero with half-inch deviations progressing upward and downward from that point. The scale should not be more than four inches wide.

In taking the bobbing test, the subject stands with toes even with the front edge of the bench and touching the edges of the scale. The arms and trunk are bent forward, fingers in front of the scale. The subject then bobs downward forcefully three or four times, reaching equally with the fingers of both hands. The knees must be kept straight. The score is the lowest point reached in the series of bobbings. An alternative test score is the reach attained and held for two or three seconds.

Poley [46] obtained a reliability coefficient of .93 for the standing bobbing test, with college women as subjects. Scott and French also describe a sitting bobbing test in the reference.

Wells and Dillon sit and reach test.[47] The equipment for this test consists of a platform scale, two gymnasium (stall-bar) benches, and a piece of rubber matting about four feet square. The platform scale consists of a scale similar to that used by Scott and French, described above, with a center line marked zero, and with plus and minus scales on either side of the zero line. The support for this scale is in the form of an elongated plus sign made of 11-inch boards resting on their edges. For convenience, these are referred to as the cross board and the stem board. Footprints are outlined on the

---

[45] M. Gladys Scott and Esther French, *Evaluation in Physical Education* (St. Louis: C. V. Mosby Company, 1950), p. 181.

[46] Margaret Poley, "A Study of the Postural Characteristics of College Women as Related to Build," Microcarded Doctoral Dissertation, State University of Iowa, 1948.

[47] Katharine Wells and Evelyn Dillon, "The Sit and Reach: A Test of Back and Leg Flexibility," *Research Quarterly,* Vol. XXIII, No. 1 (March 1952), p. 115.

cross board, one on either side of the stem board. The scale is attached to the upper edges of the support in such a way that when the subject is seated on the floor with the feet against the footprints, the zero line coincides with the near surface of the cross board and the minus values are toward the subject.

The equipment is placed near a wall. The two benches are placed side by side on their sides about 12 inches apart, with their legs against a wall. The scale is placed between the benches with the cross board braced against the benches. The rubber matting is spread on the floor in front of and partially under the scale.

In taking the test, the subject sits on the rubber matting, legs separated just enough to straddle the stem board, with the feet placed on the footprints and pressed firmly against the cross board. The arms are extended forward with the hands placed palms down on the upper surface of the scale. In this position, the subject bobs forward four times and holds the position of maximum reach on the fourth count. The knees must remain straight. If the hands reach unevenly, the hand reaching the shorter distance determines the score. The score is taken to the nearest half inch.

Kraus-Weber floor-touch test. This test will be described in Chapter 8, as an item in the Kraus-Weber Test of Minimum Muscular Fitness. Suffice it to say here that it consists of the ability to touch the floor from a standing position, keeping the knees straight.

An evaluation. The importance of trunk-hip flexibility in motor performance is yet to be proved satisfactorily. In a number of studies, low correlations were obtained between motor ability tests and body flexibility. McCue [48] found that college women who had a past history of greater physical activity tended to be more flexible than did less active college women. Olson,[49] also with college women, found no significant relationship between flexibility measures and the Scott Motor Ability Test. However, she did obtain low relationships between lateral trunk flexibility and throwing distance and between knee flexibility and jumping, running, and body

[48] Betty F. McCue, "Flexibility Measures of College Women," *Research Quarterly,* Vol. XXIV, No. 3 (October 1953), p. 316.

[49] Barbara Olsen, "An Investigation of the Relationship of Ankle, Knee, Trunk, and Shoulder Flexibility to General Motor Ability," Microcarded Master's Thesis, University of Oregon, 1956.

maneuverability performances. With college athletes, Leighton [50] presented evidence that the number and kind of specialized flexibility performance abilities vary significantly among different specialized skills, and that these variations do not occur for all movements nor for the same movements among different special skill groups.

It has been quite well established by a number of investigators that girls at most ages have greater trunk-hip flexibility than boys. Also, boys appear to lose in flexibility as they enter the adolescent period, although they do not lose amplitude in all areas of the body.[51] With boys 10 to 18 years of age, Leighton [52] found that flexibility abilities varied with age: eight decreased progressively, seven decreased erratically, and one showed little or no change. In a study by Hupprich and Sigerseth,[53] girls were found to increase in flexibility from six to twelve years of age, and then showed a decline.

The correlations between flexibility and anthropometric measures are low. With college women, Wilson and Scott [54] reported correlations between the Scott and French standing bobbing test and the following: .16 with height, .15 with trunk length, .29 with arm length, and .30 with trunk and arm length. Mathews, Shaw, and Bohnen [55] obtained similar results, again with college women. These latter investigations obtained the following intercorrelations between flexibility tests for hip flexibility: .95 between Kraus-Weber and Wells sit and reach tests, .80 between Kraus-Weber and Leighton flexometer tests, and .74 between Leighton flexometer and Wells sit and reach tests.

---

[50] Jack R. Leighton, "Flexibility Characteristics of Four Specialized Skill Groups of College Athletes," *Archives of Physical Medicine and Rehabilitation,* Vol. XXXVIII, No. 1 (January 1957), p. 24.

[51] Joseph M. Forbes, "Characteristics of Flexibility in Boys," Microcarded Doctoral Dissertation, University of Oregon, 1950.

[52] Jack R. Leighton, "Flexibility Characteristics of Males Ten to Eighteen Years of Age," *Archives of Physical Medicine and Rehabilitation,* Vol. XXXVII, No. 8 (August 1957), p. 494.

[53] Florence L. Hupprich and Peter O. Sigerseth, "The Specificity of Flexibility in Girls," *Research Quarterly,* Vol. XXI, No. 1 (March 1950), p. 25.

[54] Marjorie Wilson and M. Gladys Scott: Reported in Scott and French, *op. cit.,* p. 184.

[55] Donald K. Mathews, Virginia Shaw, and Merla Bohnen, "Hip Flexibility of College Women as Related to Length of Body Segments," *Research Quarterly,* Vol. XXVIII, No. 4 (December 1957), p. 352.

CABLE-TENSION STRENGTH TESTS

In medicine, physical therapists have used "manual" tests to measure the strength of muscle groups weakened or impaired as a result of disease or injury. These tests have been used to determine the strength status of affected muscle groups at the beginning of therapeutic exercise and, periodically, during the period of treatment in order to follow their improvement. In applying these tests, the examiner subjectively estimates the ability of muscles to overcome gravity and resistance applied manually. Williams [56] has presented the development and use of this form of testing. Daniels, Williams, and Worthingham [57] have carefully described the techniques involved in the administration of these tests. An early objective-type test for measuring the strength of muscles activating various joint movements was devised by Martin,[58] in which a spring balance was used for measuring the strength of twenty-two muscle groups. In this test a sling was fastened to the extremity with the pull at right angles to the long axis of the limb. An assistant held the spring balance, fastened to the other end of the sling. The subject contracted the muscle being tested and held it against the pull of the spring balance.

More recently, Clarke [59] adapted the tensiometer,[60] an instrument designed to measure the tension of aircraft control cable, for testing the strength of individual muscle groups. Cable tension is determined from the force needed to create offset on a riser in a cable stretched between two set points, or sectors. This tension can be converted into pounds on a calibration chart. Thirty-eight strength tests were subsequently devised to measure the strength of muscles activating the following joints: fingers, thumb, wrist, forearm, elbow, shoulder, neck, trunk, hip, knee and ankle.

Research in the construction of these tests included: determina-

---

[56] Marian Williams, "Manual Muscle Testing: Development and Current Use," *Second Congress Proceedings,* World Confederation for Physical Therapy, 1956, p. 115.

[57] Lucile Daniels, Marian Williams, and Catherine Worthingham, *Muscle Testing* (Philadelphia: W. B. Saunders Company, 1947).

[58] E. G. Martin, "Tests of Muscular Efficiency," *Physiological Review,* Vol. I (1921), p. 454.

[59] H. Harrison Clarke, *Cable-Tension Strength Tests* (Chicopee, Mass.: Brown-Murphy Co., 1953).

[60] Manufactured by the Pacific Scientific Co., Inc., 1430 Grande Vista Avenue, Los Angeles, California.

tion of body position which permitted greatest application of strength for each joint movement, selection of the joint angle which resulted in the strongest movement, and the study of such factors as the position of the pulling strap and the effect of gravity upon the test scores. The effectiveness of the following four instruments for recording muscle strength was studied: cable tensiometer, Wakim-Porter strain gauge, spring scale, and Newman myometer.[61] As reflected by objectivity coefficients, the tensiometer has greatest precision for strength testing (.90 and above). It was the most stable and generally useful of the instruments.

A complete description of the equipment needed and of the testing techniques for administering the various cable-tension strength tests appear in Clarke's *Manual* (see footnote 59). One test only will be presented here, as an illustration of the procedures involved. This test is for knee extension strength, illustrated in Figure 7.9 and described as follows:

Starting Position
1. Subject is sitting, backward-leaning position; arms extended to rear, hands grasping sides of table.
2. Knees on side tested in 115 degrees extension (use goniometer).

Attachments
1. Regulation strap around leg midway between knee and ankle joints at right angles to the limb.
2. Pulling cable attached to hook at lower end of testing table.

Precautions
1. Prevent lifting buttocks.
2. Prevent elbow flexion.

Hull-scale norms have been constructed for twelve of these tests for boys at seven, nine, twelve, and fifteen years of age.[62]

In addition to the use of cable-tension tests for the measurement of muscle strength, Clarke and Herman[63] found that a resistance load equal to 50 per cent of the strength of the muscles, tested by

---

[61] H. Harrison Clarke, "Comparison of Instruments for Recording Muscle Strength," *Research Quarterly*, Vol. XXV, No. 4 (December 1954), p. 398.

[62] James Harrison, "The Construction of Cable-Tension Strength Test Norms for Boys Seven, Nine, Twelve, and Fifteen Years of Age," Microcarded Master's Thesis, University of Oregon, 1958.

[63] David H. Clarke and Edward L. Herman, "Objective Determination of Resistance Load for Ten Repetitions Maximum for Quadriceps Development," *Research Quarterly*, Vol. XXVI, No. 4 (December 1955), p. 385.

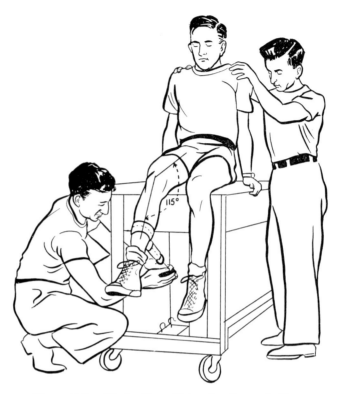

Figure 7.9. Clarke Knee Extension Strength Test.

cable-tension methods (strap attached to ankle), was found to be a reasonably satisfactory method of objectively determining the amount of weight necessary for a maximum of ten repetitions in exercising the knee extensor muscles. Nearly a straight-line decrease in the mean number of repetitions resulted when the weights used varied from 30 to 50 per cent of knee extension strength.

STRENGTH DECREMENT INDEX

The Strength Decrement Index (SDI) is proposed as a test of muscle fatigue.[64] The basic concept of this test is that an immediate effect of fatiguing muscles is to reduce their ability to apply tension. This phenomenon is the same as the muscular weakness ex-

---

[64] H. Harrison Clarke, Clayton T. Shay, and Donald K. Mathews, "Strength Decrement Index: A New Test of Muscle Fatigue," *Archives of Physical Medicine and Rehabilitation*, Vol. XXXVI, No. 6 (June 1955), p. 376.

perienced when a person chins himself: at the start, he chins fairly easily, but soon is no longer able to do so.

The SDI is the proportionate loss of strength in a given muscle group resulting from physical exertion. The formula for its computation is:

$$\text{SDI} = \frac{\text{Si} - \text{Sf}}{\text{Si}} \times 100$$

in which: Si = Initial strength: taken before exercise.
Sf = Final strength: taken after exercise.

The SDI has been used in conjunction with the cable-tension strength tests. For a given muscle group, e.g., the knee extensors, strength tests are given before and immediately after fatiguing exercise. The proportionate strength loss indicates the resultant degree of fatigue. The control of muscular fatigue may well be a factor in certain types of disabilities; the SDI will permit the physical educator to regulate exercise approximately to a predetermined amount.

SELECTED REFERENCES

Clarke, H. Harrison, *A Manual: Cable-Tension Strength Tests*. Chicopee, Mass.: Brown-Murphy Co., 1953.
———, "Recent Advances in Measurement and Understanding of Volitional Muscular Strength," *Research Quarterly*, Vol. XXVII, No. 3 (October 1956), p. 263.
Cureton, Thomas K., "Bodily Posture as an Indicator of Fitness," *Supplement to the Research Quarterly*, Vol. XI, No. 2 (May 1941), p. 348.
Hupprich, Florence L., and Peter O. Sigerseth, "The Specificity of Flexibility in Girls," *Research Quarterly*, Vol. XXI, No. 1 (March 1950), p. 25.
Lee, Mabel, and Miriam M. Wagner, *Fundamentals of Body Mechanics and Conditioning*. Philadelphia: W. B. Saunders Company, 1949.
Leighton, Jack R., "Flexibility Characteristics of Males Ten to Eighteen Years of Age," *Archives of Physical Medicine and Rehabilitation*, Vol. XXXVII, No. 8(August 1957), p. 494.
Phelps, W. W., R. J. H. Kiphuth, and C. W. Goff, *The Diagnosis and Treatment of Postural Defects*, 2nd. ed. Springfield, Mass.: Charles C Thomas, 1956.

CHAPTER EIGHT

Strength Tests

The majority of tests previously considered for measuring the physical fitness of individuals have been designed primarily to measure only certain aspects of physical condition. The school medical examination is not ordinarily conducted to appraise physical fitness. It is essentially a fact-finding procedure, in which physical defects are discovered and subsequently, through a follow-up service, corrected so that the physical fitness of the student may be improved. Cardiovascular tests may be used as supplements to the medical examination, especially as checks on the condition of the circulatory system itself. Posture tests reveal certain physical deformities and habitual body positions that may contribute to lessened efficiency of visceral and other internal organs. These tests, however, are inadequate to evaluate the physical condition of the individual; none serves as an index of the physical development of the human body.

Consequently, a test is needed that will measure objectively the fitness of the body as a whole; a test that will be sensitive to the effects upon the organism of lack of exercise, of faulty health habits, and of organic drains; *a test that can be understood, interpreted, and used by individuals trained in physical education.* Not only is a test needed for evaluating the physical fitness benefits of the physical education program, but such a test is needed also to select those boys and girls who are deficient in this essential quality, so that their particular needs may be studied and improved.

Strength tests, although they do not measure all aspects of fitness as the physical educator views the problem, do deal with a basic element of the individual's general physical status. They have been used successfully in practical field situations, both as a means of selecting students for developmental classes, and for general classification in physical activities. The former use will be discussed in this chapter; the latter, in Chapter 12.

The idea of using strength tests as a measure of physical condition is not new. Feats of strength and trials of endurance, practiced by savage tribes as well as by civilized man, have come down through the ages. Nor is the idea of combining strength tests into a formal battery for the purpose of measuring athletic ability a new one, for Dudley A. Sargent, M.D., in 1880 proposed such a battery in which the individual elements were measured by calibrated mechanical instruments. It was not until 1925, however, when Dr. Frederick Rand Rogers standardized testing procedures and developed norm tables for their interpretation, that the relationship between physical condition, athletic performance and muscular strength was demonstrated.[1]

The Rogers Physical Fitness Index Battery

In selecting the individual elements composing the PFI battery, Rogers tried to include only tests that would measure most of the large muscles of the body. As a result, the complete test involves the following muscle groups: forearms, upper arms, shoulder girdles, back, and legs. Most of the large muscles not tested are antagonistic to those tested—Rogers' composite test of seven elements is a reduction from ten tests given by Sargent.

With the construction of norm tables for many combinations of sex, age, and weight, two major scores are possible—the Strength Index and the Physical Fitness Index—each of which has a distinctly different purpose. Rogers, by the construction of these norm tables, created the PFI, a score—and even a concept—unknown to Sargent.

The Strength Index. The Strength Index is the gross score obtained from the six strength tests plus lung capacity. It is proposed as a measure of *general athletic ability* and should be conceived neither as a measure of skill in any particular sport nor as a measure

---

[1] Frederick Rand Rogers, *Physical Capacity Tests in the Administration of Physical Edcucation* (New York: Bureau of Publications, Teachers College, Columbia University, 1926).

of physical fitness. It is with this measure, scored in kilograms and points rather than pounds and points, that Sargent was familiar. The old Sargent test was an athletic ability test only.

The Physical Fitness Index. The Physical Fitness Index is a score derived from comparing an achieved Strength Index with a norm based upon the individual's sex, weight, and age. It is a measure of basic physical fitness elements.

THE ADMINISTRATION OF THE PFI TESTS

The Physical Fitness Index Test may be used for both boys and girls, the elements being the same for both sexes except that the pull-up and push-up tests for girls are less strenuous than those for boys. The various parts of the test, in the order in which they are usually administered, are described in detail in the following paragraphs.

In all tests the subject should be encouraged to do his best *but should not be driven;* in fact, it is safer in the long run to stop the subject just before he begins his apparent "last pull-up," for example. "Normal strains of effort" should be encouraged; "extreme strains" should be discouraged.

Age, Height, Weight

The age, height, and weight of the individual should be recorded, according to the following instructions:

1. Age should be taken in years and months, as, 15 years, 7 months.
2. Height and weight should be taken in gymnasium uniforms, and recorded at the nearest half-inch and pound, respectively.

Lung Capacity

Lung capacity is measured in cubic inches with a *wet spirometer* (Figure 8.1).

1. The spirometer should be equipped with an extra-length rubber hose (36 to 42 inches), filled with water to within one inch of the top, and placed at such a height that all subjects can stand erect when beginning the test. A good arrangement for the majority of students is to place the base from four to four and one-half feet from the floor.
2. An individual wooden mouthpiece, the most hygienic, is used for each subject. The mouthpieces should not be handled by the tester, but should

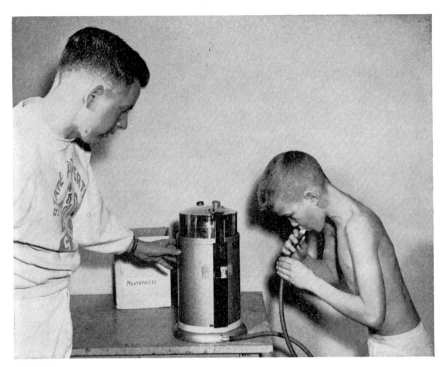

Figure 8.1.   Test of Lung Capacity with Wet Spirometer.

be inserted into the tube by the subject being tested. The wooden mouth-piece may be used repeatedly if thoroughly sterilized by boiling, steam-ing, soaking for half an hour in an antiseptic solution, such as zephiran aqueous solution, $\frac{1}{1000}$. A glass mouthpiece is not recommended unless some method can be devised for instantaneous sterilization.

3. The subject should take one or two deep breaths before the test. Then, after the fullest possible inhalation, he should exhale slowly and steadily while bending forward over the hose until all the air within his control is expelled. Care should be taken to prevent air from escaping either through the nose or around the edges of the mouthpiece, and to see that a second breath is not taken by the subject during the test. If the test is improperly performed, or if, in the opinion of the tester, the pupil did not do his best, it should be repeated after an explanation of the precautions necessary to make the test a successful one.

4. The tester should watch the indicator closely to note when it reaches the highest point.

5. The rubber plug at the base of the spirometer should be removed when lowering the inner can after a test has been administered. Care should be taken in lowering this can so that the water is not spilled. If at any time the inner can should "bobble" and refuse to rise higher with con-

tinued blowing into the hose, additional water is required. This situation will occur if there is an insufficient amount of water in the can, which may happen if the water level has been lowered through spilling.

Grip Strength

A *manuometer*, or *hand dynamometer*, of the rectangular type, is used to measure grip strength, both right and left hands being tested (Figure 8.2).

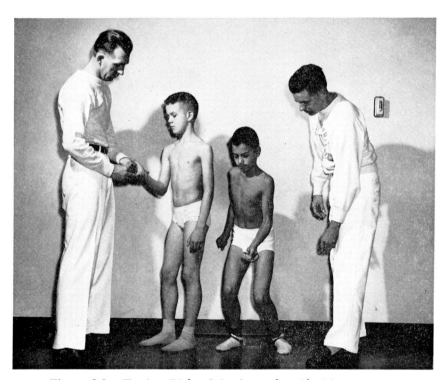

Figure 8.2. Testing Right Grip Strength with Manuometer.

1. The tester should take the right-hand corner of the manuometer between the thumb and forefinger of his right hand and place it in the palm of the subject's hand while holding the hand to be tested with his left hand in such a manner that the convex edge of the manuometer is between the first and second joints of the fingers and the rounded edge is against the base of the hand. The thumb should touch, or overlap, the first finger. The dial of the manuometer should be placed face down in the hand.

2. In taking the test, the subject's elbow should be slightly bent and his hand should describe a sweeping arc downward as he squeezes the

manuometer. The hands should not be allowed to touch the body, or any object, while the test is being administered. If they do, the score should not be read at all, and a retest should be given after a short rest period of 30 seconds.

3. The right hand should be tested first and then the left. Scores should be read to the nearest pound.
4. A cake of magnesium carbonate should be available for dusting the hands if they should become moist and slippery.
5. The indicator should be returned to zero after each test.

The Back and Leg Dynamometer

The back and leg dynamometer is the instrument used in measuring the strength of both back and leg muscles.

1. Several back and leg dynamometers are on the market, the better ones being rather expensive. The instrument selected should be easy to read, should be calibrated in pounds, and should be capable of measuring a lift of at least 2,500 pounds. The chain purchased with the dynamometer should be at least 24 inches in length, and the handle should be from 20 to 22 inches long.
2. Certain dynamometers are equipped to measure compression, or crushing strength. In testing for back and leg strength, the handles supplied for this purpose should be removed. The outer edge of the dynamometer carries the scale for measuring lifting strength, while the inner scale is for crushing power. Care, therefore, should be taken to read back and leg lifts from the outer scale only.
3. Small pointers of white adhesive with the weight indicated on the broad ends may be placed at each hundred-pound interval on the dial to facilitate reading the lifts.
4. The dynamometer base should be placed on a small elevated platform (a stall bar bench will serve nicely), so that the tester may sit in a chair before the instrument in the administration of the tests. The wooden base, however, should not be fastened to this platform. It is very important that this base be solid and steady so that the subject will have a feeling of security throughout the test.
5. The handle or cross-bar may be taped to facilitate firm handling by the subject, and a block of magnesium carbonate or chalk should be supplied with which to dust the hands if they are moist and slippery.
6. In all lifting tests, the feet should be placed parallel, about six inches apart, with the center of the foot opposite the chain. To save the tester's time and energy, foot outlines should be painted on the base to indicate the position of the feet.
7. In back and leg lifts, the tester should guard against any snap resulting from a kink in the chain, which might jar the indicator beyond the true lift made by the subject.

Back Lift (Figure 8.3)

1. With the feet in the proper position on the base of the dynamometer, the subject should stand erect with the hands on the front of the thighs,

187

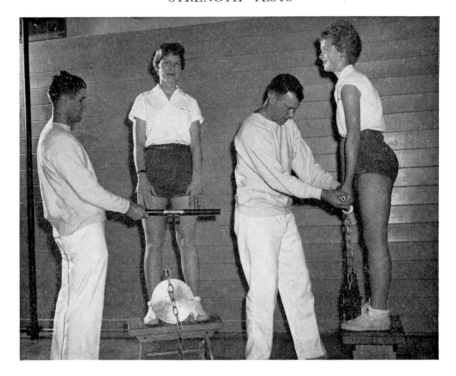

Figure 8.3.   Back Lift with Dynamometer.

fingers extended downward. The tester should then hook the chain so that the bar level is just below the finger tips. The subject should grasp the handle firmly at the ends of the bar, with thumb clenching fingers and *with one palm forward and one palm backward.* When the subject is in position to lift, the back should be slightly bent at the hips, so that he will not completely straighten when lifting, but the legs should be straight with no bend at the knees. The head should be up and eyes directed straight ahead.

It is highly important not to bend the back too much, as the resultant poor leverage is conducive to a poor lift as well as to the possibility of strain. With the back properly bent, however, there is very little likelihood of injury from lifting.

2. The subject should lift steadily. Care should be taken to keep the knees straight. The tester should grasp the subject's hands firmly during the lift.

3. The subject's feet should be flat on the platform. It is necessary to retest after shortening the chain, if he attempts to lift by standing on his toes. Any initial lateral sway should be immediately checked.

4. At the end of lifting effort, the back should be almost straight. If not, repeat the test.

Leg Lift (Figure 8.4)

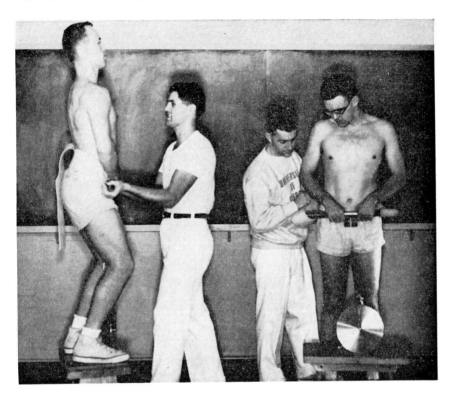

Figure 8.4.   Use of the Belt in Testing Leg Strength.

Two methods have been proposed for administering the leg lift on the back and leg dynamometer. These methods may be characterized as "without the belt" and "with the belt." Everts and Hathaway [2] perfected the belt technique in order to aid both the subject and the tester in obtaining more objective results and to improve the validity of the PFI battery itself. The belt technique is now advocated and has been generally adopted by physical educators as the standard technique in the administration of the test. Consequently, the leg lift with the belt only is described below.

---

[2] Edgar W. Everts and Gordon J. Hathaway, "The Use of the Belt to Measure Leg Strength Improves the Administration of Physical Tests," *Research Quarterly,* Vol. IX, No. 3 (October 1938), p. 62.

1. The subject should hold the bar with both hands together in the center, both palms down, so that it rests at the junction of thighs and trunk. Care should be taken to maintain this position after the belt has been put in place and during the lift.
2. The loop end of the belt is slipped over one end of the handle or cross-bar: the free end of the belt should be looped around the other end of the bar, tucking it in under so that it rests next to the body. In this position, the pressure of the belt against the body and the resultant friction of the free end against the standing part holds the bar securely. The belt should be placed as low as possible over the hips and gluteal muscles.
3. The subject should stand with his feet in the same position as for the back lift. The knees should be slightly bent. Maximum lifts occur when the subject's legs are nearly straight at the end of the lifting effort. Experienced testers become adept at estimating the potential lift by noting the degree of muscularity of the subject's legs; as a consequence, they will start the stronger subjects at a lower chain link, so as to allow for the extra distention in the dynamometer. If too high a link is used, the subject's knees may snap into hyperextension during the lift, although an alert tester can always anticipate such an occurrence and interrupt the performance.
4. Before the subject is instructed to lift, the tester should be sure that the arms and back are straight, the head erect, and the chest up. These details are of great importance to accurate testing. Beginners will err in results by from 100 to 300 or more pounds if the single detail of leg-angle is wrong. Therefore, even experienced testers repeat leg-lift tests for most subjects immediately, changing slightly the length of chain— *even by twisting, if a link seems too great.*
5. Record the best of two to three tests.

Pull-up Test for Boys (Figure 8.5)

The boys' pull-up test is administered from a chinning bar to which, preferably, rings have been attached. This arrangement permits the wrists to twist naturally as the subject performs the test. The rings should be high enough from the floor so that the feet of the tallest boy do not touch the floor when performing the test. If this is impossible, it will be necessary for tall individuals to bend their knees in order not to touch the feet on the floor in lowering the body to a straight-arm hang.

1. In taking the pull-up test, the subject hangs from the rings by his hands, and chins himself as many times as he can. In executing the movement, he should pull himself up until his chin is even with his hands, then lower himself until his arms are straight. He should not be permitted to kick, jerk, or use a kip motion. (Without rings, use forward hand grip.)
2. Half-counts are recorded if the subject does not pull all the way up, if he does not straighten his arms completely when lowering the body, or if he kicks, jerks, or kips in performing the movement. Only 4 half-counts are permitted.

190

Figure 8.5. Pull-Up Test, or Chinning the Bar, for Boys.

Pull-up Test for Girls (Figure 8.6)

For the girls' pull-up test, preferably, rings should be loosely attached (in order to permit the hands to twist naturally as the subject performs the test) to either an adjustable horizontal bar or one bar of the parallel bars which may be conveniently raised and lowered. A mat should be laid on the floor to prevent the feet from slipping.

1. The rings should be adjusted to approximately the height of the apex of the sternum, thus requiring each girl to pull approximately the same proportion of her weight. Time may be saved in adjusting the bar if the girls are arranged by heights at the beginning of the test.
2. The girl should grasp the rings with palms outward and should slide her feet under the bar until the body and arms form approximately a right angle when the body is held straight. The weight should rest on the heels.
3. The test is to pull up (with the body held perfectly straight) as many

191

Figure 8.6. Pull-Up Test for Girls.

times as possible. The girls should pull a dead weight, the exercise being performed by the muscles of the arms and shoulder girdles only.
4. If the body sags, if the hips rise, or if the knees bend in a kip motion, or if the subject does not pull completely up or go completely down, half-credit only is given up to 4 half-credits.

A. E. Gay, of Lockport, New York, Public Schools, has perfected a device that greatly improves the procedure for administering the girls' pull-up test. This device consists of a platform with an adjustable heel rest which may be raised or lowered depending upon the height of the girl being tested, the rings remaining at a fixed height. The whole testing procedure is thus considerably simplified.

Push-up Test for Boys (Figure 8.7)

The push-up test for boys may be administered either on the regular gymnasium parallel bars or on wall parallels (or "dipping bars"). The regulation parallel bars are much to be preferred, since their width and height may be adjusted to the height of the subject.

Figure 8.7. Push-Up Test, or Dipping, for Boys.

1. The bars should be adjusted at approximately shoulder height.
2. The subject should stand at the end of the parallel bars, grasping one bar in each hand. He jumps to the front support with arms straight (this counts *one*). He lowers his body until the angle of the upper arm and forearm is less than a right angle, then pushes up to the straight-arm position (this counts *two*). This movement is repeated as many times as possible. The subject should not be permitted to jerk or kick when executing push-ups.
3. At the first dip for each subject, the tester should gauge the proper distance the body should be lowered by observing the elbow angle. He should then hold his fist so that the subject's shoulder just touches it on repeated tests.
4. If the subject does not go down to the proper bent-arm angle or all the way up to a straight-arm position, half-credit only is given, up to 4 half-credits.

Push-up Test for Girls (Figure 8.8)

The push-up test for girls is executed from a stall bar bench, or a stool, 13 inches high by 20 inches long by 14 inches wide. It should be placed on a mat about six inches from a wall so that subjects will not take a position too far forward.

Figure 8.8. Push-Up Test for Girls.

1. The girl should grasp the outer edges of the bench or stool at the nearest corners and assume the front-leaning rest position, with the balls of her feet resting on the mat and with her body and arms forming a right angle.
2. The test is to lower the body so that the upper chest touches or nearly touches the near edge of the stall bar bench, then raise it to a straight-arm position as many times as possible. In performing the test, the girl's body should be held straight throughout.
3. If the body sways or arches, or if the subject does not go completely down or does not push completely up, half-credit is given, up to 4 half-credits.

General Instructions for Pull-up and Push-up Tests

1. After four half-credits have been recorded in the push-up and pull-up tests for both boys and girls, no more should be allowed for partial performance.
2. At the fifth incomplete exercise, it is advisable to stop the test and repeat after a rest period.
3. Counting should be audible to the subject, the count being made sharply at the end of each evolution and the reason for each half-count briefly given at the time it occurs.
4. The subject should rest five minutes between the pull-up and push-up tests unless fewer than three counts have been made. No rest periods are necessary between the other parts of the test.

194

STRENGTH TESTS

Scoring

Scoring of the Physical Fitness Index tests is accomplished in the following manner:

Arm Strength: Arm strength is scored according to the following formula:

(pull-ups + push-ups) $\left(\dfrac{W}{10} + H - 60 \right)$, in which W represents the weight in pounds, and H the height in inches. Fractions are corrected to whole numbers.

For example, a boy pulls up 7 and pushes up 8 times. His weight is 155 pounds and his height 68 inches.

$$(7 + 8)\left(\frac{155}{10} + 68 - 60 \right), \text{ or } (15) \times (16 + 8),$$

which gives an arm strength of 360 pounds. If the subject is below 60 inches in height, height should be disregarded, the formula thus becoming:

$$(\text{Push-ups} + \text{Pull-ups}) \times \left(\frac{W}{10} \right).$$

Strength Index: The Strength Index, or SI, is the total score determined by adding together the scores made on each test item: lung capacity, right grip, left grip, back strength, leg strength, and arm strength.

The Norm: The norm charts are based upon sex, weight, and age, the normal score being changed for each two-pound increase in weight and for each half-year increase in age. Instead of interpolating to determine the *norm* for those individuals between points on the norm chart, the weight above and the age below should be taken. For example, if an individual weighs 151 pounds, the norm at 152 should be taken; if he is 16 years and 5 months of age, the norm at 16 years should be taken.

As norm charts have been prepared for PFI tests both when the belt is used in the leg lift and when it is not used, care should be taken to use the proper chart in scoring the tests. Norm charts (with belt) appear in Appendix B, Tables XIX to XXII inclusive.

Physical Fitness Index: The Physical Fitness Index is computed from the following formula:

$$\text{PFI} = \frac{\text{Achieved SI}}{\text{Normal SI}} \times 100.$$

A standard card should be used for recording the scores made on the PFI test. Spaces for several tests should be provided on this card to allow for retests, together with annual tests over a period of years. Such a card is illustrated in Figure 8.9. A sample PFI problem appears on this card.

DEPARTMENT OF ATHLETICS AND PHYSICAL EDUCATION, SYRACUSE UNIVERSITY
MINIMUM ESSENTIALS TEST RECORDS

Date	9/19/59	11/25/59										TEST SUMMARIES
Age	½0 M3	½0 M5	Y	M	Y	M	Y	M	Y	M		
Weight	126	125										MEDICAL
Height	65 in.	65 in.		in.		in.		in.		in.		Regular
Multiplier	18	18										Modified
Pull-ups	7	11										Physical Fitness Index
Push-ups	11 18	15 26										
Arm Strength	324	468										SWIMMING
Leg Lift	820	1020										
Back Lift	260	330										
Left Grip	88	95										SKILL TESTS
Right Grip	110	114										
Lung Capacity	212	214										
Strength Index	1814	2241										
Normal S. I.	2134	2134										
P. F. I.	85	105										

Name REC, RUDY .... College B.A. .... Year 1963

Figure 8.9.   PFI Score Card with Sample Tests.

SUGGESTIONS FOR ADMINISTERING THE PFI TESTS [3]

Many problems are encountered in admistering the Physical Fitness Index tests efficiently and accurately. Several suggestions that may prove helpful are given below; others that apply to testing in general will be found in Chapter 16.

1. *Accurate instruments:* The accuracy of testing instruments should be checked at least once a year. A rough check on the back and leg dynamometer may be made by suspending several known weights from it and reading the scores on the dial. A new instrument in use at Chautauqua, New York, was found to be calibrated at one-half the actual score. On checking, the physical director (weight, 150 pounds) registered only 75 pounds when hanging from the dynamometer. In a study by Clarke and Geser,[4] the mean right grip strength scores for 34 college men obtained with three manuometers purchased from two manufacturing concerns were as

---

[3] The PFI testing instruments may be obtained from the following sources: Back and leg dynamometer, testing to 2500 pounds, and belt: Fred Medart Products, Inc., 3535 De Kalb Street, St. Louis 18, Missouri; Manuometer and wet spirometer: Narragansett Gymnasium Equipment Company, Railroad and Rollins Street, Centralia, Missouri.

[4] H. Harrison Clarke and L. Richard Geser, "Comparison of Three Manuometers," *Research Quarterly,* Vol. XXVIII, No. 2 (May 1957), p. 173.

follows: 136 pounds, 124 pounds, and 103 pounds. Murray [5] describes a number of ways for the physical educator to check the accuracy of this and other testing instruments.

2. *Trained testers:* Trained testers are essential, for, unless tests are given properly and accurately, the results will be misleading and, thus, the time spent in giving them worse than wasted. Mathews [6] demonstrated pronounced differences between skilled and unskilled testers in results obtained in administering the PFI test. For all test items, the skilled testers obtained significantly higher mean scores than did the unskilled testers. For example, the skilled testers obtained a mean PFI of 107; for the unskilled testers, the mean was 90. [7] The correlations between the scores obtained by the skilled and unskilled testers were satisfactory, .99 and .89 respectively. However, for all other tests, they were .81 and below; the correlation for leg lift was .48. Hubbard and Mathews [8] found that, when testing for leg lift strength, higher scores were achieved when the subjects attained a maximum lift and then lunged backward (a practice which is not a permissible PFI testing technique).

Contrary to Mathews, Cousins [9] did not find significant differences between means for trained and untrained testers in the administration of grip strength tests. However, in Cousin's study, grip strength was tested with a tensiometer placed in a special device; this arrangement restricted the freedom with which the instrument could be manipulated by the subject as compared with the one used by Mathews. Van Dalen and Peterson [10] and Wear [11]

---

[5] Kenneth Murray, "Calibration and Uses of Fitness Tests in Westmount High School, Quebec," *Supplement to the Research Quarterly,* Vol. VI, No. 1 (March 1935), p. 12.

[6] Donald K. Mathews, "Comparison of Testers and Subjects in Administering Physical Fitness Index," *Research Quarterly,* Vol. XXIV, No. 4 (December 1953), p. 442.

[7] Some, but by no means all, of this difference may be due to the skilled testers giving the second test to all subjects; the subjects, therefore, had the benefit of some experience in taking the test, which may logically have increased their scores.

[8] Alfred W. Hubbard and Donald K. Mathews, "Leg Lift Strength: A Comparison of Measurement Methods," *Research Quarterly,* Vol. XXIV, No. 1 (March 1953), p. 33.

[9] George F. Cousins, "Effect of Trained and Untrained Testers upon Administration of Grip Strength Tests," *Research Quarterly,* Vol. XXVI, No. 3 (October 1955), p. 273.

[10] D. B. Van Dalen and C. A. Peterson, "A Comparative Study of the Administration of the Manuometer," *Physical Educator,* Vol. VII, No. 2 (May 1950), p. 52.

[11] C. L. Wear, "Further Study of the Administration of the Manuometer," *Physical Educator,* Vol. IX, No. 3 (October 1952), p. 82.

obtained significantly higher grip strength scores when the manuometer was placed with the dial toward the palm than when placed
with the dial turned outward.

Thus, careful attention to the prescribed detail of administering
these strength tests is imperative for proper results. The back and
leg strength tests are the most difficult to administer and require not
only proper instruction and supervision but a great deal of practice. One must give several hundreds of these tests before he
qualifies as a good back and leg tester.

3. *Organization for testing:* With a sufficient number of trained
testers available, the next problem is to organize procedures so that
a maximum number of pupils are tested during each hour or day
of testing. Economy in testing time requires that pupils be made
available in a continuous, unbroken procession. The method of
testing pupils during their physical education class period results
in tremendous loss of time, conservatively estimated at from 30 to
40 per cent, as the testing line must be started and stopped each
period.

With pupils readily available, testing stations should be set up in
such a manner that pupils can pass from one to another in a continuous line. Plans should be made carefully so that student lines
do not cross when passing from station to station. The stations
should be as follows:

Station 1: Age, height, and weight: record cards, scales, stadiometer.
Station 2: Lung capacity: wet spirometer.
Station 3: Grip strength: manuometer.
Station 4: Back and leg strength: preferably two back and leg dyna-
mometers, two belts, and three dynamometer handles.
Station 5: Pull-ups (boys): Horizontal bar (or substitute) and rings.
Pull-ups (girls): Adjustable horizontal bar (or one bar of the
parallel bars, Gay's apparatus, or substitute) and floor mat.
Station 6: Push-ups (boys): Parallel bars or wall parallels (or substitute).
Push-ups (girls): Stall bar bench and mat.
Station 7: Scoring Method A: four scorers, each of whom makes one of the
following calculations: (*a*) arm strength, (*b*) strength index, (*c*) normal-
strength index, and (*d*) physical fitness index (an adding machine or a slide
rule is very helpful in scoring).
Scoring Method B: an electrical calculator (one operator and an
assistant to look up norms). By either method, A or B, PFI's can be calculated
as fast as the tests are given.

The advantages of this method of testing and calculations by a
large staff are many and important. Chiefly, it increases the effi-

ciency of the testing and also the interest of the subjects, their respect for physical education, their understanding of results, and their cooperation in follow-up work to improve their own fitness.

Special mention should be made of organization procedures that may be followed in administering back and leg lifts rapidly. Owing to the extra operation of placing the belt on the subject, more time is necessary for administering the leg lift than for any other single test in the PFI battery. Two methods may be followed to reduce the time necessary for the test, as follows:

a. If two back and leg dynamometers are available, one may be used for the back lift and the other for the leg lift. With an extra tester and two handles and two belts for the latter instrument, the belt can be adjusted to one subject while the subject preceding him is taking the lift. The subject is thus ready for the lift as soon as he takes his place for the test.

b. If only one back and leg dynamometer is available, the order of the tests may be reversed, giving the leg lift first and the back lift last. With an extra tester and a second handle, the belt can be adjusted to one subject while the subject preceding him is taking the back lift. Obviously, back and leg lifts cannot be given as rapidly with one instrument as with two, but the procedure described will reduce considerably the testing time from what otherwise would be required for these tests.

With a sufficient number of trained testers, therefore, with pupils available in a continuous procession, and with the testing apparatus arranged on the gymnasium floor as indicated above, it is a comparatively easy task to test pupils at the rate of one a minute, or sixty per hour.

4. *Order of tests:* Rogers originally contended that the order of administering his strength test items should be maintained in the following order: lung capacity, grip tests, back lift, leg lift, pull-ups, and push-ups. However, Allen [12] found that the order in which test items were administered did not influence the results obtained with the MacCurdy Force Index. The MacCurdy index contains the same test items as the PFI, except pulls and pushes on a dynamometer are substituted for pull-ups and push-ups. Thus, the exact order of PFI test administration is not essential, except the pull-ups and push-ups should be last to avoid possible carry over of fatigue effects to the other strength efforts. In this situation, however, some time can be saved, without adverse effect, by testing lung capacity during the rest period between pull-ups and push-ups.

___

[12] James H. Allen, "Influence of Order upon the MacCurdy Force Index," Microcarded Doctoral Dissertation, Indiana University, 1956.

5. *Practice tests:* It is essential that physical fitness tests be administered accurately, and that the derived PFI of a pupil selected for the development program (special physical education classes) be his true score. The physical educator should doublecheck on the test results of his low group. If the testing period is preceded by class sessions during which the tests have been taught and practiced, he may be reasonably sure of his results. If, however, this has not been possible, it is advisable to retest low students before studying their individual cases or starting developmental programs. This procedure is especially important if pupils have not been previously tested. Retests are advisable, also, if the situation at the time of the annual tests does not approximate normal conditions. For example, the initial tests in one school system were conducted at a time when many pupils had been absent from school because of measles and many others had just been vaccinated. The retests in this situation, quite naturally, showed many significant increases. In addition, pupils who feel they can "do better" on the test should be allowed to repeat it. Fundamentally, the physical educator should be sure that the score assigned to a low-fitness pupil is an accurate one. A little extra time spent at this point will be well worthwhile in the saving of pupil- and teacher-time later on.

6. *Warm-up period:* A few light calisthenic exercises are advisable before students take the Physical Fitness Tests. Better results are achieved through this brief warm-up period, and there is less likelihood of sore muscles following the completion of the test.

Accuracy of the PFI Tests

The reliability and objectivity of the Physical Fitness Index tests, when administered by competent testers, were established by Rogers [13] and have since been verified by other investigators working independently. With tests taken four months apart, the self-correlations ranged from .86 for leg lift to .97 for lung capacity; the self-correlation for the Strength Index was .94.

The question is sometimes asked: "Since PFI tests do not measure all the larger muscles of the body, is the test an entire body strength

---

[13] Rogers, *op. cit.,* p. 32.

test?" In this connection, it should be pointed out that the close relationship and interdependence of muscles tend to develop antagonistic muscles equally in large-muscle activity programs. Therefore, a measure of a proper sampling of muscle groups should be sufficient to determine the general condition of all. The intercorrelations between the strength of the various muscles tested are fairly high, as shown in Table III.[14] These relationships are quite satisfactory, showing that each is contributing significant elements to the total test. A high intercorrelation would indicate that the two items were measuring much the same thing and that one could be safely eliminated.

TABLE III

INTERCORRELATIONS BETWEEN STRENGTH TESTS

	Grip Strength	Back Strength	Leg Strength	Arm Strength	Lung Capacity
Grip Strength	—	.61	.65	.61	.52
Back Strength	.61	—	.67	.60	.54
Leg Strength	.65	.67	—	.58	.30
Arm Strength	.61	.60	.58	—	.06
Lung Capacity	.52	.54	.30	.06	—

THE PFI AS A MEASURE OF PHYSICAL FITNESS

Physical Fitness Elements

The Physical Fitness Index battery contains test items for two basic elements of physical fitness, muscular strength and muscular endurance. It does not contain items which measure the circulatory-respiratory type of endurance, so essential in sustained running, swimming, and the like. Thus, the PFI does not measure all aspects of fitness, as the physical educator views the problem.

Muscular strength and muscular endurance are not the same, although they are related. Individuals with greatest muscular strength have greatest absolute endurance; however, stronger muscles tend to maintain a smaller proportion of maximum strength

---

[14] Luis F. Sambolin, "Extent of Relationship between Several Selected Strength and Cardiovascular Tests." Unpublished master's thesis, Syracuse University, Syracuse, N. Y., 1943.

than do weaker muscles. Tuttle and associates [15] obtained a correlation of .90 between the maximum strength of the back and leg muscles and their absolute endurance; the correlation between the strength and relative endurance (average strength maintained) was −.40 and −.48 for back and leg muscles respectively. Clarke [16] has summarized other muscular strength-endurance relationships from the literature. The need for including both strength and endurance elements in physical fitness testing is demonstrated.

In order to understand the PFI better and to evaluate its significance, two important concepts should be made clear. First, in order for a condition to affect strength, it must have systemic implications, that is, be total-body in its reaction. For example, if one has a sore toe, it might be an inconvenience and an annoyance, but it would not affect one's strength or lower his PFI. When, however, that same toe becomes infected, a systemic condition is established, muscles weaken, and the PFI drops. If, therefore, such conditions as body fatigue, lack of exercise, improper diet, diseased tonsils, abscessed teeth, ulcers, cancers, and the like, have total-body reactions, the strength of the muscles is affected—and the PFI declines.

The second important concept is that the PFI is a generalized index, as the name implies—not a diagnosis. It may be compared to the use of a clinical thermometer by a physician. If the thermometer reading indicates that the individual has a temperature above normal, it tells the physician that something is wrong, not what that something is. In like manner, a low PFI indicates a lack of physical condition, a lowered body vitality, but not what the cause might be. Like the patient with a fever, the individual with a low PFI should be studied in order to determine the cause of this condition. The analogy may be carried further. Individuals with high or rapidly changing temperatures almost always need a physician's care. Individuals with low, high, or rapidly changing PFI's need the physical educator's care, and they may or may not also need the attention of physicians.

---

[15] W. W. Tuttle, C. D. Janney, and J. V. Salzano, "Relation of Maximum Back and Leg Strength to Back and Leg Strength Endurance," *Research Quarterly*, Vol. XXVI, No. 1 (March 1955), p. 96.

[16] H. Harrison Clarke, "Muscular Strength-Endurance Relationships," *Archives of Physical Medicine and Rehabilitation*, Vol. XXVIII, No. 9 (September 1957), p. 584.

Validity of the Physical Fitness Index

In studying the validity of the PFI as a measure of physical fitness, Chamberlain and Smiley [17] selected at random a group of 65 Cornell University students. Physical Fitness Tests were administered to these students, who were given by the University staff of examining physicians a careful physical examination upon which estimates of their health statuses were based. In this group, 52 of the 65 students were given the same classification in both the physicians' estimates and the test—an 80 per cent agreement.

The correlation between the two ratings was .60, although Chamberlain and Smiley state that the true correlation is probably .65 or above, owing to the fact that it was possible to use only three class intervals in making the computation. This correlation is considered rather high when it is remembered that it compares well with physicians' estimates of other health factors.

Moreover, the correlation coefficient between medical ratings and PFI's is twice as significant as between teachers' judgments of intelligence and I. Q.'s.[18] Scores on the *Stanford Revision and Extension of the Binet-Simon Intelligence Scale* correlate .48 with teachers' judgments of intelligence. Reduced to "predictive indices," the results are as follows:

	r	P.I.
Medical Ratings and PFI	.65	.24
Teachers' Ratings and I.Q.	.48	.12

Two other types of evidence may be cited in support of the PFI as related to physical fitness status, as follows: the fitness significance of a change in strength and the implications from case studies of pupils with low PFI's.

Significance of a change in strength: A number of studies have been conducted showing the significance of a change in strength to a change in physical fitness. The effects of illness, fatigue, and organic drains upon the strength of the body are shown, for example, by experiments with grip strength. In these studies, the manuometer was used to make a daily record of grip strength, and any changes that occurred were noted.

---

[17] C. G. Chamberlain and D. F. Smiley, "Functional Health and the Physical Fitness Index," *Research Quarterly*, Vol. II, No. 1 (March 1931), p. 193.
[18] Frederick Rand Rogers, *Fundamental Administrative Measures in Physical Education* (Newton, Mass.: Pleiades Company, 1932), p. 43.

Only the original investigation by Rogers [19] will be reported here as an illustration of the use of grip strength as a *measure* of changing body condition. This experiment was performed on an adult male subject who, after being trained in grip-test technique, tested himself daily or oftener. Following are several of his observations: (a) his grip strength dropped 30 points (from 170 to 140) before he was aware of approaching influenza; (b) an unusually fatiguing day (90 holes of golf and a square dance) resulted in no change in grip strength at bed time, but a drop of 30 points was recorded the next morning; (c) severe fatigue of the forearms caused drops of 35 to 60 points, depending upon the degree of exhaustion induced, with corresponding delay in return to normal.

Representative case studies: The mass of material contained in case studies of pupils with low Physical Fitness Indices gives considerable evidence of the significance of the PFI in revealing physical condition. The danger of citing such cases is that they may lead to misunderstanding in interpreting the PFI. It is true that there are many cases on record in which low or declining PFI's have indicated the presence of organic drains within the individual. The number of such cases, however, is relatively small: the majority of low-fitness students require merely the proper amount and kind of exercise, the modification of health habits, relaxation programs, and the like.

Nor is the discovery of such defects necessarily a reflection upon the competence of examining physicians: physicians cannot detect internal strains or drains that affect health, especially within the limited time and with the techniques available for school examinations. It is also the case that these functional disorders may not have been present at the time the medical examinations were given. Occasionally, too, PFI tests reveal muscular weakness or declines in strength long before these changes can be noted by subjective examinations. Such PFI discoveries lead to proper investigations and thus disclose organic drains.

Space does not permit an accounting of the many case studies reported of low-fitness boys and girls. Over a period of years, however, physical educators working day by day with this test in the field have discovered through proper referral such conditions as the fol-

---

[19] F. R. Rogers, "The Significance of Strength Tests in Revealing Physical Condition," *Research Quarterly*, Vol. V, No. 3 (October 1934), p. 43.

lowing: thyroid deficiency, spinal meningitis, encephalitis, anemia, post-malarial condition, ulcer, cancer, syringomyelia, tuberculosis, and emotional strain. Subsequent improvement in strength scores following effective treatment is a typical experience in following such cases.

After studying carefully the case studies of 50 college freshmen and sophomores with low PFI's, Page [20] described the average college "low PFI student" as follows: John Doe, 20 per cent overweight, high scholastic aptitude (although doing poor scholastic work), below normal in social adjustment, lives at home or commutes, is employed, did not participate actively in the high-school physical education program, is not (at first) particularly interested in physical activity, is lacking in physical skills, and has such faulty health habits as smoking, insufficient sleep, and incorrect diet.

Similar results were obtained from case studies of 78 low PFI college students by Coefield and McCollum.[21]

PFI FOR GIRLS

The advisability of using the PFI test in girls' physical education programs has frequently been questioned. It has been argued that girls are not and should not be particularly interested in feats of strength or in big muscles, and that it is a serious mistake to adapt girls' programs from those proposed for boys. There is much to be said for this point of view: psychologically, the PFI does not ideally fit into the concept of girls' physical education.

The crux of this situation, however, lies in a fuller understanding of the need for strength in the realization of values of importance to girls. Certainly girls recognize the need for body grace and poise. Yet, these qualities cannot be developed in girls without body strength. This being true, *adequate strength* is essential for girls in order that they may realize objectives which to them *are* important. Sufficient strength and vitality to meet the demands of everyday life and with sufficient reserve to enjoy leisure and for emergencies are essential for both boys and girls.

---

[20] C. Getty Page, "Case Studies of College Men with Low Physical Fitness Indices." Unpublished Master's Thesis, Syracuse University, Syracuse, N. Y., 1940.

[21] John R. Coefield and Robert H. McCollum, "A Case Study Report of 78 University Freshman Men with Low Physical Fitness Indices," Microcarded Master's Thesis, University of Oregon, 1955.

The PFI, therefore, can be used in girls' programs with its ultimate motivation being directed toward their specific objectives: the concept of a reasonably strong body should be presented in order that girls may be graceful and well poised.

THE SELECTION OF PFI CASES FOR FOLLOW-UP WORK

Limitations of Norms

Before pupils can be intelligently selected for individual attention in physical fitness programs, the limitations of norms must be understood. Norms are derived from testing many subjects and determining averages from these data, a different average being established in the PFI test for every combination of age, weight, and sex. Consequently, the establishment and application of norms for all subjects in a particular designation do not allow for the many factors that make individuals "normally" different. This difficulty is not confined alone to norms applied to physical fitness testing; *it is true wherever norms are used in human measurement.*

Often norms do not fit extreme cases. In establishing norm tables, a sufficiently large number of cases usually is not available to describe adequately individuals at the upper and lower ends of the scale so that typical performances can be determined. In terms of the Physical Fitness Tests, this exception means the very large and the very small individuals. The old form of the PFI test (leg lift without the belt), for example, was criticized because many athletes obtained low scores. With the revised form of the test, however, this is not true. The average PFI of majors in physical education, nearly all of whom had been outstanding athletes in high school and many of whom are important members of university athletic teams—a high percentage of well-built, rugged individuals—is around 110. It may be argued that even this average is not high enough for such a select group. These are large men with average SI's of 2883. One such person, who weighed 200 pounds, had an SI of 5100 and a PFI of 147.

It is readily admitted, however, that the norms for the PFI test can be improved. The use of the present norm charts in conjunction with somatotyping is one possibility which should be considered.

Willgoose and Rogers [22] obtained the following results from testing 300 university male students: students with primary mesomorphic component had a mean PFI of 107; those with primary ectomorphic component, approximately 100; and those primarily endomorphic, approximately 70. A correlation of −.93 (13 cases) was obtained between degrees of endomorphy and PFI, indicating that the more weighted an individual is in this component the lower his score. The correlation of PFI with ectomorphy was .52 (19 cases); and with mesomorphy, .09 (104 cases). It was found that a degree of endomorphy is a limiting factor to relative strength for predominantly mesomorphic individuals. The low insignificant correlation between PFI and ectomorphy indicates that the third component may not influence PFI scores to any great extent.

As a part of a longitudinal study of growth in adolescence, Jones [23] found that individual differences in the rate of physiological maturing during adolescence are associated with marked differences in growth patterns of static dynamometric strength (right grip, left grip, push and pull). In fact, he concludes, so close is this association that growth in strength may itself be regarded as a puberal indicator and also as a secondary sexual characteristic. Also, between the ages of 13 and 16, boys who mature early (in terms of skeletal age) tend to be stronger than the group average; boys maturing late tend to be weaker. Similar results were obtained for girls, classified as early or late-maturing on the basis of age at menarche. Logically, therefore, strength scores may also be interpreted in relation to physiological age and to individual factors of early or late maturation.

The High PFI

Another factor that further complicates the selection of pupils in need of individual fitness programs is the high PFI individual, as there is abundant evidence to support the contention that his condition *may* be dangerous. Individuals with such scores may be "on edge," "keyed up," about to "go stale," or even in danger of a nervous breakdown.

---

[22] Carl E. Willgoose and Millard L. Rogers, "Relationship of Somatotyping to Physical Fitness," *Journal of Educational Research*, Vol. XLIII, No. 9 (May 1949), p. 704.

[23] Harold E. Jones, *Motor Performance and Growth* (Berkeley: University of California Press, 1949), Chap. 4.

A median PFI of 150, with but six cases below 95, was recorded in testing 116 boys and girls from 10 to 16 years of age in a Massachusetts state rest camp for children with tubercular tendencies. The most noticeable condition of these children on entering camp was an extreme nervousness, characterized by inability to relax, to sleep during rest periods, and to get to sleep at night. Elizabeth Zimmerli [24] has reported several cases of extremely high PFI's running from 156 to 202. These individuals were variously described by the following characteristics: over-trained, overactive, highstrung, overstimulated, overanxious, overambitious, overdeveloped. Ellis H. Champlin, Director of Physical Education at Springfield College, sums up this condition when he calls these individuals "activity drunkards." The individual with a high PFI, at any rate, should be given special attention by the physical educator.

The Selection of PFI Cases for Study

It is readily apparent from the above that the selection of PFI cases for study and treatment is not so simple as many believe. It is now realized that the designation of "all below" an arbitrary PFI point, such as 85, as "needing individual care" is inadequate, since by so doing many cases in need of special developmental programs are missed. Actually, there are at least three groups needing special consideration:

1. *Individuals with PFI's in the lower ranges.* The abnormally weak obviously need attention. The physical educator should decide upon the number of pupils for whom he can provide individual programs and select a large portion of these from the low PFI scores.

2. *Individuals whose PFI's decline on repeated tests, regardless of their PFI level.* Such drops are usually definite danger signs, indicating changes in physical condition which need to be checked. It is essential, after each general testing period, to examine all record cards to discover whose PFI's are dropping. A drop of from five to ten points is significant if tests are accurately given. This is an important procedure and should not be neglected.

3. *Individuals with PFI's in the upper ranges.* As has been noted above, often an extremely high PFI indicates that the individual may be over-trained, overactive, high-strung, overstimulated, over-

---

[24] Elizabeth Zimmerli, "Case Studies of Unusual Physical Fitness Indices," *Supplement to the Research Quarterly*, Vol. VI, No. 1 (March 1935), p. 246.

developed. A PFI of 150 is considered sufficiently high to warrant investigation for factors that may cause this condition, and to provide a program of rest and relaxation if indicated. It should be recognized, of course, that high PFI's may be due to the development of excellent physiques through participation in such activities as weight lifting, gymnastics, modern dance, and the like.

Suggested Changes in the PFI Tests

Since its origin, the Physical Fitness Index battery has been repeatedly changed in procedures, norms, and interpretations. While the PFI test remains as described above, there have been a number of modifications proposed.

Oregon Simplification

While the Physical Fitness Index and the Strength Index have been used effectively in school and college physical education programs, many users readily acknowledge that the following extraneous factors prevent their more general use: cost of testing equipment, time required for giving the test to many students, and necessity for well-trained testers. As a consequence, Clarke and Carter [25] undertook a simplification of this battery for boys at each of the following school levels: upper elementary school, junior high school, and senior high school. The following multiple correlations were obtained between the Strength Index as criterion and the test items composing the SI battery as experimental variables.

School Level		R	Test Items
Upper elementary school		.977	Leg lift, back lift, push-ups.
Junior high school	A	.987	Leg lift, arm strength.
	B	.998	Same tests, with right grip added.
Senior high school	A	.985	Leg lift, arm strength.
	B	.996	Same tests, with back lift added.

Regression equations for each of the above multiple correlations were computed. By use of the appropriate equation, the physical educator is able to estimate approximately the SI each boy would have achieved had he taken the full test. Thus, the regular SI norms

---

[25] H. Harrison Clarke and Gavin H. Carter, "Oregon Simplification of the Strength and Physical Fitness Indices for Upper Elementary, Junior High, and Senior High School Boys," *Research Quarterly*, Vol. XXIX, No. 4 (March 1959).

to determine each boy's PFI may be used. The regression equations are as follows:

Upper Elementary School Boys

SI = 1.05 (leg lift) + 1.35 (back lift) + 10.92 (push-ups) + 133.

Junior High School Boys

A: SI = 1.33 (leg lift) + 1.20 (arm strength) + 286
B: SI = 1.12 (leg lift) + .99 (arm strength) +
     5.19 (right grip) + 129

Senior High School Boys

A: SI = 1.22 (leg lift) + 1.23 (arm strength) + 499.
B: SI = 1.07 (leg lift) + 1.06 (arm strength) +
     1.42 (back lift) + 194.

In Appendix B, Tables XXIII, A-E, tables for the ready computation of all regression equations are provided. Following is an illustration of this process for a junior high school boy, 14 years 5 months of age and 149 pounds in weight (A equation):

Test Item	Score	Repression Weighting
Leg lift	1260	1676
Arm strength	480	576
Constant		286
Predicted Strength Index		2538

From the norm chart, Table XIX, this boy's norm for age and weight is 1878. Thus, his predicted PFI is 135.

The second, or B, equations for the junior and senior high school boys, of course, approximate each boy's actual SI with a greater degree of accuracy than do the first, or A equations. The degree of accuracy for these predictions is reflected in the standard error of estimates. For the junior high school boys, this error is approximately 2.5 times greater for the A equation; for the senior high school boy, it is about twice as large.

Use of Tensiometer

The most expensive instrument necessary for administering the PFI test is the back and leg dynamometer. Also, the two tests given with this instrument are the most difficult to administer in the battery. This is especially true for the leg lift, where considerable judgment is necessary in placing the subject at the start of the test so that his knees will be nearly straight at the end, as the dynamometer spring elongates somewhat as pressure is applied. As a consequence, Kennedy [26] sought to substitute the tensiometer for the dynamometer in back and leg lift testing; this instrument is much cheaper than the dynamometer and the pull is against a cable which does not stretch.

The capacity of the tensiometer used was 800 pounds, which was sufficient to measure back lifts directly. However, for the leg lift test, a lever system was devised, which permitted lifts up to 2400 pounds. The correlations between strength scores obtained with the dynamometer and tensiometer were .92 and .95 for the back and leg lifts respectively. The means and standard deviations obtained with the two instruments for these tests were comparable. Thus, it was demonstrated that the tensiometer could be substituted for the dynamometer in back and leg strength testing without essential loss of validity for these tests.

McCloy's Revisions

McCloy has proposed three changes in the PFI battery: one known as his Strength Index Revision; a second, as the Athletic Strength Index; the third, as the Pure Strength Index.

1. *Strength Index Revision.*[27] Two changes in the PFI battery are suggested: a different formula for computing arm strength, and the elimination of lung capacity. Otherwise, the test items remain the same, except that the old method of testing leg strength (without the belt) is followed.

In discussing arm strength determined from push-ups and pull-ups, McCloy states that the formula used by Rogers unduly penalizes the individual who is small and unduly rewards the person whose dipping and chinning are above the average. He experimentally developed the following formula for the computation of chinning and dipping strength.

---

[26] Frank T. Kennedy, "A Comparison of the Tensiometer to the Dynamometer in Back and Leg Lifts for College Men," Microcarded Master's Thesis, University of Oregon, 1956.

[27] C. H. McCloy and Norma D. Young, *Tests and Measurements in Health and Physical Education,* 3rd ed. (New York: Appleton-Century-Crofts, Inc., 1954), p. 129.

Boys: Chinning *or* dipping strength = 1.77 (weight) +
3.42 (chins or dips) — 46.

Chinning *and* dipping strength = 3.54 (weight) +
3.42 (pull-up + push-ups) — 92.

Girls: Chinning strength = .67 (weight) + 1.2 (chins) + 52.
Dipping strength = .78 (weight) + 1.1 (dips) + 74.

In subsequent studies, correlations of the approximate magnitude of .95 were obtained between McCloy's arm strength score and body weight for both college men and junior high school boys.[28] These high relationships are due to the heavy weighting given to body weight in the McCloy formula.

McCloy advocates the elimination of lung capacity from the PFI battery on the grounds that lung capacity is not a test of strength. The use of lung capacity in the PFI battery has been argued by others, so an understanding of its characteristics is important. Weisman [29] found from numerous tests that if one has 10 per cent less vital capacity than is normal for age, sex, and occupational class, it is probable that he is suffering from some constitutional disturbance; if he is as much as 15 per cent below normal, this is almost certain. In an extensive study of respiratory muscle function, Dail and Affeldt [30] conclude that the deficiency of respiratory reserve, as expressed in per cent normal vital capacity, is the integration of several factors, which may include any of the following: strength endurance and adaptation, limitation of lung movement, distribution pattern of body weakness, body position, and presence of heart or lung disease, as well as certain technical factors.

Cureton [31] reviewed the experimental literature on lung capacity in an attempt to determine whether it was properly regarded as a strength test, a flexibility test, a circulatory-respiratory test, or a test of thoracic size. He concluded that breathing capacity was a reflection predominantly of body size, as indicated principally by surface area, height, weight, or chest girth. Clarke [32] reported high cor-

---

[28] H. Harrison Clarke, "Relation of Physical Structure to Motor Performance of Males," *Contributions*, No. 6, American Academy of Physical Education, 1958.

[29] Samuel A. Weisman, *Your Chest Should Be Flat* (Philadelphia: J. B. Lippincott Company, 1938), pp. 30, 42.

[30] Clarence W. Dail and John E. Affeldt, "Vital Capacity as an Index of Respiratory Muscle Function," *Archives of Physical Medicine and Rehabilitation*, Vol. XXXVIII, No. 6 (June 1957), p. 383.

[31] Thomas K. Cureton, "Analysis of Vital Capacity as a Test of Condition for High School Boys," *Research Quarterly*, Vol. VII, No. 4 (December 1936), p. 80.

[32] Clarke, *op. cit.*

relations for junior high school boys between lung capacity and maturity, anthropometric, and strength measures. Among his correlations were the following: .86 with McCloy's Classification Index (based on age, height, and weight), with height, and with the composite score on twelve cable-tension strength tests; .84 with McCloy's Athletic Index; .80 with Strength Index and with skeletal age. Davis [33] obtained a correlation of −.61 between lung capacity and time in the 200-yard swim, which was the highest correlation for any of his variables as related to swimming time.

McCloy's Strength Index revision correlates .77 with a battery of four track and field events. As a prediction of strength factor, validity is .94; reliability is .96; and objectivity is high. Norms based upon sex, age, and weight are available in the reference both with and without lung capacity: for boys, ages 11 to 18; and for girls, ages 11 to 17. When the belt is used in the leg lift, these norms are inappropriate.

2. *Athletic Strength Index.*[34] In constructing an Athletic Strength Index (boys only), McCloy weighted the test items in his revision of the Strength Index so as to give the total amount of strength usable in athletic events. Two formulas are given, as follows:

Long form: Right grip + left grip + .1 (back lift) + .1 (leg lift) + 2 (chinning strength) + dipping strength − 3 (weight).
Short form: Same, except omit back and leg lifts.

The two forms of the test were correlated with a criterion composed of six track and field events. The coefficients of correlation were the same, .91. Norms for boys based on weight and age, for ages 11 to 18, are available in the reference.

3. *Pure Strength Index.*[35] Through factor analysis, McCloy found that two elements emerge from strength tests: one of these is "pure" strength or force; the other is dependent on body size. To predict "pure" strength, he gave the following weighting: .5 (R + L grips) + .1 (leg lift) + chinning strength + dipping strength. The test items were administered and scored in accordance with his revision of the Strength Index. No norms have been published, which makes this revision the only one of the three proposed by McCloy without a means of obtaining from the index a score comparable to the PFI.

---

[33] Jack F. Davis, "Effects of Training and Conditioning for Middle Distance Swimming," Microcarded Doctoral Study, University of Oregon, 1955.
[34] C. H. McCloy, *op. cit.*, pp. 25-26.
[35] *Ibid.*, p. 26.

Strength Tests for Girls

Many of the strength batteries presented above are as applicable for girls as for boys, especially the following: the Rogers Strength Index and Physical Fitness Index; McCloy's Strength Index and PFI norms; and Chamberlain's revision. Several investigations in this field, however, have been directed toward the construction of tests to measure the general athletic ability of girls, rather than toward measures of relative strength. Criteria have generally been athletic events. Norm charts are based on the standard-score technique, rather than on weight and age or some other such relative measure. As a result, these tests are comparable *in purpose* to the Strength Index, but not to the Physical Fitness Index. Presentation of these tests, therefore, will be found in Chapter 12.

Kraus-Weber Muscular Tests

Emerging from their clinical practice in physical medicine and rehabilitation, Kraus and associates [36] have presented tests of "minimum muscular fitness," commonly known as the Kraus-Weber tests. Originating in a posture clinic, the tests were further developed as a basic means of measurement in the treatment of low back pain; 80 per cent of a total of over 4,000 patients, free from organic disease, were unable to pass one or more of the test items. When treated with therapeutic exercise, they improved as their test results improved. In an eight-year follow-up, it was found that as the patients stopped exercising, they again failed the tests as their back complaints reappeared.

The Kraus-Weber (K-W) Tests of Minimum Muscular Fitness consist of six items. They are proposed as tests which indicate the level of strength and flexibility for certain key muscle groups below which the functioning of the whole body as a healthy organism seems to be endangered. As described here, the tests are graded on a pass or fail basis, although the authors provide a means for scoring partial movements from 1 to 10. Descriptions of these tests follow.

---

[36] Hans Kraus and Ruth P. Hirschland, "Minimum Muscular Fitness Tests in School Children," *Research Quarterly*, Vol. XXV, No. 2 (May 1954), p. 178.

Test No. 1 (Figure 8.10A): Strength of the abdominal plus psoas muscles. The subject is in a supine lying position, hands behind the neck; the examiner holds his feet down. The test is to perform one sit-up.

Figure 8.10. Kraus-Weber Test of Minimum Muscular Fitness.

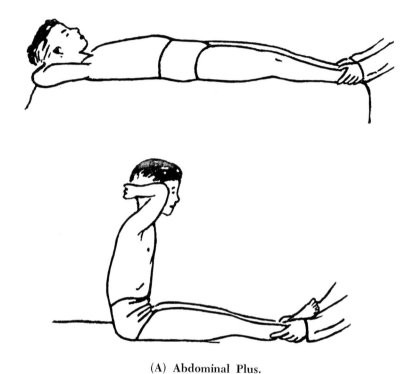

(A) Abdominal Plus.

Test No. 2 (Figure 8.10B): Strength of the abdominal muscles without the help of the psoas. The subject is in the same position as for Test No. 1, except the knees are bent with the heels close to the buttocks. The test is to perform one sit-up.

Test No. 3 (Figure 8.10C): Strength of the psoas and lower abdominal muscles. The subject is supine with hands behind the neck; the legs are fully extended with the heels 10 inches off the table. The test is to hold this position for 10 seconds.

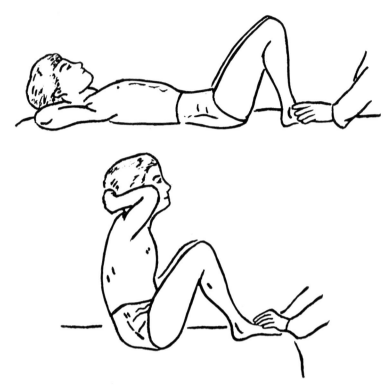

(B) Abdominal Minus.

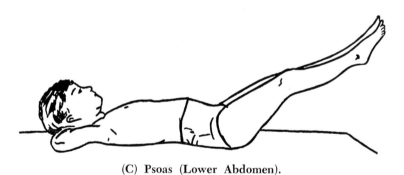

(C) Psoas (Lower Abdomen).

Test No. 4 (Figure 8.10D): Strength of the upper back muscles. The subject lies prone with a pillow under hips and lower abdomen, hands behind the neck; the examiner holds his feet down. The test is for the subject to raise his chest, head, and shoulders and hold them without touching the table for 10 seconds.

216

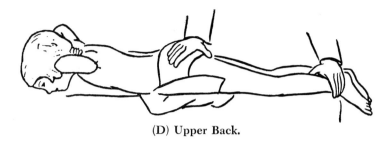

(D) **Upper Back.**

Test No. 5 (Figure 8.10E): Strength of the lower back. The subject is in the same position as Test No. 4, except the examiner holds his chest down. The test is for the subject to raise his legs off the table, with knees straight, and hold this position for 10 seconds.

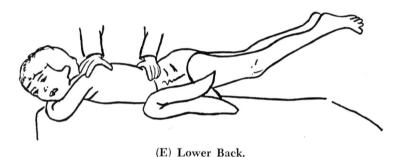

(E) **Lower Back.**

Test No. 6 (Figure 8.10F): Length of back and hamstring muscles. The subject stands erect in stocking or bare feet, hands at his sides, feet together. The test is for the subject to lean down slowly and touch the floor with the finger tips; this position is held for three seconds. Bouncing is not permitted. The examiner should hold the knees of the person being tested in order to prevent any bend and to detect a slight bend in case it occurs.

(F) **Length of Back and Hamstring Muscles.**

217

With these tests, Kraus and Hirschland examined 4,458 eastern United States school children from both urban and rural communities, and compared their achievement with 3,156 Swiss, Austrian, and Italian children. The results of this testing revealed that 57.9 per cent of the United States children and only 8.7 per cent of the European children failed one or more of the tests. Ample verification of the failure rate of United States children on K-W tests has been provided by surveys in Indiana,[37] Iowa,[38] Oregon [39] and elsewhere; the percentages of failures in these states were 45.1, 66.1, and 38.1 respectively.

As experience with K-W testing has been gained, several characteristics of the tests as applied to United States children have become obvious. Among these are the following:

1. The flexibility test (length of back and hamstring muscles) has produced by far the greatest number of failures. Nearly twice as many boys as girls fail this test; in the Oregon sample, of those failing at least one test, the percentages were 59.4 for boys and 33.0 for girls.

2. For the abdominal minus psoas test (No. 2), the opposite was the case; again, in the Oregon survey, 35.2 per cent of the girls and 18.8 per cent of the boys who failed one or more of the tests, failed this one.

3. Very few children fail the two back strength tests; of nearly 1,200 children in the Oregon group, only three failed the upper back test and 11 failed the lower back test. Almost identical situations occurred in the Indiana and Iowa studies.

4. Girls have a lower failure rate than boys on the entire K-W test, but this is due to their much lower failure rate on the flexibility test. When the strength tests only are considered, the boys show superiority.

5. For both sexes, there is a definite decrease in strength failures

[37] Marjorie Phillips and associates, "Analysis of Results from the Kraus-Weber Test of Minimum Muscular Fitness in Children," *Research Quarterly,* Vol. XXVI, No. 3 (October 1955), p. 314.

[38] Margaret Fox and Janet Atwood, "Results of Testing Iowa School Children for Health and Fitness," *Journal of Health, Physical Education, and Recreation,* Vol. XXVI, No. 7 (September 1955), p. 20.

[39] Glenn Kirchner and Don Glines, "Comparative Analysis of Eugene, Oregon, Elementary School Children Using the Kraus-Weber Test of Minimum Muscular Fitness," *Research Quarterly,* Vol. XXVIII, No. 1 (March 1957), p. 16.

as children become older; however, the opposite is true for the flexibility test, as these failures increase with age.

6. The percentage of K-W failures is much lower in schools where strong physical education programs exist. Furthermore, participation in vigorous body-building activities will rapidly reduce the failure rate in any school.

Many questions have been raised relative to the validity of the K-W tests in evaluating the muscular fitness of school children. It should be remembered that they are proposed by the originators as minimum fitness tests. It is surprising that so many United States boys and girls fail such simple tests; actions to correct this situation can certainly be justified. However, they should be supplemented or replaced by more complete tests, which extend through all levels of fitness, as soon as time and resources permit.

Conclusion

In this chapter, the use of strength tests in meeting individual physical fitness needs was given primary consideration. It was assumed that physical educators have a definite responsibility in the maintenance of strength for all pupils, and especially in the development of the physical fitness of boys and girls who are deficient in this essential requisite in school and life. In order to accomplish this end successfully, it is necessary to measure accurately the physical status of schoolchildren and, by periodic re-tests, to determine their progress or lack of progress in individual programs. Strength tests have been given a greater and more severe trial in actual school situations than has any other type of physical fitness test. The better tests have been found practical. They do select pupils needing individual developmental work; progress in physical fitness can also be determined by them.

Selected References

Chamberlain, C. G., and D. F. Smiley, "Functional Health and the Physical Fitness Index," *Research Quarterly*, Vol. II, No. 1 (March 1931), p. 193.

Clarke, H. Harrison, "Muscular Strength-Endurance Relationships," *Archives of Physical Medicine and Rehabilitation*, Vol. XXXVIII, No. 9 (September 1957), p. 584.

———, "Relation of Physical Structure to Motor Performance of Males," *Contributions*, No. 6, American Academy of Physical Education. Washington:

American Association for Health, Physical Education, and Recreation, 1958.

Kraus, Hans, and Ruth P. Hirschland, "Minimum Muscular Fitness Tests in School Children," *Research Quarterly*, Vol. XXV, No. 2 (May 1954), p. 178

Rogers, Fredrick Rand, *Fundamental Administrative Measures in Physical Education*. Newton, Mass.: Pleiades Company, 1932.

———, "PFI Questions and Answers," *Journal of Health and Physical Education*, Vol. XI, No. 6 (June 1940), p. 352.

Zimmerli, Elizabeth, "Case Studes of Unusual Physical Fitness Indices," *Supplement to the Research Quarterly*, Vol. VI, No. 1 (June 1935), p. 246.

CHAPTER NINE

Motor Fitness Tests

The term motor fitness came into being during World War II. Actually, motor fitness is a limited phase of general motor ability, with emphasis placed on the underlying elements of vigorous physical activity, but does not include the primary elements of coordination and skills. It is also a more general fitness designation than physical fitness. The relationships between the three concepts may best be explained in terms of their basic elements, as shown in Figure 9.1. Thus, organic soundness and proper nutrition undergird the entire physical structure. The basic physical fitness elements are muscular strength, muscular endurance, and circulatory endurance; muscular power, agility, speed, and body balance are added to compose motor fitness; then, arm-eye, and kinesthetic foot-eye coordinations are needed for general motor ability.

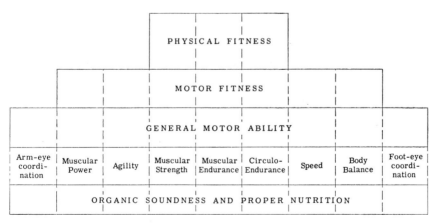

Figure 9.1. Chart of Physical Elements.

Definitions of the various elements designated in the motor fitness concept presented above are as follows:

Muscular strength: Maximum strength applied in a single muscular contraction. Example: grip strength applied to a manuometer. (This element, *per se,* is seldom found in motor fitness tests.)

Muscular endurance: Ability to continue muscular exertions of sub-maximal magnitude. Example: chinning.

Circulatory endurance: Moderate contractions of large muscle groups for relatively long periods of time, which require an adjustment of the circulatory-respiratory systems to the activity. Examples: distance running or swimming.

Muscular ("explosive") power: Ability to release maximum muscular force in the shortest period of time. Example: standing broad jump.

Agility: Speed in changing body positions or in changing direction. Examples: squat thrusts or dodging run.

Speed: Rapidity with which successive movements of the same kind can be performed. Example: 50-yard dash.

Body balance: Ease in maintaining body position. Example: hand stand.

In the above discussion, only the most fundamental elements in physical and motor fitness and general motor ability are indicated. Many other elements could be mentioned and are considered by other authors. McCloy [1] gives a much more complete coverage of these elements, presenting nine physical qualities and eighteen "motor educability" factors. For the purpose of this text, however, the smaller, basic number is considered adequate.

MOTOR FITNESS TESTS OF THE ARMED FORCES

During World War II and since, motor fitness tests were used extensively by the various branches of the armed forces. The test items, procedures for administration, scoring, and use made of test results are quite similar for the various services. While these military tests may not be applicable for the elementary and secondary schools, they do have implications for college physical education.

The pull-up and sit-up items are contained in all three test bat-

---

[1] C. H. McCloy and Norma D. Young, *Tests and Measurements in Health and Physical Education,* 3rd ed. (New York: Appleton-Century-Crofts, Inc., 1954), pp. 4-11.

teries. The Army and the Navy tests have four items in common: pull-ups, squat jumps, push-ups, and sit-ups. Both the Army and the Air Force batteries include a 300-yard shuttle run (60-yard distance), and provide for a 250-yard shuttle (25-yard distance) as a substitute when the test must be conducted indoors; the Army, however, permits a 60-second squat-thrust test as an alternate for the indoor shuttle run which, when used, makes the items in the Army and Navy tests similar. The Air Force test has the fewest test items, being limited to three: pull-ups, sit-ups, and shuttle run; the other two tests have five items each.

In the construction of the fitness tests for the armed forces, every effort was made to provide tests that could be given to a large number of men in a short period of time and that would require a minimum of equipment or apparatus in their administration. These tests can be administered to 300 to 400 men in a single hour by four testers.

Navy Standard Physical Fitness Test [2]

The Navy's test has been singled out from among the service tests for reproduction in this text, as it does not include the shuttle run and, therefore, has greater application to civilian populations. Unless the subjects have been conditioned, it is not considered appropriate to subject them to a competitive run as exhausting as those included in the Army and Air Force tests. The Navy test is intended to accomplish the following purposes:

1. To determine the physical fitness of the men at the beginning of their naval training.

2. To provide information that will aid in adapting the physical fitness program to the individual needs of the men.

3. To motivate the men toward a higher level of physical fitness.

4. To measure the progress of the men after being in service a specified length of time.

5. To provide a means of measuring the physical fitness of Navy personnel engaged in one activity as compared with the personnel engaged in other activities.

---

[2] *Physical Fitness Manual for the U. S. Navy*, Bureau of Naval Personnel, Training Division, Physical Section, 1943, Chap. 4.

J. J. Tunney, "The Physical Fitness Program of the U. S. Navy," *Journal of Health and Physical Education*, Vol. XIII, No. 10 (December 1942), p. 571.

6. To determine whether or not the physical fitness program is accomplishing the desired result.

The Navy test consists of five items, as follows: squat-thrusts, sit-ups, push-ups, squat jumps, and pull-ups. T-score tables for the test have been constructed using as a basis a group of well-conditioned naval personnel. These tables appear in Appendix B, Table XXIV. Directions for administering the various test items are given below.

1. *Squat-Thrusts:* To test large-muscle speed, power, agility, and coordination.

a. Starting Position: The subject is "at attention."

b. Movement: The following four-part exercise is performed as rapidly as possible for one minute: (1) Bend knees and hips and place hands on the floor (squat-rest position). Fingers should point forward; arms may be between, outside of, or in front of the bent knees. (2) Extend legs backward until body is straight from shoulders to heels (front-leaning rest). (3) Return to squat-rest position. (4) Stand straight. In the upright position, the subject may lean forward, but his chest must be in front of an imaginary line drawn from chin to toes.

The subject will make faster time on this test if he does not take a full knee bend but rather bends knees only to a right angle, and if he keeps the shoulders in front of the hands when the legs are thrust back.

c. Scoring: One point is given for the successful performance of each complete squat-thrust.

Following are violations of proper form in executing the squat-thrusts: (1) hands are not placed within eight inches of the feet in the squat position; (2) feet start backward before the hands are placed on the floor; (3) hips are kept above shoulder line when the feet are back; and (4) subject does not straighten up on the fourth count. One point deduction is given for each violation.

2. *Sit-Ups:* To test the strength and endurance of the abdominal muscles.

a. Starting Position: The subject lies on his back on the floor, knees straight, feet approximately 12 inches apart, with hands clasped behind head; an assistant kneels on the floor and holds the soles of the subject's feet against his (the scorer's) knees, pressing them firmly to the floor.

b. Movement: The subject performs the following movement as many times as possible: (1) Raise the trunk, rotating it somewhat to the right, and bend forward far enough to touch the *right* elbow to the *left* knee. (The knees may be slightly bent as the subject sits up.) (2) Lower the trunk to the floor. (3) Sit up again, but rotate the trunk to the left and touch the *left* elbow to the *right* knee. (4) Again lower the trunk to the floor, and continue. The subject must not pause during the test. The movement must be continuous either when leaning forward to touch the knee or when lowering the trunk to the floor.

c. Scoring: One point is given for each complete movement of touching elbow to knee. No score should be counted if the subject unclasps hands from head, keeps knees bent when lying on the back or when beginning the sit-up, or pushes up from an elbow. The subject "sits-up" as many times as possible, without resting on the floor.

3. *Push-Ups:* To test the strength and endurance of the extensor muscles of the arms and shoulder girdles.

a. Starting Position: The subject lies face downward, with hands on the floor at the sides of the shoulders, fingers pointed forward, and toes resting on the floor.

b. Movement: The subject performs the following movement as many times as possible: (1) Raise body from floor by straightening arms so that body is straight from shoulder to heels, with weight resting on hands and toes. (2) Lower body by bending elbows until chest touches the floor. In the Army test, the chest should touch the tester's hand.

c. Scoring: One point is given every time the subject's arms are completely straightened and the exercise is correctly done. No scores are given if (1) arms are bent at the top of the movement; (2) any part of the body other than the hands, toes, and chest touch the floor after the test has begun; (3) shoulders are pushed up first while hips are stationary near the floor; or (4) hips are raised upward and backward before shoulders are pushed up. There should be no penalty for hips being slightly out of line if the whole body is moving upward at about the same speed. In the Army test, penalties for form violations of one-half point only are given.

4. *Squat-Jumps:* To test the strength and endurance of the leg muscles.

a. Starting Position: The subject stands with hands clasped palms down on top of the head; the feet are from four to six inches apart, with the heel of the left foot on a line with the toes of the right foot.

b. Movement: The subject performs the following movement as many times as possible: (1) Drop to a squat on the right heel. (2) Immediately spring upward with both knees straight; while off the floor, interchange the position of the feet so that the right foot is in front; and drop to a squat on the left heel. (3) Repeat the movement, each time interchanging the feet. The upper part of the body should be kept fairly erect. The action should be continuous throughout.

The most common errors in performing squat-jumps are getting the feet too far apart, front and back, and failing to squat down on the rear heel. The test should be carefully demonstrated, and the subjects should be given some practice in performing the test.

c. Scoring: Each time the subject springs from the squat position, he should be given one credit. A movement is not scored if the subject (1) fails to descend to a complete squat, (2) fails to straighten his legs completely while in the air, (3) fails to interchange his legs, or (4) removes hands from his head.

5. *Pull-Ups:* To test the strength and endurance of the flexor muscles of the arms and shoulder girdles.

a. Starting Position: The subject hangs from a horizontal bar, using the forward grasp, in which the thumbs and palms face away from the body (the reverse grasp is acceptable in the Navy test, although the forward grasp is recommended), and the elbows straightened out. If the bar is not high enough for the subject to hang without touching his feet to the floor, he should bend his knees enough for clearance.

b. Movement: The subject chins himself as many times as possible, as follows: (1) Pull body up until chin is brought above level of the bar; legs may be raised if he does not kick or "kip." (2) Lower body until elbows are straight.

c. Scoring: Each time the subject pulls his chin above the bar in correct form, he is given credit for one pull-up. He should not be credited with a pull-up if (1) the arms are not straight at the beginning of the pull-up, (2) the chin is not raised above the bar, (3) a kick or "kip" movement is used, or (4) he stops to rest.

Additional instructions for administering the test provide for: (1) a warm-up calisthenic drill preceding the testing; (2) instruction in and demonstration of the exact techniques for performing each test item correctly; (3) sufficient number of practice trials in preceding class periods to insure proper understanding of test procedures; and (4) five-minute rest period between the events of the test. Navy men are encouraged to practice test events as conditioning exercises. Scoring tables are placed on bulletin boards in barracks and aboard ship so that men may follow their progress.

Equipment required for the administration of the Navy test consists only of a watch and a bar or other support for chinning. When properly organized, it can be administered to several hundred men in an hour. Statistical evidence concerning the accuracy with which the test is administered and the validity of the test as a measure of physical fitness has not been reported.

The Naval Pre-Flight Program also provided for an extensive fitness appraisal program.[3] The following items were included in the testing process: jump and reach, push-ups, chinning, speed-agility run, pack and step tests, screening posture and foot conditions, and measurements of age, height, chest circumference, and abdominal circumference.

Other Armed Forces Tests

USAF Physical Fitness Test.[4] The United States Air Force motor fitness test was designed to measure cardio-respiratory endurance, muscular strength, speed, coordination, and power. The test items are as follows: unlimited sit-ups, pull-ups, and 300-yard shuttle run (outdoors) or 250-yard shuttle run (indoors). On the record card appears the scoring table for each part of the test and for the total score on all three items. The ratings given are classified into five

---

[3] United States Naval Institute, *Mass Exercise, Games, Tests*, Chap. 6, "Physical Appraisal of Cadets" (Annapolis: United States Naval Institute, 1943). Now available from A. S. Barnes and Company, New York.

[4] Air Force Manual, 160-26, *Physical Conditioning* (Washington: Government Printing Office, 1956).

performance categories: excellent, very good, good, poor, and very poor.

Army Physical Efficiency Test.[5] The Army's motor fitness test is designed to measure the principal elements of muscular endurance, circulatory endurance, agility, and coordination. This test has undergone several revisions. Starting with ten test items, it was reduced to seven during World War II. As the seven-item battery required two days to administer, the test was subsequently reduced to the following five items: pull-ups, squat-jumps, push-ups, sit-ups, and 300-yard shuttle run. This battery is recommended when the test can be given on a dry level area of sufficient size to accommodate the shuttle run (60-yard distance). A second battery, which is used when testing cannot be done outdoors is identical with the first, except that either the 250-yard indoor shuttle run or the 60-second squat-thrust test is substituted for the last event.

United States Military Academy Physical Efficiency Test.[6] A physical proficiency test of the motor-fitness type is used for admission to and retention at the United States Military Academy. A number of events have been scaled; exact items in the battery vary each year. A representative battery for a single year is as follows: dips, 100-yard shuttle run (20-yard laps), sit-ups, and softball throw.

Evaluation of Service Tests

In constructing the Air Force motor fitness test, fifteen items were selected as measuring the elements to be included in the test. The three items finally selected correlated .86 with the fifteen items.[7] Validity for the Army test was studied by Esslinger and McCloy [8] with 220 troops who had completed intensive basic training at Fort Knox, Kentucky, and 324 men of the 125th Infantry Regiment. Test items selected for the test battery showed high critical ratios between the upper and lower 25 per cent of these troops.

Mathews, Shay, and Clarke,[9] as part of pack-carrying studies con-

---

[5] Department of the Army Field Manual FM21-20, *Physical Training* (Washington: Government Printing Office).

[6] United States Military Academy, West Point, N. Y.

[7] Leonard A. Larson, "Some Findings Resulting from the Army Air Forces Physical Training Program," *Research Quarterly*, Vol. XVII, No. 2 (May 1956), p. 144.

[8] Arthur A. Esslinger, University of Oregon, unpublished data.

[9] Donald K. Mathews, Clayton T. Shay, and H. Harrison Clarke, "Relationship Between Strength Loss in Pack Carrying and Certain Motor-Physical Fitness Criteria," *Research Quarterly*, Vol. XXVI, No. 4 (December 1955), p. 426.

ducted for the Climatic Research Laboratory, Army Quartermaster Corps,[10] determined the relationships between muscular fatigue caused by carrying military packs under field conditions and various motor-physical fitness tests. The college men serving as subjects were conditioned from six marches carrying the combat load of the rifleman. On the final march, the subjects carried 61 pounds with a rucksack for 7.5 miles at a rate of 2.5 miles in 50 minutes. The highest multiple correlation obtained was −.92 between the strength loss of major muscle groups involved and the Strength Index; the correlations between the Navy, Air Force, and Army motor fitness tests were −.57, −.51, and −.49 respectively. In terms of predictive index, the Strength Index had 3.4 times greater predictive value than did the Navy test, while the Navy test exceeded the Army test by 38 per cent.

In this study, too, the Army motor fitness test correlated well with the other two tests for conditioned subjects, as follows: .88 with the Navy test and .86 with the Air Force battery. The correlation between the Navy and Air Force tests was much lower (.48). The correlations of the Strength Index with the three service tests ranged from .32 to .50. The correlations of the Physical Fitness Index with the service tests were: .80 with the Army test, .63 with the Air Force test, and .49 with the Navy test.

THE INDIANA MOTOR FITNESS TESTS

Motor fitness tests have been constructed at the University of Indiana for the following age groups: college men, high-school boys, high-school girls, and elementary-school children.

College men.[11] In constructing a motor fitness test for college men, Bookwalter empirically proposed the following four Motor Fitness Indices, based upon five simple test items:

---

[10] H. Harrison Clarke, Donald K. Mathews, and Clayton T. Shay, "Strength Decrements from Carrying Various Army Packs on Military Marches," *Research Quarterly*, Vol. XXVI, No. 3 (October 1955), p. 253.

[11] Karl W. Bookwalter and Carolyn W. Bookwalter, "A Measure of Motor Fitness for College," *Bulletin of the School for Education*, Indiana University, Vol. XIX, No. 2 (March 1943).

Karl W. Bookwalter, "Further Studies of Indiana University Motor Fitness Index," *Bulletin of the School of Education*, Indiana University, Vol. XIX, No. 5 (September 1943).

I. (chins + push-ups) × vertical jump
II. (chins + push-ups) × standing broad jump
III. (straddle chins + push-ups) × vertical jump
IV. (straddle chins + push-ups) × standing broad jump

These indices were related to a 12-item criterion composed of two or more measures each of strength, velocity, motor ability, and endurance. The highest correlation (.86) was obtained with Motor Fitness Index I. Nearly as high a coefficient (.84) was obtained when straddle chins was substituted for regular chinning (Motor Fitness Index III). The other two indices may also be considered acceptable, as the correlations were: .82 with Index II, and .81 with Index IV.

Descriptions of the test items needed for the four Motor Fitness Indices are described below. When the test description appears elsewhere in this text, the page reference only is made.

1. *Chins:* Same as for "pull-ups" page 190, except either a palms-forward or a palms-backward grip may be used.

2. *Straddle chins:* With individuals paired for approximate height, the subject being tested lies on his back clasping the hands (finger hold) of his partner who stands astride him, body erect. The subject chins as many times as possible, each time raising his body, back straight and in line with legs, until chest meets firm resistance from partner's thighs.

3. *Push-ups:* Page 225.

4. *Vertical jump:* Page 303, measured to nearest one-fourth inch.

5. *Standing broad jump:* The subject toes a line which is four feet from the edge of a pit, or first lines on a mat, and jumps forward from both feet. If a pit is used, the measurement is taken from and at right angles to the take-off line to the nearest point touched by any part of the body. If a mat is used, lines may be marked in two- to six-inch intervals and the distance between lines estimated. Measurements are made to the nearest inch. The best of three jumps is recorded.

Norms, based on the six-sigma scale, for the five tests included in the four motor fitness indices for college men, are presented in Appendix B, Table XXV. An illustration of the scoring process is as follows:

	Performances	*Scale Scores*
Chins	10 times	65
Push-ups	25 times	73
Standing broad jump	86 inches	51

Applying the scale scores to Index II: $(65 + 73) (51) = 7038$. This figure is divided by 100 and rounded off to the nearest whole number. Thus, the final score of this subject is 70, his Motor Fitness Index. The following rating scale provides a means of interpreting this Index:

Rating	*Motor Fitness Index*
A or Superior	85 and up
B or Good	59 to 84
C or Normal	33 to 58
D or Fair	7 to 32
F or Inferior	6 or less

In the references, achievement scales based upon McCloy's Classification Index I are available for each of the four Indiana Motor Fitness Indices.

High school boys and girls.[12] A motor fitness test for high school boys and girls was constructed, composed of the following four test items: straddle chins, squat-thrusts for 20 seconds, push-ups, and vertical jump. Directions for administering all but the girls' push-up test have been described in this chapter. The girls' push-up test is the same as the boys, except push-ups are performed from the knees, rather than the toes. For validity, the battery correlates .77 with a criterion of twelve motor fitness items.

A motor fitness score is obtained by multiplying the sum of the raw scores on the first three items of the test by the score on the vertical jump; this product is divided by 10 and rounded off to the nearest whole number. For example, a girl performs on this test as follows: straddle chins, 12; squat thrusts in 20 seconds, 8; push-ups, 15; vertical jumps, 20. The motor fitness score equals $(12 + 8 + 15) (20) = 700 \div 10 = 70$.

Norms based upon the McCloy Classification Index for boys and height-weight class divisions for girls appear in Tables XXVI and

---

[12] State of Indiana, *Physical Fitness Manual for High School Boys*, Bulletin No. 136. Department of Public Instruction, Indiana, 1944, pp. 5-13.

State of Indiana, *Physical Fitness Manual for High School Girls*, Bulletin No. 137, rev. ed. Department of Public Instruction, Indiana, 1944, pp. 21-29.

XXVII, Appendix B. To continue scoring the girl in the above illustration: her height is 63 inches; her weight, 115 pounds. From Table XXX, Appendix B, her height-weight classification falls medium for height and medium for weight, hence MM. Entering Table XXVI, column MM, her motor fitness score of 70 is "average."

For scoring a boy, the following illustration is given. His performances were: straddle chins, 25; squat thrusts in 20 seconds, 12; push-ups, 22; vertical jump, 25. Thus, his motor fitness score equals: $(25 + 13 + 22)\ (25) = 1500 \div 10 = 150$. McCloy's Classification Index I is: 20 (age) + 6 (Height) + Weight.[13] Age is reckoned to the last half year; and height, to the last full inch. In the illustration, the boy is 18 years of age (do not exceed age 17 in the formula), 70 inches tall, and weighs 150 pounds. His Classification Index, then, is: $20\ (17) + 6\ (70) + 150 = 190$. Entering Table XXVII, column 885-919, the boy's score of 150 is graded as "Good."

Elementary-school motor fitness test.[14] Accepting the four-item Indiana Motor Fitness Test for high-school pupils, Franklin and Lehsten, under the direction of Bookwalter, adapted it for elementary-school boys and girls, grades four to eight. As relatively few tests exist at the elementary level, this battery is especially important. The test items are administered in the manner described above.

Norms for this test have been established for each of six groups determined from McCloy's Classification Index I. The norm charts for this test appear in Appendix B: Table XXVIII for boys and Table XXIX for girls. No validity evidence for elementary-school pupils is given.

OREGON MOTOR FITNESS TEST

On two different occasions, Oregon motor fitness tests have been constructed. Research on the most recent of these tests was conducted separately for boys and girls each at the elementary, junior high, and senior high school levels by graduate students at the University of Oregon and Oregon State College. The motor fitness ele-

---

[13] Consult Table XXX, Appendix B, for a table which permits the ready computation of McCloy's Classification Index I.

[14] C. C. Franklin and N. G. Lehsten, "Indiana Physical Fitness Tests for the Elementary Level (Grades 4 to 8)," *The Physical Educator*, Vol. V, No. 3 (May 1948), pp. 38-45.

ments and suggested test items for each element were proposed by a statewide committee. The elements selected for this test were: arm and shoulder girdle strength and endurance, abdominal strength and endurance, muscular power, running speed and endurance, agility, and trunk flexibility.

The construction of the tests followed essentially the same pattern for both sexes at the three school levels. Potentially useful test items were assembled for each of the several motor fitness elements. These test items were administered twice, each time by a different tester, to a random sample of subjects who were representative of the sex and age group for which the test was intended; objectivity coefficients were computed based on the repeated tests. At this point, those test items were discarded which had low objectivity coefficients and which did not discriminate between levels of performance. A composite of the remaining test items served as the criterion of motor fitness; the test items to compose each motor fitness battery were selected by multiple correlation procedures. The multiple correlations for three-item batteries ranged from .91 to .95.

As a consequence of the studies, it was possible to select the same test items for boys and for girls at the three school levels. The test items for boys are: pull-ups, jump and reach, and 160-yard potato race. Directions for administering these tests are as follows:

1. *Pull-ups:* Page 190, performed with palms outward.

2. *Jump and reach:* Same as vertical jump, p. 303.

3. *160-yard potato race:* Three circles, each one foot in diameter, are drawn on the floor in line with each other. Circle one is behind and tangent to a starting line. The center of circle two is 50 feet from the starting line, and circle three is 70 feet from the starting line. One 2″ x 4″ block, or eraser, is placed in circle two, and a second one in circle three. From a standing start, the subject (a) runs to circle two, picks up the block, returns to circle one and places it in the circle; (b) he then runs to circle three, picks up the block and carries it to circle one; (c) he immediately picks up the first block, carries it back to circle two; (d) he then returns to circle one, picks up the second block and carries it to circle three; (e) finally, he races back across the starting line. The blocks must be placed, not dropped or thrown, in the proper circle each time.

Three or four stations are possible in giving this test so that a number of students may compete at once. In this instance, a comparable number of spotters are necessary. As the first runner approaches the finish line, the starter counts the seconds in a loud voice. Each spotter observes his contestant and records the time as he crosses the finish line. The score is the elapsed time in seconds.

The Oregon motor fitness test items for girls are: hanging in arm-flexed position, standing broad jump, and crossed-arm curl-ups. These tests are given as follows:

1. *Hanging in arm-flexed position:* The subject stands on a stool or table placing her hands shoulder width apart, palms outward, on a one-inch standard horizontal bar or ladder with elbows flexed to permit the chin to be level with the bar. The support is removed. The girl holds her chin at the level of the bar as long as she can do so. (The legs should remain extended throughout.) The score is the number of seconds the student is able to maintain some flexion in the elbow, preventing the elbow from straightening.

2. *Standing broad jump:* Page 229.

3. *Crossed-arm curl-ups:* The subject assumes a lying position on the back with knees bent at approximately a right angle, soles of the feet flat on the floor, hip width apart; the arms are folded and held against the chest. The girl's feet should be held down firmly by a partner. The test consists of raising the trunk to an erect sitting position and returning to a back-lying position as many times as possible. The feet must remain on the floor throughout the test; the elbows must be kept down and the arms not used to help the body sit up; bouncing from the floor is not permissible; resting during any phase of the performance is not allowed. The score is the number of times the girl raises herself correctly to a sitting position.

T-scale scoring charts for the junior and senior high school boys' and girls' Oregon motor fitness tests are provided in Appendix B, Tables XXXI and XXXII.

NSWA PHYSICAL PERFORMANCE TEST [15]

The National Section on Women's Athletics (NSWA) has proposed a motor fitness test for high school girls consisting of eight

---

[15] Eleanor Metheny, Chairman, "Physical Performance Levels for High School Girls," *Journal of Health and Physical Education,* Vol. XVI, No. 6 (June 1945).

items designed to evaluate muscular control and coordination, speed, agility of movement, and "strength to move the body and implements used in work and play." The following five-item test battery is suggested when circumstances do not permit use of all eight items: standing broad jump, basketball throw for distance, potato race *or* ten-second squat thrusts, unlimited sit-ups, and push-ups *or* pull-ups.

The test items are given in much the same way as described for the other tests above, with the following exceptions: the potato race is for 60 yards. Two lines are drawn on the floor 30 feet apart. Two blocks or erasers are placed beyond the second line. The subject stands behind the first line; on signal, she runs to the first line, picks up one block, runs back to the first line, and places (not throws) the block behind the line; she then returns to the first line, picks up the second block, and runs back over the first line with the block in her hand. The performance is scored in seconds and tenths of a second.

In the basketball throw, the girl throws from behind a line. Only one step is permitted in performing this test, but both feet must remain behind the throwing line until the ball has left the hand. The score is the distance in feet the ball travels in the air. Scoring may be facilitated by marking parallel lines on the floor at intervals of five feet.

A six-sigma scoring chart for this test appears in Appendix B, Table XXXIII.

OTHER MOTOR FITNESS TESTS

A large number of other motor fitness tests have been proposed. While many of these are very worthy instruments, space does not permit their complete presentation in this text. However, several of these are briefly described below. The references may be consulted for more detail.

The University of Illinois Motor Fitness Tests [16]

In developing motor fitness criteria, Cureton recognized six components, as follows: endurance, power, strength, agility, flexibility,

---

[16] Thomas K. Cureton, *Physical Fitness Appraisal and Guidance* (St. Louis: C. V. Mosby Company, 1947), Chap. 13.

and balance. Fourteen-item and 18-item test batteries were developed, validated against a 30-item criteria. A validity coefficient of .87 is reported for the 14-item test.

Subsequently, a seven-item motor fitness test was proposed for use when greater administrative simplicity is desired. The items in this battery are: dive and roll, medicine ball put, bar vault, chinning, leg lifts and sit-ups (agility run may be substituted), breath-holding, and man-lift. Scoring is simplified by using the pass or fail plan. This procedure screens out the subjects poor in ability, and does not require a severe effort on the part of the majority of subjects.

Motor fitness tests were also constructed for high-school girls.[17] A single-period test of six items and a double-period test of 12 items are available.

The JCR Test [18]

The JCR Test is a three-item battery consisting of the vertical jump (J), chinning (C), and 100-yard shuttle run (R). In the shuttle run, the subject covers a ten-yard course ten times, with the aid of bankboards to assist him in making the turn. The test is intended to measure the ability of the individual to perform fundamental motor skills, such as jumping, chinning, running, and dodging, which involve the basic elements of power, speed, agility, and endurance. Reliability coefficients ranging from .91 to .97, and validity coefficients from .59 to .90, are reported for the test. Six-sigma scale scoring tables are available. In a subsequent study, a low but definitely positive relationship was found between the JCR Test and success in primary and advanced levels of pilot training.[19]

Elder Motor Fitness Test [20]

Elder developed a motor fitness test designed to evaluate the following eight basic components: strength, endurance, power, agility,

---

[17] Mary E. O'Connor and Thomas K. Cureton, "Motor Fitness Tests for High School Girls," *Research Quarterly,* Vol. XVI, No. 4 (December 1945), pp. 302-314.

[18] B. E. Phillips, "The JCR Test," *Research Quarterly,* Vol. XVIII, No. 1 (March 1947), pp. 12-29.

[19] B. E. Phillips, "Relationships Between Certain Aspects of Physical Fitness and Success in Pilot Training," *Journal of Aviation Medicine,* Vol. XIX (June 1948), pp. 186-203.

[20] Haskell P. Elder, "Appraising the Physical (Motor) Fitness of Junior High School Boys," Microcarded Doctoral Dissertation, Springfield College, 1958. Materials obtained from author, 12002 Weatherby Rd., Los Alametose, Calif.

flexibility, speed, balance, and body size and age. The composite score on fourteen motor fitness items served as the criterion for the selection of tests to compose the final battery. The tests thus selected were: floor push-ups, standing broad jump, trunk flexion forward, Cozens' dodge run, and 20-second squat thrusts. This battery was found to differentiate well between eight groups considered to be different in terms of their "physical fitness," ranging from "top athletes" to boys who were absent because of illness fifteen or more days during a twenty-week period. Six-sigma scale norms are available for six divisions of the California Classification System, which is based on the boy's age, height, and weight.

New York State Physical Fitness Test [21]

The New York State test is designed to provide schools with a convenient instrument for periodic evaluation of status and progress in motor fitness of boys and girls in grades four through twelve. The elements tested in this battery are: posture, accuracy, strength, agility, speed, balance, and endurance. A manual containing directions for administering this motor fitness test, together with norms and record forms, has been published.

A.A.U. Junior Olympics [22]

The Amateur Athletic Union of the United States has proposed motor fitness standards designed for the "motivation of boys and girls six to fifteen years of age to increase athletic sports participation for the development of physical fitness." Official certificates of achievement may be obtained for boys and girls who meet the standards in five required and one optional event. The required events are: sprints, walk and run, sit-ups, pull-ups, and standing broad jump. The optional events consist of push-ups, baseball throw, continuous hike for distance, and running high jump. The standards are on a pass-or-fail basis. Separate standards are provided for boys and girls; the standards change for each two years' increase in age.

---

[21] *The New York State Physical Fitness Test: A Manual for Teachers of Physical Education* (Albany, N. Y.: Physical Education Bureau, State Education Department, 1958).

[22] Amateur Athletic Union, 233 Broadway, New York City.

California Physical Performance Test [23]

The California Physical Performance Test involves the use of five groups of events, as follows: power of the legs, muscular strength and endurance of the arms and shoulder girdles, abdominal strength and endurance, running speed, and agility, coordination, and body control. When more than one test is listed in a group, one is marked "preferred." An "alternate" test may be substituted in each group if the pupil's interests or the facilities and equipment are such as to warrant the substitution; "optional" tests may be given in addition to the preferred or alternate tests if desired. Norms for boys and girls are based on the California classification plan.

AAHPER Youth Fitness Test Manual [24]

Under the chairmanship of Paul A. Hunsicker, University of Michigan, a committee of the American Association for Health, Physical Education, and Recreation selected the following items to form the AAHPER youth fitness test battery: pull-ups, sit-ups, 40-yard shuttle run, standing broad jump, 50-yard dash, softball throw for distance, and 600-yard run-walk. Three aquatic tests are also presented in the manual. Norms are based on the Neilson-Cozens (California) Classification Index. Data for the norms were obtained from an extensive sample of 8500 boys and girls in grades five through twelve from schools throughout the United States.

EVALUATION OF MOTOR FITNESS TESTS

The wide use of a motor-fitness type of test has evolved since World War II. These tests are designed to secure ease of operation; little training is required to master the testing techniques involved; with good administration, large numbers can be given the tests in a short time by a few testers; and self-scoring is, in some instances, encouraged. In other words, a major consideration has been to test as easily, as economically, and as simply as possible. Such practices are desirable, provided, of course, that the validity and accuracy of the test are not sacrificed. Although much remains to be studied

---

[23] *California Physical Performance Test,* Bureau of Health Education, Physical Education, and Recreation, California State Department of Education, Sacramento, California.

[24] *AAHPER Youth Fitness Test Manual,* American Association for Health, Physical Education, and Recreation, 1201 Sixteenth Street, N.W., Washington 6, D.C.

in relation to the effectiveness of these tests as fitness appraisal instruments, several researches have recently been reported which throw some light on this problem. Certain of these findings and observations will be given below.

Sit-ups

The widely used sit-up test is proposed as a measure of the strength and endurance of the abdominal muscles. This test, however, has been the subject of considerable controversy. For example: Is a person who can perform 100 sit-ups proportionately more fit than he who can do only 50? And how account in fitness terms for the phenomenal sit-up records of 500, 1,000, 2,000, and more?

Both DeWitt [25] and Wedemeyer [26] studied two-minute and un-limited sit-ups, and concluded that no markedly significant relationships existed between sit-ups and abdominal strength and endurance. DeWitt's criterion of abdominal strength was a direct pull upward on a dynamometer when lying supine on a table with shoulders over the edge to permit anchoring the instrument to the floor; his criterion of abdominal endurance was the length of time the body could be held clear of the floor while in a sitting position, hands clasped back of head, and feet on floor under bottom rung of stall bars. As a criterion of abdominal strength, Wedemeyer tested his subjects with the Martin "breaking" method while each was in a sitting position, trunk at an angle of 45 degrees with the floor; as a criterion of endurance, the subjects went through a training period and the initial and final results were compared. In this latter study, after strength reached a certain level, further improvement in the number of sit-ups was accompanied by no significant increases in strength; also, the endurance factor appeared to improve more than did strength.

Karpovich and associates at the School of Aviation Medicine, Randolph Field,[27] obtained a correlation of .38 between unlimited

---

[25] R. T. DeWitt, "A Study of the Sit-up Type of Test as a Means of Measuring Strength and Endurance of the Abdominal Muscles," *Research Quarterly*, Vol. XV, No. 1 (March 1944), pp. 60-63.

[26] Ross Wedemeyer, "A Differential Analysis of Sit-ups for Strength and Muscular Endurance," *Research Quarterly*, Vol. XVII, No. 1 (March 1946), pp. 40-47.

[27] Peter V. Karpovich, Raymond A. Weiss, and Edwin R. Elbel, "Relation Between Leg-Lifts and Sit-Ups," *Research Quarterly*, Vol. XVII, No. 1 (March 1946), pp. 21-23.

sit-ups and leg-lifts (legs lifted to vertical from supine-lying position as many times as possible). Although statistically significant, this correlation is too low for the exercises to be used interchangeably for testing purposes.

While the validity of the sit-up test as an indicator of the condition of the abdominal muscles is doubtful, Mathews [28] questions the use of the straight-leg sit-up from a physiological point of view. He points out that the test performed in this position is performed primarily with the iliopsoas muscles, particularly if the back is arched. Thus, as this muscle is attached to the bodies of the lumbar vertebrae, it may, in persons with weak abdominal muscles, cause serious strain at the lumbosacral joint. As a consequence of these observations, Mathews urges that the sit-up test with knees flexed be used.

DeWitt [29] compared the average number of chins college men could do grasping the bar with palms in, with palms out, and with kipping and kicking. He found that his subjects averaged two more chins with the palms-in than with the palms-out grip. The kick-kip method produced slightly more chins than the palms-in method. This study points to the need for indicating the specific grip to be used in pull-ups when including this test in a test battery.

Inter-Relationships

Brown [30] studied the relative effectiveness of twelve physical-motor test batteries, with college men at Southern Methodist University as subjects. A criterion score consisting of performances on the twelve batteries was established. The highest correlations obtained with this criterion were: .84 with McCloy's Motor Ability Test, .84 with Rogers' Strength Index, .81 with Larson's (Outdoor) Motor Ability Test, and .80 with the Indiana Motor Fitness Test. Several of these tests are classified in this text as general motor ability tests, as presented in Chapter 12. However, the relationships reported by Brown show the close relationship existing between

---

[28] Donald K. Mathews, *Measurement in Physical Education* (Philadelphia: W. B. Saunders Company, 1958), p. 90.

[29] R. T. DeWitt, "A Comparative Study of Three Types of Chinning Tests," *Research Quarterly*, Vol. XV, No. 3 (October 1944), pp. 249-251.

[30] Howard S. Brown, "A Comparative Study of Motor Fitness Tests," *Research Quarterly*, Vol. XXV, No. 1 (March 1954), p. 8.

motor fitness and motor ability. This relationship was pointed out at the beginning of this chapter.

With male freshmen at Indiana University, Cousins [31] conducted a multiple factor analysis with 26 items typically used in motor fitness tests. These items supposedly measured strength, speed, agility, endurance, power, balance, flexibility, and coordination. Four factors were isolated, as follows: arm extensor endurance, power of leg extensors, power of hip extensors, and power of thigh flexors. These factors, however, were identified with considerable reservation because of the low factor loadings and communalities; the presence of a specific factor or factors not isolated, therefore, is indicated. Cousins also concluded that strength appeared to be the most significant factor in body agility and that the power of the hip extensors had a high relationship with ability in the dashes.

Mathews, Shay, and Clarke [32] obtained various correlations between the service motor fitness tests and the test items composing these tests with conditioned college students. The most significant of these relationships were as follows:

1. Time in 300-yard shuttle run: −.81 with Army test, −.74 with Air Force test, −.72 with Strength Index, −.66 with Physical Fitness Index, and −.61 with Navy test.
2. Number of squat thrusts in one minute: .79 with Navy test and .62 with the Army test.
3. The following multiple correlations were obtained:
   a. Physical Fitness Index, .99: leg lift, squat thrusts, and sit-ups.
   b. Strength Index, .98: leg lift and squat thrusts.
   c. Army Physical Efficiency Test, .95: 300-yard shuttle run, sit-ups, and squat jumps (.92 without squat jumps).
   d. Navy Standard Physical Fitness Test, .93: squat thrusts, squat-jumps, and 300-yard shuttle run.
   e. Air Force Physical Fitness Test, .82: 300-yard shuttle run and sit-ups.

Self-Scoring

Self-scoring, as suggested for some of the tests, may be seriously questioned. There is a large chance for error in catching one's time or a partner's time at the finish of the runs as the seconds are called off by the timer. The practice of appointing a judge for each individual is much better. Also, unless carefully checked, such tests as chinning or dipping will result in many partial movements being

[31] George F. Cousins, "A Factor Analysis of Selected Wartime Tests," *Research Quarterly*, Vol. XXVI, No. 3 (October 1955), p. 277.
[32] Mathews, Shay, and Clarke, *op. cit.*

scored as complete. Securing straight elbows in the pull-up test and sufficient elbow bend in dipping is difficult even with competent testers present. And, too, if the individual knows that important decisions affecting his future depend upon his scores, the tendency is to become lax in carrying out the exact requirements of the tests.

SELECTED REFERENCES

Brown, Howard S., "A Comparative Study of Motor Fitness Tests," *Research Quarterly*, Vol. XXV, No. 1 (March 1954), p. 8.

Cousins, George F., "A Factor Analysis of Selected Wartime Tests," *Research Quarterly*, Vol. XXVI, No. 3 (October 1955), p. 277.

Cureton, Thomas K., *Physical Fitness Appraisal and Guidance*, Chap. 13. St. Louis: C. V. Mosby Company, 1947.

Larson, Leonard A., "Some Findings Resulting from the the Army Air Forces Physical Training Program," *Research Quarterly*, Vol. XVII, No. 2 (May 1946), pp. 144-164.

Mathews, Donald K., Clayton T. Shay, and H. Harrison Clarke, "Relationship Between Strength Loss in Pack Carrying and Certain Motor-Physical Fitness Criteria," *Research Quarterly*, Vol. XXVI, No. 4 (December 1955), p. 426.

PART THREE

Social Efficiency

CHAPTER TEN

Physical Education and
Social Efficiency

Social efficiency was defined in Chapter 1 as the development of desirable standards of conduct and of the ability to get along with others. Too frequently in physical education this development is considered merely as a concomitant of the activity program, functioning automatically and requiring neither special planning nor definite programs designed to achieve these results. Character development does continuously take place in all life's activities. This constitutes an obligation and a challenge to physical educators to *see to it* that social development takes the right direction; carefully planned programs should be instituted to realize this objective of physical education.

The physical educator may utilize a number of procedures to achieve the greatest benefits from his efforts to improve the social efficiency of his pupils. In this chapter several such expedients are listed, and the uses of measurement in their development process are pointed out.

TEAM SPORTS

In the social efficiency program, special emphasis should be given to sports activities. All kinds of competitive athletics provide many situations requiring individual and social responses. However, team sports should be included in the physical education program for their unique social value, if for no other reason, and no pupil who is physically able to participate should be exempt from these experiences.

While one must consider relative merits, close-knit team sports, such as basketball, soccer, lacrosse, football, and water polo, offer a unique opportunity through their maximum reliance on team play, for the development of such desirable social traits as co-operation, voluntary subjugation of self for the good of the group, leadership, and followership. All athletics foster such traits as loyalty, quick thinking, initiative, courage, self-control, and a host of other equally desirable characteristics. The realization of such social outcomes is achieved by setting up standards of conduct and applying proper motivation to carry them through. Mores of conduct can be developed by the application of good educational procedures. Such positive slogans as "Play the game," "Play fair," "Hit the line hard," "Follow through," "Play together," "One for all and all for one," are examples of a realistic language for human conduct, indicating the direction and dynamic appeal of such training when properly conducted.

Furthermore, as expressed by Goodwin Watson: "There is no more fundamental human longing than the desire to be an accepted member of a social group." [1] The individual who feels himself isolated, or an outcast, may develop all sorts of undesirable behavior traits. Team sports provide opportunities for all individuals to be members of a group, to participate in group activities, to strive with others toward the accomplishment of desirable goals of achievement. For most pupils, the opportunity itself will be a sufficient incentive. For the isolated pupil, however, wise guidance is essential if he is to experience emotionally the merging of himself with the group.

Social Acceptability

Social acceptance is an important requisite for satisfactory personal and social adjustment. Lack of social status frequently results in discontent and unhappiness; attainment of status once lacking may produce marked changes in an individual's personality and feeling of well-being. Obtaining and maintaining social acceptabil-

---

[1] Goodwin Watson, "Personality Growth through Athletics," *Journal of Health and Physical Education*, Vol. IX, No. 7 (September 1938), p. 408.

ity is particularly important during adolescence, as an emerging interest in social, especially heterosexual, relationships is characteristic of this age.

The learning of physical skills is an important element in social adjustment. It often constitutes the difference between the development of social, well-integrated individuals and unsocial, retiring types. The physical education program, therefore, has "a strategic position for contributing to the development of individual students in their personal-social relations." [2]

In connection with the Berkeley Growth Studies, Harold E. Jones [3] reported that boys high in physical strength tend to have good physiques, to be physically fit, and to enjoy a favored social status in adolescence. Boys who are low in strength show a tendency toward asthenic physiques, poor health, social difficulties and lack of status, feelings of inferiority, and personal maladjustment in other areas. In interpreting this social phenomenon, the "pile-up" effect of associated biological factors should be considered. Individuals low in strength are frequently found to have an accumulative assortment of handicaps, and those high in strength frequently show an imposing variety of physical advantages. Thus, those at the strength extremes were deficient or superior not in one but in many aspects of size, build, health, and fitness, each of which makes its additive contribution. It is not surprising that these multiple defects or advantages should be reflected, not merely in physical activity, but also in social participation and in the individual's own attitudes and self-appraisal.

A further discussion of the relationship of physical education to social acceptability appears in Chapter 13.

ABILITY GROUPINGS

In this text, equating the powers of opposed individuals and groups has been classified primarily as a phase of the social development program. Other values, however, have not been lost sight of, as the purposes to be served by ability grouping in physical educa-

---

[2] Lois H. Meek, Chairman, *The Personal-Social Development of Boys and Girls with Implications for Secondary Education.* New York: Committee on Workshops, Progressive Education Association, 1940, p. 204.

[3] Harold E. Jones, "Physical Ability as a Factor in Social Adjustment in Adolescence," *Journal of Educational Research,* Vol. XL (December 1946), pp. 287-301.

tion are at least three in number: (1) pedagogical advantages; (2) desirable attitudes toward physical education; and (3) social development.

Pedagogical Advantages

Ability grouping is an important pedagogical procedure. There is no doubt in the minds of experienced teachers that class instruction is more efficient when the abilities of groups are similar. Heterogeneous grouping presents a serious problem in class instruction, as class work usually will be geared to the ability of the less able pupils. Instruction adapted to the ability of the average student becomes too difficult for the poor performers and too easy for the good ones. Equating, however, brings together pupils of near equal ability, all of whom are ready for instruction on approximately the same level. Skills may thus be taught effectively and efficiently.

Homogeneous grouping, too, may be far more important in physical education than in scholastic phases of the educational program, as the manner of an individual's participation in many physical activities—what he does, how he reacts—depends to a large extent upon the *actions* of those participating with him. For example, the greatest football player cannot catch a forward pass if the ball is badly thrown, or make long runs against comparable opposition if his own line and blocking backs do not function efficiently in removing potential tacklers from his path; the basketball player cutting for the basket cannot shoot effectively unless the ball is thrown to him properly and in a way in which he can handle it, and unless he can avoid defensive guards attempting to block the shot. Correlative and oppositive efforts of this sort are not required in English, mathematics, or other academic classes.

Ability grouping has been fairly well done in classroom work. Within certain limits, of course, academic grade classification is a reasonably satisfactory arrangement for mental activities. The fact that pupils have been promoted to a certain grade, although differing in such factors as social maturity, intelligence, interest, and industriousness, is at least partial evidence that they have attained a certain academic level. To use grades in school, or study halls, as the only means of classifying pupils for physical education, however, as is usually done, is grossly unsatisfactory, as such important elements as physical size and maturity, physical fitness, strength, speed, and ability to learn new skills bear but small relation to academic abilities. Also, especially in high school and college, previous experience and training in physical education activities differ far more widely than do these qualities in academic subjects. It may be assumed, for example, that an entering freshman in college has had certain definite educational training in such subject-matter fields as English, science, social studies, and so forth. In physical education, nothing can be taken for granted, as many college freshmen have had little—or even no—training in physical skills. Such differences, therefore, unless equated in some way, markedly handicap the physical education program.

Desirable Attitudes Toward Physical Education

Physical educators desire to insure real and lasting interest in physical education activities, not only that their program may be more attractive, but that their pupils may carry on desirable physical activities during their leisure time and engage in them after graduation. But the development of desirable attitudes depends upon the amount of individual skill acquired by the participant and upon satisfying experiences in the activities themselves. In equating the abilities of students, opportunity for individual success is increased. Under such conditions pupils compete with equals and thus have the satisfaction of extending themselves and their opponents and of winning a *fair share* of contests. The interest of all participants is therefore largely assured, neither contestant (or team) winning easily or losing badly.

That equating the competing powers of teams is an essential factor in conducting a successful intramural program has been demonstrated repeatedly. One need only observe the practices of professional sports promoters to have a convincing argument: the achievement of initial equality and great doubt of the outcome is their prime aim—in boxing, baseball, hockey, and the like. In horse racing, even weight handicaps are added to insure exciting—that is, fair, equal—chances.

In school practice, also, eligibility rules are enforced primarily to achieve equality. During the writer's many years of experience in conducting high-school and college intramural programs, the equating of competing teams has always been carefully planned, with deliberate scheduling of opposing teams of similar ability. In

249

intramural sports, a close game should be regarded as a successful one from the standpoint of the director; for, above all, the interest of all competitors is maintained and return matches are the rule. A lop-sided score represents failure: failure to maintain the interest especially of the players on the losing team.

With equated intramural teams, many of the most exciting and interesting games (for the contestants) have been played by "dub" teams previously equated. One has only to observe the interest in these leagues to be completely convinced of the value of ability grouping. All players realize that the contests remembered the longest, exciting the greatest interest, and discussed in later years with the greatest enthusiasm were the ones played against opponents of equal ability, where the game was hard fought and the score close. To be sure, winning the game is important; but, when the game is played against decidedly inferior opponents, it is a victory devoid of lasting satisfaction. For the intramural director, loss of interest due to uneven contests should be a matter of serious concern.

Social Development

The third value of ability grouping is in providing a setting for desirable social experiences. When competing individuals or teams are evenly matched, players are more active, cooperation is essential, and initiative and courage are necessary requisites to playing the game successfully. In fact, all of the physical, mental, emotional, and social qualities of the individual are at a premium when playing hard-fought, closely contested matches. In unequal contests, the winning players are not required to exert themselves, teamwork is not particularly important, "grandstand" players may perform without jeopardizing the success of their teams, individuals are not stimulated to display initiative, and head work, loyalty, and fortitude are not essential elements of the game. The losing team may either fight through under great odds, a desirable outcome, or, as is usually the case, lose interest and coast through in any way to complete the contest. When each new effort is met with overwhelming superior power and ends in disappointment, or when the slightest effort produces success, there is little encouragement for continuing.

It may be argued that certain advantages result from heterogeneous situations. The excellent performer may benefit socially from helping those who are less skilled, thus developing a tolerant and understanding attitude toward beginners. The poor performer, on the other hand, is given a better concept of possible excellence in physical activities and is perhaps extended beyond his ordinary performance by participating with more highly skilled contestants. Many physical educators, therefore, may wish to provide occasional opportunities for participation of this sort. As a regular practice, however, the advantages of homogeneous grouping in physical education far outweigh the disadvantages.

PLAYER CONTROL OF CONTESTS

Pupil responsibility and initiative are essential to the development of pupil leadership. Physical education is especially rich in opportunities for the exercise of these qualities. Every game provides a setting for developing pupil leadership by permitting the players themselves to plan, direct, and control their own contests. The extensiveness of this opportunity is especially apparent when one considers the large number of contests conducted in physical education classes and in intramural leagues.

The guidance of the physical educator, however, should be a very definite part of this plan. He should capitalize on opportunities to drive home in this natural setting important lessons in citizenship. A democratic state may thereby be approached, and one that is particularly rich in social experiences.

SUCCESS EXPERIENCES

An important factor in developing confidence and poise in boys and girls, which will in turn pave the way for wider personality adjustments, is for them to realize success experiences. Physical education activities should be so selected and arranged that the individual has a chance to succeed, and will do so a fair share of the time. To be met constantly with defeat or to be subjected repeatedly to activities beyond one's ability to perform can only result in feelings of impotence and inferiority, culminating in defeatism and withdrawal from people and from life situations. On the other hand, to present the pupil with an activity he can readily learn, despite its possible elementary nature, to face him with a situation he can master, or to place him with and against others of his own ability will result in his increased interest, self-assurance, and willingness to attempt progressively more difficult assignments. The application of the success principle will be the starting point in the unfolding of full personalities of many hitherto retiring introverts.

SOCIAL EDUCATION

The development of the individual for social living is an essential task of education; in this task, physical education naturally shares. Boys and girls must be prepared to live in a complex, highly interdependent society, to participate responsibly in a democracy which is no longer only nationally oriented but envisages an international society based on the brotherhood of man, and to be committed irrevocably to a moral and spiritual way of life. Accomplishment of these very vital objectives is the greatest need apparent in life today. All of our science, all of our technology, all of the truly great achievements of the mind, and all the physical fitness and athletic skills will be ineffectual in the face of a society with unrestricted competition and with a world based upon unrestricted power politics.

Social stability and progress in a democracy is dependent upon the conviction that self-interest is interwoven with the social good and the social welfare. Cooperation is learned as common interests and common activities are carried out by the team or group.[4] Voluntary cooperation, contrary to the idea of the survival of the fittest, is essential to all forms of life. Fundamentals of such social development are an appreciation of individual personality, an assumption of responsibility for the consequences of one's own conduct, an acceptance of the concept of moral equality, and a desire to achieve excellence.

The mere participation in activities, no matter how potentially useful, will not automatically result in desirable social outcomes. Any sport can be presented in a manner to develop either desirable or undesirable modes of conduct. Good sportsmanship may be obvious in some athletic contests, while unsportsmanlike acts may

---

[4] Charles C. Cowell, *Scientific Foundations of Physical Education* (New York: Harper & Brothers, 1953), p. 119.

be rife in others; well-coordinated team play may be evident in the way some teams compete, while a collection of individual stars, each playing for his own glory, may characterize other teams. The teacher or coach is the key to social education: social growth can be no better than the understanding and ability of the teacher to develop those qualities needed in men today for the sake of the years to come. As expressed by the Educational Policies Commission: ". . . the teacher of sports is usually one of the most influential members of the school community in the shaping of moral and spiritual values." [5]

Many of the activities of physical education may be used to provide a realistic laboratory experience in democratic living. Sports participation knows no racial barriers, national restrictions, or differences in creed: sports achievement is widely recognized and acclaimed regardless of the origins of the competitor; the code of a sportsman is realistic and universal and knows no special privileges; "fair play" is an experience in the application of law and justice; each competitor recognizes and accepts his appropriate role in the team effort. In order to realize these goals, the welfare of the participant, not the athletic record of the school, must always be the first consideration.

Boys and girls need to know what respect for authority means; they should be given a vision of a more desirable state toward which to strive and of which they themselves may not be cognizant; and they must learn to make wise choices and to develop *for themselves* worthy standards of conduct. The physical educator deals many times with emotionalized attitudes developed under the stress of actual pressure; character may thus be emphasized as underlying and integrating all behavior of the individual. Wise guidance is essential if best results are to be attained.

MEETING INDIVIDUAL NEEDS

Individuals vary in social characteristics and needs as widely as they do in the physical characteristics and needs discussed in earlier chapters of the text. Too frequently, however, school pupils are treated en masse, with occasional reprimands and punishments

---

[5] Educational Policies Commission, *Moral and Spiritual Values in the Public Schools* (Washington: National Education Association, 1951), p. 68.

meted out to the few incorrigibles and the overly mischievous, no matter how different their temperaments, how varied their interests, how peculiar their social characteristics, or how pressing their social problems may be. No attempt is made to understand the individual; he is lost in the shuffle.

If the individual is to develop socially in such a way as to indicate high probability of a social rather than a self-centered or predatory career, individual needs must be determined; and treatment must be based upon measurement of the individual pupil, recorded regularly during the successive phases of his maturation. For those with social problems, individual diagnosis to discover the cause of the condition should be made and appropriate steps for its correction instituted. Retests from time to time should be given in order to determine the progress being made. If no progress is recorded as a result of the retests, the case should again be reviewed, gone into even more thoroughly, and possibly referred to psychologists or psychiatrists.

Need for Objective Tests

Measurement in relation to the social development of boys and girls may take a number of directions. Most significant among these are the following:

1. *Measurement of social efficiency.* The physical education teacher should utilize the better tests of social efficiency and conduct appropriate follow-up procedures for those in need. He should develop ability to recognize behavior problems and to know their meaning. He should take steps to discover the origin of the child's behavior disturbances, looking for dominant behavior tendencies. The physical educator's chief concern, however, should be with the appearance of these unsocial attitudes and psychic anomalies which at first seem insignificant but which later may lead to neurotic or serious social maladjustment. Tests to aid physical education teachers in measuring personality and character traits are presented in the next chapter.

2. *Ability grouping.* Ability grouping may be accomplished roughly by judgment or by "choosing sides." However, it is also possible to use tests for this purpose. Tests of general motor abilities are discussed in Chapter 12.

3. *Physical fitness.* The causes of many cases of social maladjustment have been traced to physical sources. Obviously, one is not a very social being when he has a splitting headache or when he is fatigued. Eyestrain may be the cause of irritation, lack of attention, and disciplinary problems in the classroom. Organic defects, resulting in lowered physical vitality and general bodily weakness, may result in poor grades and inability to take part in the activities of the school, thus promoting failure and retardation, with their attendant undesirable effects upon the social development of the pupil. A foundation of abundant health and vitality is a major asset in the development of a socially adjusted individual. Physical fitness measurement was considered in Part II of the text.

4. *Individual competence.* Competence in physical skills, resulting in the development of confidence and poise, involves the acquiring of a satisfactory degree of proficiency in various physical education activities. Tests of such activities appear in Chapter 14.

Selected References

Collings, E., "Learning By Socialized Doing," reported by Sidney L. Pressey and J. Elliott Janney, *Casebook of Research in Educational Psychology.* New York: Harper & Brothers, 1937.

Cook, Lloyd and Elaine, *School Problems in Human Relations.* New York: Mc-Graw-Hill Book Company, Inc., 1957.

Cowell, Charles C., *Scientific Foundations of Physical Education.* New York: Harper & Brothers, 1953.

Educational Policies Commission, *Moral and Spiritual Values in the Public Schools.* Washington: National Education Association, 1951.

Meek, Lois H., chairman, *The Personal-Social Development of Boys and Girls with Implications for Secondary Education.* New York: Committee on Workshops, Progressive Education Association, 1940.

Russell, Bertrand, *Education and the Good Life.* New York: Boni and Liveright, 1926.

Watson, Goodwin, "Personality Growth Through Athletics," *Journal of Health and Physical Education*, Vol. IX, No. 7 (September 1938), p. 408.

CHAPTER ELEVEN

Measurement of
Social Efficiency

In the preceding chapter it was pointed out that the field of physical education is particularly rich in opportunities for social experiences, since pupils participate actively and wholeheartedly in activities requiring many and varied social responses. These experiences develop social traits. Further, definite programs can be devised to develop desirable traits and to suppress undesirable ones.

A major obstacle to rapid progress in the development of social efficiency, however, is the difficulty of measuring social character. Without adequate tests, a really strong program of social development is impossible, regardless of the number and nature of the general procedures employed to realize this objective. In fact, without measurement, the physical director cannot tell whether he is actually developing desirable social traits in any or all of his pupils. An understanding of pupil social characteristics is thus the base upon which this aspect of the physical education program must be built. Moreover, determining the effects of such programs upon the individual can be done only by retests of these individuals from time to time. Thus, like the physical development program, the social efficiency program of the physical educator must be essentially an individual program, the physical educator adapting procedures to meet individual needs *after such needs have been determined through measurement.*

Moreover, in the development of social efficiency, physical educators should be interested in two fundamental aspects of this problem. First, does physical education develop desirable behavior in relation to the physical activities in which the pupils participate? Second, are these same qualities carried over into school and life activities? The real success of any physical educator's attempt to improve pupils' social efficiency may very well be identified with the degree of transfer achieved. But particularly should he be familiar with the actual social problems of his pupils as a means of directing his teaching toward specific individual problems.

In measurement, therefore, consideration should be given to social traits functioning in physical education, in school, and in out-of-school situations. As physical education tests of social efficiency are confined primarily to behavior responses in physical education activities without reference to individual traits in other school and life activities, tests in the fields of education and psychology measuring similar qualities will be included in this chapter. *The physical educator, consequently, who uses the latter type of test will be in a position to meet the broad social needs of his pupils and to plan definitely for the carry-over of specific traits in individual cases.*

Behavior Rating Scales

So far, in physical education, the tests proposed for measuring social efficiency have been confined largely to ratings based upon the judgment of observers. The best of these tests are based upon a rating of behavior frequencies. In this method, the rater estimates the frequency with which he observes certain types of behavior in the individual being rated, thus having the advantage of specific data to guide his judgment. For example, the test contains statements classified under subheads of a general trait, which might be as follows. The ratings would be based upon whether the behavior occurs "never," "seldom," "fairly often," "frequently," or "extremely often":

Sportsmanship
 a. Acts like a good sport toward opponents.
 b. Razzes, teases, or bullies opponents.
Ethics
 a. Takes decisions, wins and loses, in good spirit.
 b. Takes advantage of lax officiating.
 c. "Crabs" about officiating.

McCloy's Behavior Rating Scale [1]

McCloy proposed one of the first behavior rating scales in physical education. In this scale, nine traits are listed: leadership, active qualities, attitudes, self-control, cooperation, sportsmanship, ethics, efficiency, and sociability. A total of 37 typical trait actions are listed under the nine traits, each of which is rated by the judges on a scale of 5 to 1, with 5 representing "good" behavior. The frequencies are designated by such descriptive terms as: "extremely often," "frequently," "fairly often," "seldom," "never." The assurance of the rater is also indicated opposite each trait action, as follows: 0 (a mere guess), 1 (slight inclination), 2 (fair assurance), 3 (positive assurance).

Blanchard's Scale [2]

Blanchard utilized 85 trait actions classified under the nine traits suggested by McCloy. These trait actions were evaluated by 16 physical education teachers, and the 45 receiving the highest ratings were selected as the basis for his study. Three major criteria were used in the selection of the final trait actions, as follows: (1) median of the average deviations of the total scores of four teacher and eight student raters (indicating consistency of ratings); (2) the reliability of teacher and student scores per trait action; and (3) the intercorrelation of each trait with the remainder of its category.

Twenty-four trait actions were finally selected for the behavior frequency rating scale. The reliability of this battery is .71 and the intercorrelation of one trait action with the rest of the items in its category is .93. The complete scale appears in Figure 11.1.

Cowell Social Behavior Trend Index [3]

In identifying a socially well-adjusted student, Cowell presented the following description: "One who has a feeling of social security as the result of his social skills, his social 'know how,' and because he is accepted and 'fits into the group.' One who feels 'at home in the

[1] C. H. McCloy, "Character Building in Physical Education," *Research Quarterly,* Vol. I, No. 3 (October 1930), p. 42.

[2] B. E. Blanchard, "A Behavior Frequency Rating Scale for the Measurement of Character and Personality in Physical Education Classroom Situations," *Research Quarterly,* Vol. VII, No. 2 (May 1936), p. 56.

[3] Charles C. Cowell, "Validating an Index of Social Adjustment for High School Use," *Research Quarterly,* Vol. XXIX, No. 1 (March 1958), p. 7.

MEASUREMENT OF SOCIAL EFFICIENCY

Name:...........................Grade:...................Age:.................Date:...............

School:.................................Name of Rater:...........................

BEHAVIOR RATING SCALE

Personal Information	No Opportunity to Observe	Never	Seldom	Fairly Often	Frequently	Extremely Often	Score
Leadership							
1. Popular with classmates................		1	2	3	4	5	
2. Seeks responsibility in the classroom.......		1	2	3	4	5	
3. Shows intellectual leadership in the classroom		1	2	3	4	5	
Positive Active Qualities							
4. Quits on tasks requiring perseverance......		5	4	3	2	1	
5. Exhibits aggressiveness in his relationship with others...........................		1	2	3	4	5	
6. Shows initiative in assuming responsibility in unfamiliar situations................		1	2	3	4	5	
7. Is alert to new opportunities..............		1	2	3	4	5	
Positive Mental Qualities							
8. Shows keenness of mind................		1	2	3	4	5	
9. Volunteers ideas........................		1	2	3	4	5	
Self-Control							
10. Grumbles over decisions of classmates......		5	4	3	2	1	
11. Takes a justified criticism by teacher or classmate without showing anger or pouting..		1	2	3	4	5	
Co-operation							
12. Is loyal to his group.....................		1	2	3	4	5	
13. Discharges his group responsibilities well...		1	2	3	4	5	
14. Is co-operative in his attitude toward his teacher		1	2	3	4	5	
Social Action Standards							
15. Makes loud-mouthed criticism and comments		5	4	3	2	1	
16. Respects the rights of others..............		1	2	3	4	5	
Ethical Social Qualities							
17. Cheats		5	4	3	2	1	
18. Is truthful		1	2	3	4	5	
Qualities of Efficiency							
19. Seems satisfied to "get by" with tasks assigned		5	4	3	2	1	
20. Is dependable and trustworthy............		1	2	3	4	5	
21. Has good study habits...................		1	2	3	4	5	
Sociability							
22. Is liked by others........................		1	2	3	4	5	
23. Makes a friendly approach to others in the group		1	2	3	4	5	
24. Is friendly		1	2	3	4	5	

Figure 11.1.   Blanchard's Behavior Rating Scale.

group' and does not feel that he differs markedly from the ways the group feels are important. He has group status and is accepted by the group. One interested in the games, hobbies, and activities favored by the majority of his classmates."

After studying factors which differentiate junior high school boys who tend to participate wholeheartedly in physical education and those who are reticent to so participate, Cowell developed twelve pairs of behavior "trends" representing good and poor adjustments. As a result of a factor analysis, ten of the pairs of positive and negative behavior trends were retained as common denominators underlying good and poor adjustment. These positive and negative scales (forms A and B respectively) appear in Figure 11.2.

Cowell recommends that three teachers rate each pupil on both forms; a pupil's social adjustment score is the total of the ratings of the three teachers combining the two forms. Thus, a socially well-adjusted pupil would get a high positive score, a socially mal-adjusted pupil would receive a high negative score. These raw scores can be transposed to percentile values as prepared by Cowell from testing 222 junior high school boys. This scale appears in Appendix B, Table XXXIV.

Cowell has reported correlations of .50 and .62 between teachers' judgments of social status and scores on the Cowell's Personal Distance Scale and Who's Who Ballot respectively. He also obtained a biserial correlation of .82 between teachers' ratings of the best and worst socially adjusted boys.

Rating Precautions

Considerable care should be exercised in making ratings, as they are merely the opinions of one person in respect to the quality being considered. Masoner [4] has recommended that schools should use behavior ratings only when pupils can be observed carefully and when established principles of rating can be followed. Such factors as the experience of the raters, their understanding of the traits being rated, and their acquaintance with the subject affect the results of the ratings. Traits of character cannot be seen, but action can. However, the motive behind action may not be understood. Raters should be carefully trained in habits of observation,

---

[4] Paul Masoner, "A Critique of Personality Rating Scales," Microcarded Doctoral Dissertation, University of Pittsburgh, 1949.

the qualities to be rated being clearly pointed out so that the possibility of misunderstanding is reduced to a minimum. Also, the reliability of ratings can be increased by combining the ratings of several judges of the same pupil.

The degree of assurance of the rater should be recorded. O'Neel [5] found that ratings were usually reliable when the rater had fair or positive assurance, and that the reverse was true when he was guessing. Blanchard, on the other hand, concluded that raters' assurance columns may be eliminated, as the assurance of raters is only an index of the range of personal contact and acquaintance of the judge with the student. The best procedure for the rater is not to judge a trait action unless he has a fair acquaintance with the subject. If not reasonably sure, he should observe the subject for a time before making the ratings.

Caution must be exercised also against the "halo effect" in rating pupils, as raters tend to rate individuals whom they like, or who have fine reputations, too highly in everything, whereas the reverse is true for those whom they dislike, or who have unsavory reputations, even if such reputations are due to single-trait deficiencies. The idea of "love is blind" is indicative of this situation. Langlie [6] found this situation, and also discovered that sex differences in ratings exist, as both men and women teachers tend to rate girls as superior to boys, even though test records show an opposite trend. Also, according to Grant,[7] the "halo effect" results from the failure of a rater to discriminate between the traits of the person he is rating. This effect is recognized by the existence of high positive intercorrelations between the items in a rating scale.

McCloy [8] suggests that the "halo effect" may be partially avoided by rating each item for all individuals separately, rather than rating one individual completely before proceeding to the next. This procedure is included as a specific instruction by the Reports and Records Committee of the Commission on the Relation of School

---

[5] F. W. O'Neel, "A Behavior Frequency Rating Scale for the Measurement of Character and Personality in High School Physical Education for Boys," *Research Quarterly*, Vol. VII, No. 2 (May 1936), p. 67.

[6] T. A. Langlie, "Personality Ratings. I: Reliability of Teachers' Ratings," *Journal of Genetic Psychology*, Vol. L (June 1937), p. 339.

[7] Donald L. Grant, "An Exploratory Study of the Halo Effect in Rating." Microcarded Doctoral Dissertation, Ohio State University, 1952.

[8] C. H. McCloy, *op. cit.*

and College, Progressive Education Association.[9] Again, care and concentration on traits and their meanings will do much to counteract this effect. It will also be advantageous to confine these ratings to behavior in physical activities, without attempting to complicate the situation by introducing academic or out-of-school behavior. Behavior evaluation in the latter activities should be the result of separate ratings, or other measurement procedures, designed for this specific purpose.

Cowell Social Behavior Trend Index (Form A)

Date: _____ Grade: ____

School: _____ Age: _____

Describer: _____

Last Name   First Name

INSTRUCTIONS:--Think carefully of the student's behavior in group situations and check each behavior trend according to its degree of descriptiveness.

Behavior Trends	Descriptive of the Student			
	Markedly (+3)	Somewhat (+2)	Only Slightly (+1)	Not at All (0)
1. Enters heartily and with enjoyment into the spirit of social intercourse _____				
2. Frank; talkative and sociable, does not stand on ceremony ____				
3. Self-confident and self-reliant, tends to take success for granted, strong initiative, prefers to lead __				
4. Quick and decisive in movement, pronounced or excessive energy output _____				
5. Prefers group activities, work or play; not easily satisfied with individual projects _____				
6. Adaptable to new situations, makes adjustment readily, welcomes change _____				
7. Is self-composed, seldom shows signs of embarrassment _____				
8. Tends to elation of spirits, seldom gloomy or moody _____				
9. Seeks a broad range of friendships, not selective or exclusive in games and the like _____				
10. Hearty and cordial, even to strangers, forms acquaintanceships very easily _____				

Figure 11.2. Cowell Social Behavior Trend Index.

---

[9] Progressive Education Association, *Behavior Description,* Reports and Records Committee, 1935.

262

SOCIAL ACCEPTANCE EVALUATION

Cowell [10] has pointed out that teachers' judgments of social behavior are apt to be based on mature adult standards and to be largely indicative of the child's adjustment in dealing with adults in classroom situations. Such judgments, then, may or may not

Cowell Social Behavior Trend Index (Form B)

Date: _____ Grade: ____

School: _____ Age: _____

Describer: _____

Last Name   First Name

INSTRUCTION:--Think carefully of the student's behavior in group situations and check each behavior trend according to its degree of descriptiveness.

	Descriptive of the Student			
Behavior Trends	Markedly (-3)	Somewhat (-2)	Only Slightly (-1)	Not at All (-0)
1. Somewhat prudish, awkward, easily embarrassed in his social contacts _____				
2. Secretive, seclusive, not inclined to talk unless spoken to ___				
3. Lacking in self-confidence and initiative, a follower _____				
4. Slow in movement, deliberative or perhaps indecisive. Energy output moderate or deficient ____				
5. Prefers to work and play alone, tends to avoid group activities ___				
6. Shrinks from making new adjustments, prefers the habitual to the stress of reorganization required by the new _____				
7. Is self-conscious, easily embarrassed, timid or "bashful" ____				
8. Tends to depression, frequently gloomy or moody ____				
9. Shows preference for a narrow range of intimate friends and tends to exclude others from his association _____				
10. Reserved and distant except to intimate friends, does not form acquaintanceships readily ____				

Figure 11.2. (continued)

[10] Cowell, *op. cit.*

reflect the standards which boys and girls apply to each other. Teachers' standards may not always be realistic; they may even be oppositive to those of the students. In some such instances, the teachers' set of values may be the more desirable, as they may be based upon the broader goals of society, rather than upon possible ill-conceived goals of occasional unworthy student leaders. Nevertheless, the acceptance of students by their peers may frequently be an important form of personality evaluation. So, it may logically be contended that both forms of evaluation are desirable.

Two types of social acceptance evaluation have come into use in education. These may be designated as the social distance scale and the sociometric questionnaire. Both of these will be presented in this section.

Social Distance Scale

Social distance scales have been used in research pertaining to social psychology since 1925 when Bogardus published his *Social Distance Scale*. The Bogardus-type instrument has been used to study race attitudes and indicate social distance toward professions, religious groups, conscientious objectors, etc. Although modified for specific purposes, the general format has been maintained.

The concept of social distance has been used in education to evaluate the closeness of personal relationships. A test of this type, recently used in physical education, is the *Cowell Personal Distance Ballot*.[11] In Cowell's report, this ballot was used to represent boys' attitudes toward accepting boys. As he points out, it is possible also to determine girls' attitudes toward girls, boys' attitudes toward girls and vice-versa by various methods of balloting. A student's index on this scale depends largely on his degree of social participation in his own group and therefore, on his own "individual stimulus value."

The Cowell Personal Distance Ballot appears in Figure 11.3. The ballot is prepared by listing the names of all classmates, or other acquaintances to be evaluated. Each boy answers the ballot by checking on the seven-point scale how near to his family he would like to have each of the classmates or acquaintances listed. A Personal Distance Score is derived by adding the total *weighted* scores

---

[11] *Ibid.*

given the subject by the class or group and dividing by the total number of respondents. Division is carried to two places and the decimal point dropped. The low score is the desirable score. Cowell's percentile scale scores for boys appears in Appendix B, Table XXXV.

In a study of the social integration of a college football squad, Trapp [12] reported reliability coefficients of .91, .88, and .93 between Cowell's balloting on the same boys by the same participants at three different times during the football season. Kurth and Cowell [13] in the validation of the *Cowell Personal Distance Ballot* as a social adjustment index obtained a correlation of .84 with the students' "who's who in my group" rating and .90 with the Dean's Guidance Office Rating.

Sociometric Questionnaire

Sociometry is a promising evaluative technique for determining social status and group integration. This form of systematic determination of group structure and the individual's place in it had its chief origin in the work of Moreno,[14] first published in 1934. The sociometric test consists of asking a boy (or girl) to choose his associates for any group of which he is or might become a member. For example, the individuals within a group might be asked to choose from this group those members which they would wish to have with them in the formation of some new group, whether it be one of recreation, work, or study.

A sociometric questionnaire was utilized in the Medford Growth Study by Clarke.[15] This questionnaire required each boy to list from those in his homeroom as many as he wished in each of the following five categories:

1. List your good boy friends and boys you would like for friends.
2. List the boys you would like to go to the movies with.
3. List the boys you would like to play sports with.
4. List the boys you would like to study homework with.
5. List the boys you would invite to a birthday party.

---

12 *Ibid.*

13 Reported by: C. Etta Walters, "A Sociometric Study of Motivated and Non-Motivated Bowling Groups," *Research Quarterly*, Vol. XXVI, No. 1 (March 1955), p. 109.

14 J. L. Moreno, *Who Shall Survive?* (New York: Beacon House, 1934).

15 David H. Clarke, "Social Status and Mental Health of Boys Nine Through Fourteen Years of Age as Related to Their Maturity, Structural Characteristics, and Muscular Strength," Microcarded Doctoral Dissertation, University of Oregon, 1959.

Figure 11.3

Cowell Personal Distance Ballot

What To Do:	I would be willing to accept him:						
	Into my family as a brother	As a very close "pal" or "chum"	As a member of my "gang" or club	On my street as a "nextdoor neighbor"	Into my class at school	Into my school	Into my city
If you had full power to treat each student on this list as you feel, just how would you consider him? How near would you like to have him to your family? Check each student in *one* column as to your feeling toward him. Circle your own name.	1	2	3	4	5	6	7
1.							
2.							
3.							
4. etc.							

NOTE: The Personal Distance Score is determined by adding the total *weighted* scores given the subject by members of the class or group and dividing by the total number of respondents. Division is carried to two places and the decimal point dropped. The low score is the desirable score. The percentile scale scores in the appendix represent boys' attitudes toward accepting boys. It is possible also to determine girls' attitudes toward girls, boys' attitudes toward girls and vice-versa by various methods of balloting.

MEASUREMENT OF SOCIAL EFFICIENCY

In Clarke's study, tabulating the number of times a boy was chosen by his classmates proved an effective way of scoring the results of his sociometric questionnaire. Breck [16] investigated four methods of scoring her questionnaire as applied to college women; she found the following two methods to be of practical value: (1) tabulating only expressions of choice, assigning one point to each expression; (2) tabulating expressions of choice and deducting expressions of rejection, assigning one point for each acceptance and subtracting one point for each rejection.

SOCIAL OUTCOMES OF SPORTS

Cowell [17] has stressed that goals of personal and social development in sports participation must be made clear to the student. These goals should receive individual and group acceptance; they should be kept visible in printed form. Cowell has proposed an evaluation check-sheet on the outcomes of sports for this purpose, as shown in Figure 11.4. This instrument suggests 20 ways in which, through learning experiences in athletics, students may be motivated to change. These represent "some of the organic-physical, mental-emotional, and self-social components of the total personality." For score-minded individuals, Cowell points out, a perfect score on the check-sheet is 100.

MEASUREMENT OF GENERAL SOCIAL EFFICIENCY

The various tests discussed above in the section on "Social Acceptance Evaluation" are especially useful in judging how well boys and girls fit into the group: how well they are accepted by their peers; how well they impress teachers and others in authority who judge them. However, these evaluative instruments largely neglect another equally valuable criterion of social worth: the complex of traits such as individuality, initiative, personal integrity in the face of social disapproval, and individual creativity. While tests do not exist to measure all facets of this phase of personal and social adjustment, consideration of these traits should not be neglected.

---

[16] Sabina J. Breck, "A Sociometric Measurement of Status in Physical Education Classes, *Research Quarterly*, Vol. XXI, No. 2 (May 1950), p. 75.

[17] Charles C. Cowell, "Our Function Is Still Education!" *The Physical Educator*, Vol. XIV, No. 1 (March 1957), p. 6.

MEASUREMENT OF SOCIAL EFFICIENCY

OUTCOMES OF SPORTS: AN EVALUATION CHECK-SHEET

To What Extent Did I Learn:	(5) A Very Great Deal	(4) A Great Deal	(3) Somewhat	(2) Very Little	(1) Not at All
1. To sacrifice my own personal "whims" or desires for the good of the group or team?					
2. To test myself—to see if I could "take it," endure hardship and "keep trying" to do my best even under adversity?					
3. To overcome awkwardness and self-consciousness?					
4. To recognize that the *group* can achieve where the *individual* alone cannot?					
5. That each team member has a unique or special contribution to make in the position he plays?					
6. To share difficult undertakings with my "buddies" (teammates) because of struggling together for a goal?					
7. To respect the skill and ability of my opponents and be tolerant of their success?					
8. To make friendships with boys from other schools and to maintain good guest-host relationships in inter-school games?					
9. To feel that the school team helped break up "cliques" and factions in the school by developing common loyalty and community of interests?					
10. To consider and practice correct health and training routine such as proper eating, sleeping, avoidance of tobacco, etc.?					
11. To "take turns" and to "share"?					
12. To develop physical strength, endurance and a better looking body?					
13. To be loyal and not "let my buddy, the coach, team, or school down"?					
14. To give more than I get—not for myself but for an ideal or for one's school, town, or country?					
15. To develop a sense of humor and even to be able to laugh at myself occasionally?					
16. To think and act "on the spot" in the heat of a game?					
17. To understand the strategy—the "why" of the best methods of attack and defense in games?					
18. To understand and appreciate the possibilities and limitations of the human body with respect to skill, speed, endurance, and quickness of reactions?					
19. That in sports there is no discrimination against talent? It is performance and conduct and not the color of one's skin or social standing that matters.					
20. That nothing worthwhile is accomplished without hard work, application, and the "will to succeed"?					

(From "Our Function Is Still Education!" The Physical Educator, March 1957, pp. 6-7.)

Figure 11.4.   Cowell Outcomes of Sports: An Evaluation Check-Sheet.

In some instances, the tests presented below are helpful in this form of evaluation.

A large number of attempts have been made to construct character, personality, or social adjustment tests in the fields of education and psychology. As early as 1937, Strang [18] demonstrated that if this bibliography were extended to include not only studies in which measuring devices themselves were evaluated, but all studies concerned with the analysis and measurement of social qualities, the whole list would contain approximately four thousand titles. Although many of these tests have been hastily constructed, empirically established, and poorly standardized, a sufficient number are now available to make a scientific approach to this type of measurement.

In selecting tests for this section of the chapter, the following factors have been particularly kept in mind:

1. *The correlative value.* General social efficiency tests to be utilized by the physical educator in determining transfer values and transfer needs of social programs should measure traits developed in physical education. Thus, tests that measure social adjustment, emotional adjustment, confidence, leadership, responsibility, initiative, and so forth, have been selected.

2. *The scientific value.* Only tests that have a satisfactory degree of validity and accuracy have been considered.

3. *Comprehensiveness.* Tests representing a narrow field or involving only one or two character traits have been avoided. The comprehensiveness of the test, or the range of social behavior covered by the test, was therefore a factor in its selection.

4. *The age range.* Only tests designed primarily for secondary-school boys and girls have been considered, although tests available for elementary-school pupils have been given brief mention.

5. *Normality.* Primary consideration has been given to normal application of the tests: tests utilized to evaluate abnormal behavior or neurotic cases were avoided, as were also those designed especially for psychiatrists in dealing with advanced behavior problems. Tests selected are primarily useful in detecting incipient social problems found among so-called "normal" pupils.

---

[18] Ruth Strang, *Behavior and Background of Students in Colleges and Secondary Schools* (New York: Harper and Brothers, 1937).

6. Recognition in the field. In surveying the immense amount of material in the field of character and personality tests, a preliminary screening of the better tests was made by consulting test-evaluation studies in this area. The various Mental Measurements Yearbooks [19] were especially useful in making this evaluation. After the preliminary selection was made, these tests were studied to determine their applicability to health and physical education.

Washburne's Social Adjustment Inventory [20]

Washburne's Social Adjustment Inventory is a group test for all ages above the eighth grade and consists of 123 items arranged in questionnaire form, some of which call for more than one response. Most of the questions can be answered by writing "Yes" or "No" on a line preceding the question. The scoring key indicates the questions that attempt to measure the same trait or complex, thus providing for a grouping of the questions according to "elements." Approximately 30 to 40 minutes are needed for the administration of the test.

The primary purpose of the Social Adjustment Inventory is to determine the subject's degree of social and emotional adjustment. The score is designed to give a separate measure of development in each of several traits, which are very slightly correlated with intelligence and are highly correlated with social and emotional adjustment. The score is also designed to provide a measure of adjustment in all the traits combined. In this total score, strength in one trait may compensate for weakness in another, as is also the case in actual social situations. In the subject's score particular difficulties are revealed, a fact that is of service in diagnosis and remediation. Three of the subtests reveal primarily emotional adjustments to other people and to the environment; three reveal primarily self-organization and self-regulation.

The test contains six objective-type subtests and one essay-type subtest of social and emotional adjustment, and a subtest of truthfulness or accuracy. The subtests are as follows:

---

[19] Mental Measurements Yearbooks were published in 1938, 1940, 1948, and 1953, Oscar K. Burrow, ed. *The Fourth Mental Measurements Yearbook* was published by the Gryphon Press: Highland Park, New Jersey, 1953.

[20] John N. Washburne, *Social Adjustment Inventory.* Yonkers-on-Hudson, N. Y.: World Book Company.

270

1. *Truthfulness.* A low *t* score indicates truthfulness, or relative freedom from deliberate or unintentional inaccuracies, in answering the test questions. If an individual earns a high score (above 30) on this part of the test, the assumption is that his answers to all the questions are unreliable and the test should be discarded or considered separately.

2. *Happiness.* A low *h* score indicates satisfactory adjustment as revealed by contentment, a sense of well-being, and the feeling that life is worth while.

3. *Alienation.* A low *a* score indicates satisfactory adjustment as revealed by a sense of social membership and acceptance, of basic similarity, of common humanity with others, and of psychological security and emotional stability in social situations.

4. *Sympathy.* A low *s* score indicates satisfactory adjustment as reflected by sensitive, empathetic, non-negative responsiveness to people.

5. *Purposes.* A low *p* score indicates satisfactory adjustment as revealed in a sense of purpose.

6. *Impulse-judgment.* A low *i* score reveals satisfactory adjustment as manifest in ability to judge well between conflicting impulses, so that satisfactions which are recognized as greater, but more remote or more difficult, are not discounted in favor of easier or more immediate but obviously lesser satisfactions.

7. *Control.* A low *c* score indicates satisfactory adjustment as shown in a sense of self-control, self-regulation, and the ability to make and execute plans.

8. *Wishes.* A high *w* score shows superior social adjustment as reflected in the individual's written wishes, rated according to the development of values related to the broad realities of the individual's life circumstances.

This test required nearly ten years to complete and went through at least ten revisions. The number of groups tested have been in the neighborhood of 40 and the number of individuals well over 10,000. In nearly all experimentation, a large number of questions, presumed to be discriminatory of social and emotional adjustment, were given to adolescents paired for intelligence, age, and sex, but showing marked contrast in social and emotional adjustment, such groups as prisoners, maladjusted high-school pupils, average pupils, and well-adjusted pupils being utilized. With each revision, the questions showing least discriminatory power were eliminated and new ones were tried, most revisions showing significant refinements over the preceding ones. The result is that the difference between the number of "adjusted" and the number of "maladjusted" responses to each of the questions included is from 3 to 11 times the PE of the difference. The biserial *r* coefficient of validity is .90; the coefficient of reliability is .92. The correlations between test elements are slight, and the correlation of the test with intelligence is negligible (.17).

The Bernreuter Personality Inventory [21]

The Bernreuter Personality Inventory is a group test for high-school and college students and adults. It consists of 125 questions adapted largely from Laird's *C2 Test of Introversion-Extroversion,* Allport's *A-S Reaction Study,* Thurstone's *Neurotic Inventory,* and Bernreuter's *Self-Sufficiency Test.* The questions are answered by circling "yes," "no," or "?". About 30 minutes are required to take the test. Four separate scoring keys are applied to the questionnaire, one for each trait tested.

The *Personality Inventory* is designed, according to the author, to measure the following personality traits:

1. *Neurotic tendency.* Persons scoring high on this scale tend to be emotionably unstable. Those scoring low tend to be well balanced emotionally.

2. *Self-sufficiency.* Persons scoring high on this scale prefer to be alone, rarely ask for sympathy or encouragement, and tend to ignore the advice of others. Those scoring low dislike solitude and often seek advice and encouragement.

3. *Introversion-extroversion.* Persons scoring high on this scale are imaginative and tend to live within themselves. Those scoring low rarely worry, seldom suffer emotional upsets, and do not substitute day-dreaming for action.

4. *Dominance-submission.* Persons scoring high on this scale tend to dominate others in face-to-face situations. Those scoring low tend to be submissive.

In 1934, Flanagan,[22] using Hotaling's factor-analysis method, added two more scales for scoring the *Personality Inventory.* Flanagan called these scales "self-confidence" and "sociability."

The correlation between the four parts of the test and the corresponding four criterion tests varied from .84 to approximately 1.00. For validity coefficients, these correlations are spuriously high, since the Bernreuter inventory consists largely of items taken from the criterion tests, and the items are weighted on the basis of these tests. The validity of the inventory, therefore, is dependent upon the validity of the four criterion tests, and it may be used in place of the four separate tests previously constructed by Thurstone, Bernreuter, Laird, and Allport.

The correlations found between the various scales of the test have

---

[21] Robert G. Bernreuter, "The Theory and Construction of the Personality Inventory," *Journal of Social Psychology,* Vol. IV, No. 4 (November 1933), p. 387. Test published by Stanford University Press.

[22] John C. Flanagan, "Technical Aspects of Multi-Trait Tests," *Journal of Educational Psychology,* Vol. XXVI, No. 9 (December 1936), p. 641.

shown that, for the most part, they do not measure four different and independent traits. In fact, the correlation between neurotic traits and introversion-extroversion is so high that, for all practical purposes, the two tests must measure the same thing. Bernreuter suggests that if only one score is to be obtained from his inventory, the "neurotic tendency" scale should be used.

The Bell Adjustment Inventory [23]

The Bell Adjustment Inventory is in form very similar to the Bernreuter inventory, although the scoring is much simpler. It requires about 25 minutes to take the test and three minutes to score it. There are two forms of the test, the Student Form for high-school and college students, and the Adult Form. The Student Form provides four separate measures of personal and social adjustment, as follows:

1. *Home adjustment.* Individuals scoring high on this scale tend to be unsatisfactorily adjusted to their home surroundings. Low scores indicate satisfactory home adjustment.
2. *Health adjustment.* High scores on this scale indicate unsatisfactory health adjustment; low scores, satisfactory adjustment.
3. *Social adjustment.* Individuals scoring high on this scale tend to be submissive and retiring in their social contacts. Individuals with low scores are aggressive in social contacts.
4. *Emotional adjustment.* Individuals with high scores on this scale tend to be unstable emotionally. Persons with low scores tend to be emotionally stable.

In the *Adult Form,* provisions are made for the same measures included above, and a scale for Occupational Adjustment is added.

The reliability of this test is satisfactory, ranging, for the separate items, between .81 and .85, and equaling .90 for the total score.

SRA Inventories [24]

An SRA *Junior Inventory,* grades four to eight, and an SRA *Youth Inventory,* grades seven to twelve, have been constructed to discover the problems that boys and girls say worry them most. The junior inventory contains 223 problems in the following five areas: My Health, Getting Along with Other People, About Me and My School, About Myself, and About Me and My Home. In the youth

[23] Hugh M. Bell, *The Theory and Practice of Student Counseling* (Stanford University, Calif.: Stanford University Press, 1935).
[24] Science Research Associates, Inc., 57 Grand Ave., Chicago, Ill.

inventory, there are 298 problems in nine areas, as follows: My School, Looking Ahead, About Myself, Getting Along with Others, My Home and Family, Boy Meets Girl, Health, Things in General, and Basic Difficulty. Most of the items for the inventories were selected through content analyses of "My Problems" essays written by many children in the appropriate grades. The scores for each area are obtained by counting the number of items checked by each subject.

Mental Health Analysis [25]

The Mental Health Analysis is divided into two sections, with five categories in each. Section 1 is designed to measure the presence of mental health liabilities, with the following categories: behavorial immaturity, emotional instability, feelings of inadequacy, physical defects, and nervous manifestations. Section 2 is intended to test the presence of mental health assets, with categories as follows: close personal relationships, interpersonal skills, social participations, satisfying work and recreation, and adequate outlook and goals. The selection of test items for this instrument was made from the literature and researches in the field, and from the reactions of students, teachers, principals, and employees. An item analysis further improved the quality of the total sampling of tests.

For Younger Children

The personality tests thus far discussed are usable mainly among senior high-school and college students and adults, although the SRA Junior Inventory is designed for lower grades. Several tests, however, have been devised for younger children. One of the most usable of these in school situations is the *Winnetka Scale for Rating School Behavior and Attitudes.*[26] This test is designed to rate the emotional and social aspects of the personality of children from nursery school through the sixth grade with respect to the five general categories: cooperation, social consciousness, emotional security, leadership, and responsibility. The scale was constructed by analysis of actual incidents occurring in the classroom, the data

---

[25] Louis P. Thorpe, Willis W. Clark, and Ernest W. Tiegs, *Manual of Directions: Mental Health Analysis* (Los Angeles: California Test Bureau, 1946).

[26] Dorothy Van Alstyne, "A New Scale for Rating School Behavior and Attitudes in the Elementary School," *Journal of Educational Psychology*, Vol. XXVII, No. 9 (December 1936), p. 677. Test published by Winnetka Educational Press.

being classified into situations and response levels, the final scale consisting of 13 situations. As an example of the test elements, Situation VII, classified as one of three under "emotional security," is given:

Situation VII: When faced with failure.
1. Sees cause of failure and corrects it. (10)
2. Tries to get help to overcome difficulty. (9)
3. Recovers quickly and plans new activity. (6)
4. Shows disappointment but continues activity. (4)
5. Is apparently indifferent to failure. (2)
6. Becomes discouraged easily—must succeed in order to continue activity. (1)
7. Becomes irritable, or angry, or cries. (0)

Reliability by the self-correlation method, with observations made from two to eight weeks apart, is .87 for the complete scale and from .72 to .82 for the main divisions. A validity coefficient of .71 was obtained by correlation of the test with the Social and Emotional Divisions of the *Haggerty-Olson-Wickman Behavior Rating Scale.*

This scale is especially valuable, as it can be used effectively in the early diagnosis of personality difficulties, at a time when habit patterns are being formed. Because the diagnosis is in terms of real situations, the problem of developing satisfactory behavior patterns is made specific.

One test of the inventory type might also be mentioned as useful with younger children. This is the *Link Inventory of Activities and Interests*,[27] which is suitable for children and for adolescents between the ages of 10 and 20. The purpose of this test is to measure: social initiative or aggressiveness, self-determination, economic self-determination, and adjustments to the opposite sex. A weighted combination of the scores on these traits gives a score from which a Personality Quotient (PQ) is derived. Reliability coefficients for the four parts of this test are between .70 and .88.

Precautions in the Use of Personality Tests

Although there have been many studies of personality tests, they have not yet reached the stage where their validity can be completely accepted. The criteria utilized have been mostly ratings by

---

[27] Henry C. Link, "A Test of Four Personality Traits of Adolescents," *Journal of Applied Psychology*, Vol. XX, No. 5 (October 1936), p. 527.

judges rather than psychiatric examinations. Judges' ratings are not highly reliable, even when the characteristic to be rated is well understood; when the trait is intangible and difficult to grasp, still less confidence can be placed in the ratings. Also, many of these tests are only sufficiently reliable for group use (.70 to .85).[28] As a consequence of these factors, the results of personality tests should not be considered infallible, but rather as aids in locating boys and girls who need help and guidance in making emotional and personality adjustments.

As most personality tests depend upon answers given by the subjects, the ability to obtain frank responses becomes a major problem. The desire for social acceptance results in a temptation for the subject to give answers which present him in a favorable light. Also, in contemplating his own adjustment, the individual is likely to be biased or prejudiced.[29] It is therefore necessary in administering personality tests to make every effort to establish rapport with each pupil, so that he will be willing to reveal extremely personal information about himself. Assurance must be given that the replies will be kept confidential. The pupil must be made to feel that honest answers are necessary in order that the physical education program may serve him best.

Personality is an extremely complex phenomenon with many traits acting and re-acting in numerous ways and in many combinations. Yet testing procedures must necessarily sort out and identify single traits, attempting to withdraw each from the setting in which it naturally resides. The need to reserve judgment on the status of individual traits and to attempt the association of such traits with the total personality should be kept in mind.

Not only should the individual's achieved score on each trait in a personality test be considered, but the way in which he answered each of the questions should be examined. This procedure is particularly important in studying the problems of individual students, as it provides many leads to be followed. For example: if a student gives a negative reply to the question "Do you make friends easily?" an excellent lead is provided for additional informal questions re-

[28] Arthur E. Traxler, *Techniques of Guidance* (New York: Harper & Brothers, 1945), p. 107.
[29] H. H. Remmers and N. L. Gage, *Educational Measurement and Evaluation* (New York: Harper & Brothers, 1943), p. 338.

sulting ultimately in a better understanding of the individual and a sounder basis for providing a proper educational program for him.

As with the physical self, specialized knowledge is required to evaluate, understand, and treat the social and psychological self. Medicine has been developed to care for extreme deviates from normal physical states; psychology and psychiatry have been likewise developed in the personality field. In neither of these is the physical educator qualified to practice. As a result, when extreme deviations in social and personal adjustment are suspected from testing or other procedures, the physical educator should refer them to appropriate specialists, just as readily as he now refers students with physical abnormalities to the physician.

CONCLUSION

In physical education, meager as the experience has been, rating scales, social distance tests, and sociometric questionnaires have been more effective in identifying boys and girls with personality difficulties and social problems than have the inventory-type tests. The results of several reported in Chapter 3, for example, show significant relationships of physical and motor fitness measures to peer status, leadership qualities, and personal and social traits. Personality-inventory tests were not used in any of these studies.

As a further example, Popp [30] found no significant differences on the Washburne Social Adjustment Inventory between boys grouped by highest and lowest 20 per cent on Rogers' Physical Fitness Index; also, the boys lowest on the Rogers test expressed fewer problems on the Mooney Problem Check List than did boys high on the Rogers test. Yet, when five representative administrators and teachers, who knew the boys, each independently selected the ten boys "most nearly like sons they would like to have" and the ten boys "least like sons they would like to have," the results were dramatically different. Of the boys selected in the desirable category ("most nearly like sons"), 69 per cent had high PFI's; of the boys in the undesirable category ("least like sons"), 75 per cent had low PFI's.

---

[30] James Popp, "Case Studies of Sophomore High School Boys with High and Low Physical Fitness Indices," Master of Science Thesis, University of Oregon, 1959.

MEASUREMENT OF SOCIAL EFFICIENCY

SELECTED REFERENCES

Breck, Sabina J., "A Sociometric Measurement of Status in Physical Education Classes," *Research Quarterly*, Vol. XXI, No. 2 (May 1950), p. 75.

Buros, Oscar K., ed., *The Fourth Mental Measurements Yearbook* (Highland Park, N. J.: The Gryphon Press, 1953).

Cowell, Charles C., "Validating an Index of Social Adjustment for High School Use," *Research Quarterly*, Vol. XXIX, No. 1 (March 1958), p. 7.

Hale, Patricia W., "Proposed Method for Analyzing Sociometric Data," *Research Quarterly*, Vol. XXVII, No. 2 (May 1956), p. 152.

McCloy, C. H., and Terence Hepp, "General Factors of Components of Character as Related to Physical Education," *Research Quarterly*, Vol. XXVIII, No. 3 (October 1957), p. 269.

Walters, C. Etta, "A Sociometric Study of Motivated and Non-Motivated Bowling Groups," *Research Quarterly*, Vol. XXVI, No. 1 (March 1955), p. 109.

CHAPTER TWELVE

General Motor Abilities

The social objective in physical education was discussed in Chapter 10, together with suggested procedures for its realization. With respect to these procedures, it was pointed out that equating the powers or abilities of individuals and groups is necessary to obtain the greatest benefits from physical activity programs. The present chapter deals with tests that may be used for this purpose.

BASES FOR ABILITY GROUPINGS

Homogeneous grouping of individuals for participation in a physical activity program, whether it be accomplished by judgment or by objective measurement, may follow two major procedures: (1) equating by specific activities, or (2) equating by general abilities. Each of these methods has its place in physical education; the one selected, however, will depend upon the type of program being conducted in the school.

Equating by Specific Activities

In ability grouping by specific activities, the abilities of the pupils are evaluated and the classification of the participants changed for each activity included in the program. A simple example of this procedure is the process of "choosing sides" for a game of basketball, or any other sport, during the physical education class, or informally during free-play periods. Tests might also be used to determine such groupings.

This basis for ability grouping is useful when a single physical education activity is being taught to the same group for a considerable period of time, as is often done in college programs where students elect the same activity for a quarter of the year or longer. In this situation, skill-testing of the specific activity being taught would undoubtedly be a part of the instruction program, the results of which could be used for equating or classifying purposes. Sufficient time is available to make this procedure worth while and even essential for good teaching practice. Tests of this sort are discussed in Chapter 14.

Equating by General Abilities

In grouping by general abilities, a measure of all-round athletic or motor ability is given, and groups are arranged on this basis. A test of all-round ability does not measure skill in any particular sport. An individual with a high score on such a test, however, should perform well, or have capacity for good performance after a period of instruction, in a number of athletic events. These measures do not consider previous experience in specific activities, nor do they measure such character qualities as interest, persistence, courage, and initiative. Consequently, in applying them, the best results will be obtained if some judgment is also used in placing pupils in the various groups, the physical educator being guided by his knowledge of the abilities of the different individuals, or by his subsequent observation of their performances, to make necessary adjustments and to insure proper equation.

Actually, general motor ability is complex. Many factors enter into efficient motor performance: physical, mental, emotional, and social. It is a *Gestalt*, with the whole personality dynamically organized, that results in excellent performance. Physically, motor efficiency or skill is composed of strength, endurance, speed, and the coordination or control of these elements for accuracy.[1] Cozens,[2] using his "General Athletic Ability Test" as a criterion, found that strength tests were significant measures of athletic ability among

---

[1] John D. Brock, Walter A. Cox, and Erastus W. Pennock, "Motor Fitness," *Supplement to the Research Quarterly*, Vol. XII, No. 2 (May 1941), p. 407.

[2] Frederick W. Cozens, "Strength Tests as Measures of General Athletic Ability in College Men," *Research Quarterly*, Vol. XI, No. 1 (March 1940), p. 45.

college men. Coleman's studies [3] showed that he could predict the running broad jump, 60-yard dash, velocity index, running high jump, and the 16-lb. shot-put to a satisfactory degree, with measures of strength modified by measures of velocity, height, and weight. In a factor analysis of 28 selected motor ability tests, Wegner [4] isolated four factors. One of these factors was unidentified; the other three factors were specified as follows: arm and shoulder girdle coordination, leg speed, and upper body strength. The multiple correlation for the total prediction of motor ability was .92.

McCloy [5] lists the following ten factors as prerequisite to effective learning of motor skills: muscular strength, dynamic energy, ability to change direction, flexibility, agility, peripheral vision, good vision, concentration, understanding of the mechanics of the techniques of the activities, and absence of disturbing or inhibiting emotional complications. Other factors in motor educability he summarizes as: insight into the nature of the skill; ability to visualize spatial relations; ability to make quick and adaptive decisions; sensory-motor coordination relations of eye to head, hand, or foot; sensory-motor coordination related to weight and force; judgment of the relationship of the subject to external objects in relation to time, height, distance, and direction; accuracy of direction and small angle of error; general kinesthetic sensitivity and control; ability to coordinate a complex unitary movement; ability to coordinate a complex series or combination of movements that follow one another in rapid succession; arm control; factors involved in the function of balance; timing; motor rhythm; sensory rhythm; and esthetic feeling.

On reviewing these studies, and others of a similar nature, one sees that it is obviously too difficult and too complicated for the physical educator "on the job" to attempt to measure all the elements contributing to general motor ability. He must select general or cross-section tests that have been shown to possess a high rela-

[3] James W. Coleman, "Pure Speed as a Positive Factor in Some Track and Field Events," *Research Quarterly*, Vol. XI, No. 2 (May 1940), p. 47.

James W. Coleman, "The Differential Measurement of the Speed Factor in Large Muscle Activities," *Research Quarterly*, Vol. VIII, No. 3 (October 1937), p. 123.

[4] Artnoll L. Wegner, "A Factor Analysis of Selected Motor Ability Tests," Microcarded Doctoral Dissertation, Indiana University, 1952.

[5] C. H. McCloy, "A Preliminary Study of Factors in Motor Educability," *Research Quarterly*, Vol. XI, No. 2 (May 1940), p. 28.

tionship with motor ability and that measure the elements of greatest significance.

Ability grouping by general abilities is a very useful method of classification in physical education, as individuals or groups may be equated for a wide range of activities without changing the grouping. It is particularly valuable in that type of physical education program where the activities may vary either within a single class period or from day to day, or where the same activity does not continue on consecutive days for more than a week or two at the most. Classification by individual activities would be cumbersome in these situations, as it would necessitate changing the groupings repeatedly. The great amount of time spent in testing or evaluating pupils for a number of frequently changing activities does not seem justifiable when a measure of general ability may be applied satisfactorily.

EARLY MEASURES OF GENERAL MOTOR ABILITIES

From the early days of physical education in the United States, physical educators have attempted to classify individuals roughly into equivalent groups, both for physical education class activity and for athletic competition. The change from the early emphasis on gymnastics and calisthenics to the later stress on games and sports in part created a need for general ability testing, which has continued to the present time.

A typical example of an early test of the general motor ability type, and one which has been revised in recent years, is the *Sigma Delta Psi Test*. In 1912, a national athletic fraternity, known as Delta Sigma Psi, was started at Indiana University. In order to obtain membership in the fraternity, the following achievements are required.[6]

1. 100-yd. dash		11⅗ sec.
2. 120-yd. low hurdles		16 sec.
3. Running high jump		5 ft.
4. Running broad jump		17 ft.
5. 16-lb. shot put: according to a man's weight; 30 ft. for a man weighing 160 lbs. or over.		
6. Rope climb		20 ft. in 12 sec.

---

[6] National Fraternity, Care of the School of Health and Physical Education, Indiana University, Bloomington, Indiana.

7. Baseball distance throw	250 ft.
or Javelin throw	130 ft.
8. Football distance punt	120 ft.
9. 100-yd. swim	1 min. 45 sec.
10. One-mile run	6 min.
11. Tumbling	(a) front handspring
	(b) Fence vault with
	bar at chin height.
	(c) Handstand, 10 sec.
12. Posture	Erect carriage
13. Scholarship	Eligible for Varsity
	Competition.

Note: If the candidate has won a letter in a varsity sport, he may substitute this for any of the above requirements except swimming.

The rules of the National Collegiate Athletic Association are followed for the various track and field events. In the 120-yd. low hurdle race, five standard low hurdles, 20 yards apart, are used. For the test to count, all hurdles must remain upright after the test.

In the rope climb, the contestant starts from a sitting position on the floor; the rope is climbed without the use of the legs. The legs, however, may be used in the descent.

In the timed handstand, the contestant is not allowed to advance or retreat more than three feet during the test.

Other early tests of this general type include: Detroit Decathlon utilized to select the best all-round athletes in the city of Detroit; Athletic Badge Tests devised for boys and girls in 1913 by the National Playground and Recreation Association of America; Richard's Efficiency Tests for grade schools proposed in 1914; Philadelphia Public School Age Aim Charts; Reilly's Scheme of Rational Athletics for boys and girls; California Decathlon; and Los Angeles Achievement Expectancy Tables. Later the California Pentathlon was proposed.

In the initial stages of motor or physical ability testing, the aim was to use the tests primarily to arouse the interest of boys and girls in all-round physical proficiency. Standards of achievement were set up and scoring tables were devised, on a point basis in many instances, with divisions into junior and senior groups or into various combinations of age, height, and weight. More recently, the gross scores obtained on these tests have been used to classify boys and girls into homogeneous groups. Specific physical education objectives are thus being met by organizing classes whereby effective instruction can be given and equal athletic participation can be had.

THE STRENGTH INDEX [7]

In discussing the Physical Fitness Index test in Chapter 8, the *Strength Index* was described, and its use to determine general athletic ability was mentioned. Rogers' hypothesis was that an individual with a high SI would perform well, or have potentialities for good performance after a training period, in a number of activities, and that an individual with a low SI would have athletic capabilities on a lower level. There is considerable evidence to support this hypothesis.

Experimental Evidence

Rogers [8] utilized two different methods to determine the validity of the SI as a measure of general athletic ability. In the first method, a correlation of .76 was obtained between the SI and the weighted score on the 100-yard dash, the running high jump, the running broad jump, and the bar vault. This correlation was found to be nearly twice as high as that obtained by the best combination of age, height, and weight. A second correlation between the SI and ability in a 2-lap run, standing broad jump, running high jump, 8-pound shot-put, basketball foul throw, and throwing baseballs and footballs at a specially marked target raised the coefficient to .81.[9]

Assuming that success in "making the school team" is a criterion of athletic ability, Rogers, as a second method of obtaining validity for the SI, compared the Strength Indices of major sports athletes with those scored by all other boys in the school from which the data were obtained. The resultant relationships are significant:

(*a*) Not more than five boys in 100, including the football men themselves, reached the median SI for football letter men.

---

[7] Directions for administering these tests appear in Chapter 8; the Oregon Simplification of this test is also applicable.

[8] Frederick Rand Rogers, *Physical Capacity Tests in the Administration of Physical Education* (New York: Bureau of Publications, Teachers College, Columbia University, 1925).

[9] Unless otherwise specified, all studies concerned with strength tests reported in this chapter used the old method of measuring leg lift (without the belt).

(*b*) Ten football players achieved SI's higher than 371 of the 390 boys in the school, including themselves.

(*c*) No single score was recorded above the median score achieved by the "five best athletes" or school team captains by any boy not a member of some major sports team.

Granger [10] also compared the Strength Indices of athletes and nonathletes. His data contained 104 scores of athletes in the sports of football, basketball, baseball, track and field, and tennis, and 392 scores of all other pupils. The average SI for the athletes was lower than in the study by Rogers, as Granger included tennis men, a group whose average SI was 270 points below any other of his athletic squads, a fact that would lower the SI for the entire group of athletes. In Granger's study, the difference between the letter men and the mass of pupils was 377. This result gives a critical ratio of 16.32 (that is, the difference between the two averages is 16.32 times the probable error of the difference). In this experiment, also, it was found that the average SI of the letter men was not achieved by 85.5 per cent of the mass of pupils, or, to put it another way, 90 per cent of the letter men had SI's greater than the average of the mass.

Bookwalter [11] conducted a critical evaluation of the application of some of the existing means of classifying boys for physical education activities, with a view to the determination of an administratively feasible procedure which would produce more homogeneous classification. At the elementary, junior high, and senior high school levels, the Strength Index had the highest relationships with physical performance. At the college level, McCurdy's Force Index Test, a modification of the Strength Index, was best. Gross, Greisel, and Stull [12] found that McCloy's Revision of the Strength Index gave a better index of ability to learn an unfamiliar or new activity, wrestling, than did the Iowa-Brace Test or the Metheny Revision of the Johnson Test.

As subsidiary evidence of the relationship between strength and

---

[10] An unpublished study by Walter A. Granger, Valley Stream, New York.

[11] Karl W. Bookwalter, "A Critical Evaluation of the Application of Some Existing Means of Classifying Boys for Physical Education Activities," Microcarded Doctoral Dissertation, New York University, 1938.

[12] Elmer A. Gross, Donald C. Greisel, and Alan Stull, "Relationship Between Two Motor Educability Tests, a Strength Test, and Wrestling Ability after Eight-Weeks' Instruction," *Research Quarterly,* Vol. XXVII, No. 4 (December 1956), p. 395.

general athletic ability, significant relationships have been found with the learning of motor skills. For example, Shay [13] found the following correlations between ability or speed in learning the kip or upstart on the horizontal bar:

	r	P.I.
Physical Fitness Index	.83	.45
Strength Index	.78	.37
Brace Test	.52	.16

Again, strength tests show a high relationship to skills, in this instance with the ability to learn a new skill being nearly three times as significant as the Brace Test of Motor Ability for this purpose.

Practical Application

Although objective experimental evidence is essential in determining the value of the Strength Index as a measure of general athletic ability, it is also important to "try it out" in actual practice by equating groups and recording the results of formal contests between them. This has been done in a number of situations with significant results.

For many years the SI has been used in the Albany, N. Y., schools to equate opponents in junior-high-school intramural activities.[14] In track and field competition, where pupils were grouped into four SI categories, there was a consistent improvement in the performance of the winning team as the index of the group went higher. None of the 25 teams in the first three groups would have won or placed had they competed in Group IV, the highest SI classification. At Livingston Junior High School, track meets were conducted between boys divided into six SI groups and redivided into four teams each. The median performance for all contestants in the events improved with each higher SI level. This regular improvement of performance was also found for each event, including the 75-yard dash and the 220-yard dash.

Oesterich [15] equated basketball teams by means of the Strength

---

[13] Clayton T. Shay, "The Progressive Part Versus the Whole Method of Learning Motor Skills," *Research Quarterly,* Vol. V, No. 4 (December 1934), p. 66.

[14] Walter A. Cox and Kenneth B. DuBois, "The Strength Index in Equating Intramural Teams in Albany, N. Y.," *Supplement to the Research Quarterly,* Vol. VI, No. 1 (March 1935), p. 202.

[15] Harry G. Oesterich, "Strength Testing Program Applied to Y. M. C. A. Organization and Administration," *Research Quarterly,* Vol. VI, No. 1 (March 1935), p. 197.

Index and compared the results with the "choose-up" method. The largest difference in team scores was 16, as compared with 30 for the "choose-up" method; the median difference was 3.4 as compared with 6. Eleven of the 26 games played by the test-equation method, or 44 per cent, ended either in a tie score or with a 1-point difference. The results of this study are surprising, inasmuch as the SI is not intended as a measure of basketball ability or as a measure of any other *specific* skill.

In the Melrose, Mass., high school, five games played by six touch football teams equated according to Strength Index ended either in tie scores or with the winners one touchdown ahead.[16] Decathlon participation in this school was also conducted within SI classifications, with the following results: The winner in Division I (SI of 3340) earned 974 points; the winner of Division II (SI of 2278) earned 911 points; the third-place winner in Division I (SI, 2525; 934 points) surpassed the first-place winner in Division II (SI, 2278; 911 points) in both decathlon points and SI. Similar results were obtained in all but two of 20 events included (each contestant selected ten events).[17]

Clarke and Bonesteel [18] utilized the Strength Index to equate two teams in each of three physical education classes. A series of games in touch football, speedball, field hockey, and indoor soccer was scheduled between the teams in each class. All these sports were relatively unfamiliar to the participants, and the boys were not aware that they were participating in an experiment. Thus, previous experience in game skills and differences in interests in the project were negligible factors. The number of games won and lost by the equated teams was very evenly divided. Of 64 games played by all teams in the four sports, 29, or 45 per cent, ended with tie scores. The greatest scoring difference between any two teams in all four sports was eight points, or 2.4 per cent of the total number of points scored by both teams; the least difference, three points or .9 per cent of the combined score of the two teams.

---

[16] Leonard Clark, "Melrose High School Experiments," *Supplement to the Research Quarterly*, Vol. VI, No. 1 (March 1935), p. 111.

[17] Frederick Rand Rogers, "It Has Been Done," *Journal of Health and Physical Education*, Vol. IX, No. 2 (February 1938), p. 77.

[18] H. Harrison Clarke and Harold A. Bonesteel, "Equalizing the Abilities of Intramural Teams in a Small High School," *Supplement to the Research Quarterly*, Vol. VI, No. 1 (March 1935), p. 193.

STRENGTH TESTS FOR GIRLS

The use of the Strength Index for equating the motor abilities of girls has not been so extensive as for boys. Cox and DuBois divided girls into four divisions for skating competition with fair results. Rogers suggests that the PFI, rather than the SI, might be used for this purpose.

A research study by Hinton and Rarick,[19] however, indicates the possibilities of the SI in girls' programs. These experimenters studied the relationships between the Strength Index tests and the Cubberly and Cozens Girls' Basketball Achievement Test, utilizing 64 college women as subjects. The following correlations were obtained:

	r	P.I.
1. PFI and Basketball Achievement	.47	.12
2. SI and Basketball Achievement	.81	.41

Thus, with college women, at least, a very satisfactory correlation between a specialized skill test and a general motor ability test is obtained. The correlation between the test and the SI is 3.4 times as significant (in terms of *predictive index*) as between the test and the PFI.

Hinton and Rarick also obtained a correlation of .55 between the Cubberly and Cozens basketball test and arm strength, which was the highest correlation between the test and any of the strength test variables. This finding is in agreement with McCloy's research with boys. Contrary to McCloy's recommendations, however, Hinton and Rarick concluded that lung capacity was of sufficient importance (increased R by .044) to warrant its continuance in the strength battery, even as a measure of athletic ability. These experimenters' final recommendation of a strength test for girls, with basketball ability as the criterion measure, consisted of lung capacity, back lift, and arm strength. The multiple correlation of these strength test variables with the basketball test was sufficiently high to predict basketball achievement within a 10 per cent limit above or below the basketball scores.

Several experimenters have developed strength tests especially

---

[19] Evelyn A. Hinton and Lawrence Rarick, "The Correlation of Rogers' Test of Physical Capacity and the Cubberly and Cozens Measurement of Achievement in Basketball," *Research Quarterly*, Vol. XI, No. 3 (October 1940), p. 58.

for girls which are intended to measure their general athletic ability. These tests may be used for homogeneous grouping for girls' activities, in a manner similar to that discussed above for the Strength Index.

Anderson [20] studied the following strength items in relation to a criterion measure composed of the 40-yard dash, standing broad jump, running high jump, and basketball throw for distance: items in McCloy's Strength Index; thigh flexor strength by Martin's technique; and push and pull strength (using manuometer with handle attachment). The following weighted short battery was found to correlate .53 with the criterion, which is nearly as high as for a composite of all test items studied (.55): 5 (thigh flexors) + 7 (push) + leg lift. Norms in strength T-scores for high-school girls only are available in the reference.

Again studying the athletic performance of high-school girls, Anderson [21] utilized the following strength tests: items in McCloy's Strength Index, push, pull, vertical jump, forward bends, squats, and thigh flexors. A correlation of .65 was obtained between the McCloy SI with vertical jump and a criterion composed of ratings of the athletic ability of 300 girls made by the investigator.

Although she did not construct a test, Carpenter [22] studied a number of factors pertaining to strength tests as they related to the physical performance of 100 college women. Among her conclusions were the following: (1) the methods of evaluating arm strength for women by chins and dips and pushes and pulls are unsatisfactory; (2) substituting pushes and pulls in the McCloy Strength Index is somewhat superior; (3) five of the Martin-type strength tests with grips correlated .86 with total strength; (4) factor analysis of the McCloy SI items and the Martin-type tests revealed, as would be expected, that pure strength is the outstanding factor in these tests; and (5) both strength and velocity are important factors in the athletic performance of college women.

The differential measurement of force and velocity for junior high

[20] Theresa Anderson, "Weighted Strength Tests for the Prediction of Athletic Ability in High School Girls," *Research Quarterly,* Vol. VII, No. 1 (March 1936), p. 136.

[21] Theresa Anderson, "Studies in Strength Testing for High School Girls," *Research Quarterly,* Vol. VIII, No. 3 (October 1937), p. 69.

[22] Aileen Carpenter, "A Critical Study of Factors Determining Strength Tests for Women," *Research Quarterly,* Vol. IX, No. 4 (December 1938), p. 3.

school girls was studied by Harris.[23] Thirteen events were analyzed, including McCloy's Strength Index items, vertical jump, dash, broad jump, basketball throw, 3-pound and 12-pound shot-puts, and obstacle relay. A combination of the broad jump, 3-pound shot-put, and McCloy SI was found to measure pure velocity with a multiple correlation of .91. Strength and velocity are separated into the underlying components of motor strength.

McCLOY'S GENERAL MOTOR ABILITY AND CAPACITY TESTS [24]

General Motor Ability

McCloy has also constructed a test of general motor ability that contains certain test elements quite different from those included in the Strength Index but designed to accomplish the same results, that is, to measure the "developed capacity" of an individual for participation in a wide range of physical activities. It is composed of a simple test of strength and a number of track and field events, the elements being as follows:

For boys. The strength test included is the pull-up or chinning test computed for arm strength, using McCloy's formula (see Chapter 8). The track and field events may vary according to the age and experience of the group, the selection being made by the physical educator, provided scoring tables are available for the event. However, the events selected should include one sprint (varying from 50 to 100 yards), one broad jump (either running or standing), the running high jump, and a weight-throwing event (shot-put, basketball throw, or baseball throw). These four events should be scored on McCloy's scoring tables, the sum of which is combined by special formula with chinning strength, as follows:

General Motor Ability Score = .1022 (track and field points)
+ .3928 (chinning strength).

For girls. The actual number of push-ups, rather than pull-up strength, is used in the girls' General Motor Ability Test. Three track and field events are included: a sprint, a broad jump, and a

[23] Jane Harris, "The Differential Measurements of Force and Velocity for Junior High School Girls," *Research Quarterly*, Vol. VIII, No. 4 (December 1937), p. 114.
[24] C. H. McCloy and Norma D. Young, *Tests and Measurements in Health and Physical Education*, 3rd ed. (New York: Appleton-Century-Crofts, Inc., 1954), Chap. 17.

throw, scored on McCloy's scoring tables for boys. The formula for combining these elements is:

$$\text{General Motor Ability Score} = .42 \ (\text{track and field points}) \\ + \ 9.6 \quad (\text{number of chins}).$$

In the development of the General Motor Ability Tests, results on individual test elements were correlated with the total score on a large battery of achievement tests. The elements finally selected to form the test gave as high a prediction of general motor ability as was given by any other combination of events. Other items added to this battery gave no significant additional predictive value.

McCloy correlated total track and field points with technical skill in soccer and basketball of physical education professional students, as determined by student ratings, each student in the group rating each other individual. The resulting correlations were: with soccer, .84; with basketball, .92.

General Motor Capacity

McCloy has also worked out an ingenious relationship between general motor ability and general motor capacity that may prove useful to the physical educator who plans to equate the opposing powers of groups and who wishes to analyze the individual motor problems of his students. The General Motor Capacity Test, the basis for this analysis, is designed to measure innate or inherent motor potentialities—the limits to which an individual may be developed. In this respect, the General Motor Capacity Test may be compared to an intelligence test. It is not designed to test present developed ability in any one activity, but to predict potential levels that the individual may be expected to attain. The following test items, together with the elements they purport to measure, compose this test.

1. Classification Index: general size and maturity.
2. Sargent Jump: "explosive" power of the large muscles.
3. Iowa Brace Test: motor educability.
4. Burpee (squat-thrust) Test: large-muscle speed test.

The items on the McCloy Motor Capacity Test are weighted differently for each school level. For girls it was found that the Classification Index was of little value, and it was eliminated from the battery. The correlation of the final weighted batteries with the ratings made by competent teachers was .51 for boys and .73 for girls, and with a criterion score .97 for boys and .91 for girls. The test battery may be used in a number of different ways, as follows:

1. *General Motor Capacity Score.* The G.M.C.S. is the total score on the test and is proposed as the measure of innate or inherent motor potentialities of the individual. By analogy, it may be compared with the raw score on an intelligence test.

2. *Motor Quotient.* The raw G.M.C.S. may be divided by a norm based on the Classification Index for boys and on age for girls, giving the Motor Quotient. This quotient may be compared to the Intelligence Quotient in the mental field.

3. *General Motor Achievement Quotient.* The G.M.A.Q. is a quantitative statement comparing the individual's developed motor ability and his innate motor capacity. Instead of the average G.M.A.Q. being placed at 100, the formulae for its computation were weighted so that 100 is located two standard errors of estimate above the average G.M.C.S., or at a "practical maximum." Thus, a per cent relationship of actual ability to the predicted or standard ability has been worked out. A G.M.A.Q. of 85, therefore, indicates that the individual's performance is only 85 per cent of what it would be if he were developed to his capacity.

4. *Individual analysis.* It is possible to analyze an individual's test results by transmitting the various elements to T-scores and studying the comparative scores of the individual on each item of the test.

Following the pattern established by McCloy, Carpenter [25] developed formulae for predicting general motor ability and general motor capacity for boys and girls in the first three grades. The items included in the G.M.A.S. are standing broad jump, 4-pound shot-put and body weight. For the G.M.C.S., the items are Sargent (vertical) jump, Burpee (squat-thrust) test, six Brace-type tests, and McCloy's Classification Index III. In this latter battery, five of the Johnson-type tests may be used in place of the Brace stunts. These tests are used in the same manner as described above for the McCloy batteries. Tables for ready computation of all formulae are available in the reference.

---

[25] Aileen Carpenter, "The Measurement of General Motor Capacity and General Motor Ability in the First Three Grades," *Research Quarterly,* Vol. XIII, No. 4 (December 1942), p. 444.

THE LARSON TESTS

In a study of strength tests utilizing the Rogers battery, the Mac-Curdy Test, and a new test composed of chinning, dipping, and the vertical jump, Larson [26] obtained significant correlations, as shown in Table IV, with a criterion of motor ability composed of the following 15 motor skills: bar-snap, feet-to-bar, half-lever, bar-vault, rope-climb, frog-stand, standing broad jump, running broad jump, standing hop-step-jump, football punt for distance, football pass for distance, baseball throw for distance, shot-put, dodging-run, and 440-yard run. For high-school boys, the correlations obtained between the criterion and the SI were slightly higher than those obtained between the criterion and the Larson test. With the college data, the Larson test had a clear advantage.

TABLE IV

CORRELATION OF STRENGTH TESTS WITH A CRITERION OF 15 MOTOR ABILITY ITEMS

Strength Tests	High-School Data	College Data
Rogers' SI	.84	.59
MacCurdy test	—	.52
Larson test	.83	.68

The measurement procedures for the Larson test are the same as those described elsewhere in the text: chinning and dipping, as in the SI test; and the vertical jump, as in the McCloy General Motor Capacity Test appearing in this chapter. In scoring, the raw scores must be changed into "weighted standard scores"; the sum of these equals the "Index Score." Scoring tables for college men appear in Larson's study, together with a five point classification chart for the college age group.

Subsequently, Larson [27] constructed the following two general

---

[26] Leonard A. Larson, "A Factor and Validity Analysis of Strength Variables and Tests with a Test Combination with Chinning, Dipping, and Vertical Jump," *Research Quarterly*, Vol. XI, No. 4 (December 1940), p. 82.

[27] Leonard A. Larson, "A Factor Analysis of Motor Ability Variables and Tests with Tests for College Men," *Research Quarterly*, Vol. XII, No. 3 (October 1941), p. 499.

motor ability tests, one as an indoor test and the other as an outdoor test, after experimenting with 25 motor ability items:

Indoor Test	*Outdoor Test*
1. Dodging run	1. Baseball throw for distance
2. Bar-snap	2. Chinning
3. Chinning	3. Bar-snap
4. Dipping	4. Vertical jump
5. Vertical jump	

The multiple correlations with the criterion measure were: for the Indoor Test, $R = .97$; for the Outdoor Test, $R = .98$. According to Larson, the tests do not predict or indicate specific qualities, such as endurance, coordination, sports skills, and so forth. They are valuable in that they do indicate ability in the basic elements underlying sports skills. Scoring charts for college men appear in Larson's study.

CARPENTER-STANSBURY TEST
FOR CHILDREN IN FIRST THREE GRADES

In an attempt to find a simple substitute for the Rogers Strength Index as a measure of motor ability for boys, Stansbury [28] established a criterion, known as "total points," composed of: vertical jump, 16-pound shot-put, obstacle race, baseball throw, 8-pound shot-put, 20-foot rope climb, and standing broad jump. The final selected test items consist of the following, as presented in his regression equation of weighted scores: 1.4 (8-pound shot-put in feet) + (standing broad jump in inches) + (body weight in pounds). Norms are available in the reference based upon McCloy's Classification Index for high school boys.

Carpenter [29] experimented with the Stansbury test items as applied to children in the first three grades. As a result, the following formulae were developed:

Boys: (standing broad jump in inches) + 2.3 (4-pound shot-put in feet) + (body weight in pounds).
Girls: .5 (standing broad jump in inches) + 3 (4-pound shot-put in feet) + (body weight in pounds).

---

[28] Edgar Stansbury, "A Simplified Method of Classifying Junior and Senior High School Boys into Homogeneous Groups for Physical Education Activities," *Research Quarterly*, Vol. XII, No. 4 (December 1941), p. 765.

[29] Aileen Carpenter, "Strength Testing in the First Three Grades," *Research Quarterly*, Vol. XIII, No. 3 (October 1942), p. 328.

Norms for this test are based upon McCloy's Classification Index III, with the following weightings:

Girls' norm .... .2549CI − 27.91
Boys' norm .... .3009CI − 64.60

In computing the "Physical Efficiency Index," the achieved score on the test, multiplied by 100, is divided by the individual's norm. A "PEI" of 100 indicates that the child has just the amount of motor ability that would be expected of him for his age, height, and weight. The norms for this test appear in Appendix B: Table XXXVI for boys; Table XXXVII for girls.

NEWTON MOTOR ABILITY TEST FOR HIGH-SCHOOL GIRLS [30]

Experimenting with ten test items, Powell and Howe developed the "Newton" test of motor ability for high-school girls, composed of the standing broad jump, a "baby" hurdle race and a "scramble" test. The multiple correlation of these tests with an objective criterion of 18 items, selected on the basis of strength, power, speed, and coordination, is .91. Other criteria were also used, in which these same items occupied a favored position.

Directions for giving the Powell and Howe items appear below. Six-sigma standard score achievement scales for each of the three tests in the battery and for "total points" appear in Appendix B, Table XXXVIII. In obtaining total points, the unweighted scale scores on the three tests are added directly. The decile locations for the various parts of the tests and the total achievement are given in the table, as an additional aid in judging performance.

Standing broad jump: The subject toes a starting line, two feet from the end of a gymnasium mat held firmly in place against the wall, and jumps as far as possible. The best of three trials is recorded to the nearest inch.

Baby hurdles: Ten gymnasium benches and five split bamboo sticks are used for setting up the hurdles. The first hurdle is five yards from the starting line; the others are at three-yard intervals; and an Indian club is placed three yards beyond the last hurdle. The subject runs at top speed over the hurdles, around the Indian club, and back over the hurdles to the starting line. Penalties are

---

[30] Elizabeth Powell and E. C. Howe, "Motor Ability Tests for High School Girls," *Research Quarterly,* Vol. X, No. 4 (December 1939), p. 81.

not imposed for displacing hurdles. Time is recorded to the nearest fifth of a second.

Scramble: A jumping standard is arranged with a small shelf (four feet above the floor) upon which a tap bell is fastened securely; it is placed ten feet from a wall. The subject starts from a back-lying position on the floor with both feet against the wall and the arms stretched sideways at shoulder level, palms down. At the starting signal, she gets up, runs and taps the bell twice, returns to the starting position and claps the hands on the floor twice; this performance is repeated as rapidly as possible until she has made the fourth double tap of the bell. The time is recorded to the nearest fifth of a second.

Motor Ability Tests for College Women

After extensive experimentation, Scott [31] proposed a motor ability test which may be used with college women and high-school girls. A total of 35 test items, including derived indices and measures comprised in the criteria, was included in the research. The test items were related to four criteria, as follows: (1) subjective ratings of sports ability by Scott and three student observers; (2) a number of items typical of the skills involved in the more common sports; (3) the McCloy general motor ability items for girls; and (4) a composite of the above three criteria.

The minimum battery recommended as a result of these studies consists of Scott's obstacle race, basketball throw for distance, and standing broad jump. A complete description of the test, directions for administering the test items, and T-scales for girls, women, and women majors in physical education are given in the Scott and French textbook.

Tuttle and Wendler [32] developed a procedure for measuring work capacity utilizing maximum total work output for a period of two minutes on a bicycle ergograph. Using this measure as a criterion, Scott, Moody, and Wilson [33] studied the effectiveness of the follow-

---

[31] M. Gladys Scott and Esther French, *Evaluation in Physical Education* (St. Louis: C. V. Mosby Company, 1950), Chap. 6.

[32] W. W. Tuttle and A. J. Wendler, "The Construction, Calibration, and Use of an Alternating Current Electrodynamic Brake Bicycle Ergometer," *Journal of Laboratory and Clinical Medicine*, Vol. XXX, No. 2 (February 1945), p. 173.

[33] M. Gladys Scott, Margaret Moody, and Marjorie Wilson, "Validation of Mass Type Physical Tests with Tests of Work Capacity," *Research Quarterly*, Vol. XVI, No. 2 (May 1945), p. 128.

ing test items involved in several test batteries: sit-ups, chair stepping, vertical pull, obstacle race, bounce, and Harriet Clarke's adaptation of the Brouha (Harvard step) test. The subjects were undergraduate women at the University of Iowa. Multiple correlations for two-, three-, four-, and five-item combinations of these items with work capacity range from .61 to .70. Efficiency T-scales for several of the tests were subsequently prepared.[34]

MOTOR ABILITY TESTS FOR COLLEGE MEN

Cozens Athletic Ability Test

One of the outstanding tests of general athletic ability for college men was constructed by Cozens.[35] In order to obtain a composite idea of the elements that comprise general athletic ability, Cozens

TABLE V

ELEMENTS AND TEST ITEMS COMPRISING THE COZENS TEST OF GENERAL
ATHLETIC ABILITY FOR COLLEGE MEN

Test Elements	Test Items	Score Multi-plication
1. Arm and shoulder-girdle strength	Dips	0.8
2. Arm and shoulder-girdle coordination	Baseball throw for distance	1.5
3. Hand-eye, foot-eye, arm-eye coordination	Football punt for distance	1.0
4. Jumping strength, leg strength, and leg flexibility	Standing broad jump	0.9
5. Endurance	Quarter-mile run	1.3
6. Body coordination, agility, and control	Bar-snap for distance	0.5
7. Speed of legs	Dodging run	1.0

secured judgments from 52 representative physical educators, and selected the seven deemed most important by the judges. Over 40 possible tests were collected and classified under the seven elements

[34] M. Gladys Scott and Marjorie Wilson, "Physical Efficiency Tests for College Women," *Research Quarterly*, Vol. XIX, No. 2 (May 1948), p. 62.
[35] Frederick W. Cozens, *The Measurement of General Athletic Ability in College Men* (Eugene, Oregon: University of Oregon Press, 1929).

previously chosen, one test for each element being retained after experimentation. These elements and tests appear in Table V.

In scoring this test, the raw scores are transposed into sigma scores,[36] and these are multiplied by the weights given in Table V, to obtain the relative value that each test contributes to the general quality of athletic ability. The validity and reliability of the test are high. Care, however, should be exercised in allowing unconditioned men to compete in the quarter-mile run.

Barrow Motor Ability Test

In constructing a motor ability test for college men, Barrow[37] used expert opinion in order to select eight factors of motor ability and 29 items as potential measures of these factors. On the basis of multiple correlations against a criterion consisting of the sum of performances on the 29 tests, two test batteries were chosen. For the first test battery, the correlation was .95; for the second test battery, .92. The two test batteries were as follows:

First Battery	Second Battery
Standing broad jump	Standing broad jump
Softball distance throw	Medicine ball put (6 lb.)
Zigzag run	Zigzag run
Wall pass	
Medicine ball put (6 lb.)	
60-yard dash	

Directions for administering the items in this motor ability test and norms appear in the reference.

Emory University Test

Seymour[38] restudied an eight-item motor ability test in use at Emory University. With the score on the total test as the criterion, a multiple correlation of .987 was obtained with the following four tests: softball distance throw, vertical jump, 60-yard dash, and basketball dribble.

---

[36] Sigma scoring tables based on Cozens' Classification Index are available in the following reference: F. W. Cozens, *Achievement Scales in Physical Education for College Men* (Philadelphia: Lea and Febiger, 1936).

[37] Harold M. Barrow, "Test of Motor Ability for College Men," *Research Quarterly*, Vol. XXV, No. 3 (October 1954), p. 253.

[38] Emery W. Seymour, "Classification of Emory University Male Freshmen in Physical Education Classes," *Research Quarterly*, Vol. XXIV, No. 4 (December 1953), p. 459.

MOTOR EDUCABILITY

As intelligence testing occupies an important place in education, a number of experimenters in physical education have attempted to construct tests of "motor intelligence." McCloy's General Motor Capacity Test, described above, is an important attempt of this sort. Other investigators have proposed tests of "motor educability," a term popularized by McCloy and referring to the "ease with which an individual learns new motor skills."

The Brace Test [39]

In 1927, David K. Brace published a test designed to measure "inherent motor skill." This was the first test of its kind and marked an important milestone in physical education research. The test was composed of twenty stunts, each of which was scored in terms of success or failure. The Brace Scale is low in reliability, however, and has no norms for sex, weight, or age, it being assumed that boys and girls of any size do equally well at all ages between 8 and 18. There is considerable evidence to indicate that older individuals on the whole are markedly superior to younger ones. Also, much learning occurs even during the first trial of the test. This would not be the case if the test were a true measure of native ability. In fact, little change should occur even after considerable practice. Moreover, several of the Brace tests are primarily tests of strength, and all the more difficult ones are impossible, even to the most skillful subject, unless he also possesses adequate strength.

Iowa Brace Test [40]

In an attempt to produce a test that would measure motor educability, McCloy revised the Brace Test, experimenting with 40 different stunts and retaining 21 of them, 10 of which were in the old Brace battery. From these 21 stunts, six batteries of ten stunts each were drawn up for the upper three grades of the elementary school, for the junior high school, and for the senior high school, one set on each level being for boys and one for girls. Two trials of each test were allowed, with absolutely no practice being permitted

---

[39] David K. Brace, *Measuring Motor Ability* (New York: A. S. Barnes and Company, 1927).
[40] McCloy and Young, *op. cit.*, p. 85.

299

in advance. The stunts were scored on a pass-or-fail basis. If the pupil succeeds on the first trial, he receives two points; if he fails on both trials, no points. The highest possible score for the 10 stunts in any battery, therefore, is 20. T-score tables for the test have been prepared by McCloy.

In preparing the Iowa Revision of the Brace Test, three criteria were applied to the selection of stunts, as follows: (1) The percentage of individuals passing it increased with age. (2) It had a relatively low correlation with strength, with the Classification Index, and with the Sargent Jump. In other words, it was not a measure of strength, size, maturity, or power. (3) It correlated relatively highly with track and field athletic ability when the Classification Index (or age alone for girls), the Sargent Jump, and strength were held constant to the athletic events but not to the stunt; consideration was thus given to greater skill (or a greater degree of motor educability).

In the validation of both the Brace and the Iowa Brace tests, the criterion was achievement, not ability to learn. In a later study with high-school girls,[41] a different approach to this problem was made. Various measures of motor educability were correlated with the rate of learning basketball, volleyball, and baseball skills. The highest relationship was found with the Brace Test, the next with the Iowa Brace Test, and the last with the Johnson Test. None of the tests, however, measured accurately the ease with which the subjects in the study learned new skills or relearned old ones in these three sports. Brace reports similar results in studies which he conducted in speed of learning field hockey, tennis, and aquatic skills with girls, although he did obtain a correlation of .50 with learning rhythmic skill.[42]

In later studies, Brace [43] investigated motor ability in relation to learning skills, as indicated by the following six tests: "tangle" (stunt-type) test, rhythm test, wall volley with a volleyball, ball bounce with a basketball, kick test, and target toss. The learning

---

[41] Eugenia Gire and Anna Espenschade, "The Relationship Between Measures of Motor Educability and the Learning of Specific Skills," *Research Quarterly*, Vol. XIII, No. 1 (March 1942), p. 43.

[42] David K. Brace, "Studies in the Rate of Learning Gross Bodily Motor Skills," *Research Quarterly*, Vol. XII, No. 2 (May 1941), p. 181.

[43] David K. Brace, "Studies in Motor Learning of Gross Bodily Motor Skills," *Research Quarterly*, Vol. XVII, No. 4 (December 1946), p. 242.

situation involved 90 performances of each test. He concluded that the Brace motor ability test does not measure motor learning to an extent that would justify its being classified as a test of motor educability, although it was slightly superior to the Iowa Revision in this respect.

The Johnson Test

In 1932, Johnson [44] set up a battery of tests designed to measure "native neuromuscular skill capacity." The test consists of performing the following ten exercises down the length of a 5 by 10-foot gymnasium mat, especially marked out for this purpose: (1) straddle jump; (2) stagger skip; (3) stagger jump; (4) forward skip, holding opposite foot from behind; (5) front roll; (6) jumping half-turns, right or left; (7) rock roll; (8) jumping half-turns, right and left alternately; (9) front and back roll combinations; and (10) jumping full-turns. A score of 10 is given for the perfect execution of each exercise, and points are deducted for such violations as overstepping or missing squares, failure to land on both feet at the same time, failure to maintain rhythm, improper use of the hands, turning the wrong way, and so forth. The individual's final score, therefore, is on the basis of a maximum of 100 points.

Johnson reports a validity coefficient of .69, which is low, but did not state against what criterion it was validated. Koob,[45] using the number of trials required for junior high school boys to learn a series of ten tumbling stunts, obtained a correlation of .97 between the Johnson Test and motor educability, and a correlation of .81 between the test and scores made on three track and field events. Gross, Greisel, and Stull [46] obtained low correlations between both the Metheny Revision of the Johnson Test (.33) and the Iowa-Brace Test (.46) and the ability of college men to learn wrestling. They also found that the correlation between the Metheny-Johnson and Iowa-Brace tests to be low (.40), thus concluding that the two tests were "not measures of the same ability." Cooper [47] also obtained

---

[44] Granville B. Johnson, "Physical Skill Tests for Sectioning Classes into Homogeneous Units," *Research Quarterly*, Vol. III, No. 1 (March 1932), p. 128.

[45] Clarence G. Koob, "A Study of the Johnson Skills Test as a Measure of Motor Educability." Master's thesis, State University of Iowa, 1937.

[46] Gross, Geisel, and Stull, *op. cit.*

[47] Bernice Cooper, "The Establishment of General Motor Capacity Tests for High School Girls," Microcarded Doctoral Dissertation, State University of Iowa, 1945.

a low correlation between these two tests with high school girls as subjects.

Johnson reports a reliability coefficient of .97 for the test with college men as subjects. Other experiments, however, have not found the same accuracy for the test when administered to girls. Gire and Espenschade report a reliability of .61 with high school girls; Cooper verified this correlation with .64, also with high school girls. Hatlestad [48] concludes, after administering the test to college women, that greater objectivity is needed.

Metheny [49] studied the Johnson Test and found that, with boys, four of the tests alone correlated .98 with the total Johnson score, and .93 with a criterion of learning tumbling stunts. For girls, a combination of three of the Johnson items gave a correlation of .86 with the total Johnson score. Johnson's items 5, 7, and 8 were used for both boys and girls; item 10 was added for boys.

With the elimination of six of the original Johnson items, Metheny was able to simplify the mat used in the performance of the test, as shown in Figure 12.1. A lane 24 inches wide is marked down the center of a 15-foot mat. This lane is divided into two equal narrow lanes by a center line, and into ten equal parts lengthwise by lines placed every 18 inches. These lines are alternately ¾ inch wide and 3 inches wide, the 18-inch width being measured to the middle of the line in each case.

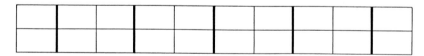

Figure 12.1. Canvas Markings for Metheny-Johnson Test of Motor Skill.

On this mat, the selected Johnson Test items are performed as follows (numbers refer to Johnson's original designations):

5. *Front Roll.* Perform rolls in entire 24-inch lane. Start with feet outside of chart. Perform two front rolls, the first within the limits of the first half of the lane (not going beyond the middle 3-inch line); the second within the limits of the second half, never touching or overreaching the lanes. *Score:* Count five points for each roll.

[48] L. Lucile Hatlestad, "Motor Educability Tests for Women College Students," *Research Quarterly*, Vol. XIII, No. 1 (March 1942), p. 10.

[49] Eleanor Metheny, "Studies of the Johnson Test as a Test of Motor Educability," *Research Quarterly*, Vol. IX, No. 4 (December 1938), p. 105.

Deduct two for overreaching side-line right or left for each roll; one for overreaching end limit on each roll; and five for failure to perform a true roll.

7. *Back Roll.* Perform two back rolls in entire 24-inch lane, one in each half of the lane. Start with feet outside of chart. *Scoring:* Score as in No. 5.

8. *Jumping Half-Turns, Right and Left Alternately.* Start with feet on first 3-inch line. Jump with both feet to second 3-inch line, executing a half-turn either right or left; jump to third 3-inch line, executing half-turn in opposite direction; continue the length of the mat, alternating directions of rotation. *Scoring:* Deduct two points for each jump in which the subject does not land with both feet on the 3-inch line, or turns the wrong way, or both.

10. *Jumping Full Turns.* Start with the feet outside the chart at about the center of the lane. Jump with feet together to second rectangular space, executing a full turn with the body right or left; continue across the mat, executing full turns, rotating in the same direction, landing on both feet in every second rectangular space. *Scoring:* Score as in No. 8, deducting two points if the subject fails to land on both feet, oversteps the square, turns too far or not far enough, or loses balance before starting the next jump.

In arranging sections for physical education on the basis of this test, Johnson suggests dividing the scores either into units based on the normal curve or into equal parts, depending upon the number of sections desired.

THE SARGENT VERTICAL JUMP [50]

The Sargent Jump, named after its originator, Dr. Dudley A. Sargent,[51] consists of a vertical leap into the air, and is primarily a test of the ability of the body to develop power in relation to the weight of the individual himself. In this jump, the individual swings his arms downward and backward, taking a crouch position with knees bent approximately to a right angle. The subject pauses in this position, to eliminate the possibility of a double jump, and leaps upward as high as possible, swinging the arms forcefully forward and upward. Just before the highest point of the jump is reached,

---

[50] Also known as the "vertical jump."
[51] Dudley A. Sargent, "Physical Test of a Man," *American Physical Education Review*, Vol. XXVI, No. 4 (April 1921), p. 188.

the arms should be swung forward and downward, motion being timed to coincide with the height of the jump. The specified arm movements in executing the jump are extremely important, the test developing serious inaccuracies without them.[52] The best of three trials should be recorded.

The distance on the Sargent Jump may be measured in a number of ways:

1. A "leapmeter" may be used consisting of an upright stand with an operating lever arm from which a cap or harness to fit the subject is suspended; resultant motion of the subject moves a guide holding a pencil on graph paper; the height of the jump is recorded in reduced size.

2. Wrapping paper two feet wide and five feet long, marked with horizontal lines one centimeter apart (each tenth line a different color), may be fastened to the wall so that the zero line is just below the standing height of the shortest subject to be tested; the distance between standing height and the top of the head at the height of the jump is recorded.[53]

3. A shorter paper with lines ruled as above may be placed on the wall near the floor; an elastic band with a button attached is placed on the subject's ankle and adjusted to the zero line on the paper; the record of the jump is the point reached by the button when the subject jumps (knees must be kept straight).[54]

4. A simple method, known as the "chalk jump," consists in having the subject make two chalk marks (chalked or wet fingers may be substituted for an actual piece of chalk) on a dark, clean wall: one made standing with the arm fully extended and the other at the height of the jump; the distance between the two marks is recorded. In a study of various methods of measuring the Sargent Jump, however, Van Dalen found the chalk and wall jumps to be inaccurate.[55]

It is generally agreed by experimenters that best results are obtained with this test after the technique of the jump has been

---

[52] Deobold Van Dalen, "New Studies in the Sargent Jump," *Research Quarterly,* Vol. XI, No. 2 (May 1940), p. 112.

[53] McCloy and Young, *op. cit.,* p. 67.

[54] Thomas K. Cureton, "Fitness of Feet and Legs," *Supplement to the Research Quarterly,* Vol. XII, No. 2 (May 1941), p. 368.

[55] Van Dalen, *op. cit.*

taught and the subjects have practiced its execution. Under these conditions, reliability coefficients have been reported at .85 [56] and .96.[57] With high school girls, Cooper [58] obtained reliability coefficients between .89 and .98. In a number of studies, the Sargent Jump was found to correlate with track and field events for men and boys at .65 and .81. With girls, slightly lower correlations were obtained.[59] This test, or the standing broad jump as a substitute for it, has been used extensively in both motor fitness and motor ability test batteries.

AGE-HEIGHT-WEIGHT CLASSIFICATION INDICES

In the past, classification schemes have been formulated based upon age, height, and weight. These were largely subjective and were never validated. In more recent years, however, an effort has been made to approach this problem scientifically. As this method of classifying pupils for physical education activities is convenient, does not require special testing equipment, and can be quickly administered, it could, if found sound, be used as a rough classifier in lieu of more complicated tests.

McCloy,[60] the first to study the best weighting of age, height, and weight, proposes the following three classification indices:

Classification Index   I = $(20 \times$ age$) + (6 \times$ height$) +$ weight
Classification Index II = $(6 \times$ height$) +$ weight
Classification Index III = $(10 \times$ age$) +$ weight

Classification Index III is particularly significant on the elementary-school level, as height was found to be a negligible factor with this group and is omitted from the formula. Classification Index I is more significant for the high-school level, where height seems of greater importance. Classification Index II is used with college men, as it was found that after 17 age ceased to make a further contribution.

[56] C. H. McCloy, "Recent Studies in the Sargent Jump," *Research Quarterly,* Vol. III, No. 2 (May 1932), p. 235.

[57] James W. Coleman, *op. cit.*

[58] Cooper, *op. cit.*

[59] Eleonore E. Adams, "The Study of Age, Height, Weight, and Power as Classification Factors for Junior High School Girls," *Research Quarterly,* Vol. V, No. 2 (May 1934), p. 95.

[60] C. H. McCloy, *The Measurement of Athletic Power* (New York: A. S. Barnes and Company, 1932).

In Table XXXIX, Appendix B, are given the divisions for classification indices proposed by McCloy, the divisions being selected on the basis of the best combination of age, height, and weight, as indicated above, and arranged by school level.

Neilson and Cozens [61] also studied the problem of classifying pupils on the basis of age, height, and weight. Their results differ somewhat from those of McCloy, but, interpreted in the same terms, their formula is:

$$\text{Classification Index} = (20 \times \text{age}) + (5.55 \times \text{height}) + \text{weight}$$

In Table XL, Appendix B, appears a chart prepared by Neilson and Cozens for easy computation of their index and classification by means of it.

The Neilson and Cozens classifying method and McCloy's Classification Index I correlate .983, indicating that either one may be used for high-school groups with equal satisfaction. McCloy's Index correlates .81 with track and field events and .57 with a number of sports skills.[62] The correlation with track and field events is comparable to that obtained with other motor ability tests reported in this chapter. However, the correlation with sports skills is not so significant as that obtained with other tests. The conclusion that may be drawn from this evidence is that the Classification Index will be found useful for rapid, tentative classifications, or when more complicated or more expensive methods are impractical or impossible, but is not so valid as other tests proposed for measuring general abilities. Also, various studies have revealed the inadequacy of age, height, and weight, in combination or singly, for the classification of secondary-school girls and college women.

Selected References

Anderson, Theresa, "Studies in Strength Testing for High School Girls," *Research Quarterly*, Vol. VIII, No. 3 (October 1937), p. 69.

Carpenter, Aileen, "An Analysis of the Relationships of the Factors of Velocity, Strength, and Dead Weight to Athletic Performance," *Research Quarterly*, Vol. XII, No. 1 (March 1941), p. 34.

---

[61] N. P. Neilson and F. W. Cozens, *Achievement Scales in Physical Education Activities for Boys and Girls in Elementary and Junior High Schools* (New York: A. S. Barnes and Company, 1934), p. 161.

[62] Joy W. Kistler, "A Comparative Study of Methods for Classifying Pupils," *Research Quarterly*, Vol. V, No. 1 (March 1934), p. 42.

Clarke, H. Harrison, and Harold A. Bonesteel, "Equalizing the Abilities of High School Teams in a Small High School," *Research Quarterly Supplement*, Vol. VI, No. 1 (March 1935), p. 193.

Cozens, Frederick W., "Strength Tests as Measures of General Athletic Ability in College Men," *Research Quarterly*, Vol. XI, No. 1 (March 1940), p. 45.

Gire, Eugenia, and Anna Espenschade, "The Relationship Between Measures of Motor Educability and the Learning of Specific Skills," *Research Quarterly*, Vol. XIII, No. 1 (March 1942), p. 43.

Larson, Leonard A., "A Factor Analysis of Motor Ability Variables and Tests with Tests for College Men," *Research Quarterly*, Vol. XII, No. 3 (October 1941), p. 499.

McCloy, C. H., and Norma D. Young, *Tests and Measurements in Health and Physical Education*, 3rd ed. New York: Appleton-Century-Crofts, Inc., 1954, Part III.

————, *The Measurement of Athletic Power*. New York: A. S. Barnes and Company, 1932.

Rogers, Frederick Rand, "It Has Been Done," *Journal of Health and Physical Education*, Vol. IX, No. 2 (February 1938), p. 77.

Willgoose, Carl E., "Use of Strength Tests in Team Equalization," *The Physical Educator*, Vol. VI, No. 1 (March 1949), p. 4.

PART FOUR

Physical Education Skills and Appreciations

CHAPTER THIRTEEN

Importance of Skills
and Appreciations

As has been stressed consistently throughout the text, the major concern of the physical educator should always be the realization of educational objectives. The methods he adopts, the activities he selects, and the tests he uses should be based upon the specific objectives he is determined to meet. In previous chapters, procedures for meeting the physical fitness and the social objectives were presented. Part IV is devoted to measurement for the development of skills and cultural appreciations, and to procedures for conducting efficient and effective programs in these areas.

PHYSICAL EDUCATION SKILLS

Physical education has a history that extends back many centuries, beginning with early Greek civilization. While they were not continuous over this entire period, physical education activities nevertheless have a rich heritage in the evolution of present-day civilization. The basis for this form of education is the learning and practice of skills in order to achieve worth while objectives. For example, gymnastics, the pentathlon, boxing, pankration, swimming, riding, fighting in armor, military maneuvers, archery, hunting, and athletic games were used by the Athenians during the fourth and fifth centuries B.C. to develop the body, an essential phase of the education of Greek youth;[1] stunts on the horizontal bar and parallel bars and other forms of gymnastics and athletics were the basis of Jahn's system of physical exercise designed to develop a physically strong nation for Germany's wars;[2] and a great variety of physical activities are included in present-day physical education programs in order to develop a physically and socially fit nation. The true basis of all physical education is to learn skills essential for physical fitness, for building character, and for use during leisure time.[3]

Physical activities differ not only in their educational content, but also in the contributions they make to specific objectives. Moreover, the contributions that any one physical activity can make are not confined to a single objective, but apply in some degree to them all. In selecting activities for his program, therefore, the physical educator should understand the educational values of these activities and should keep in mind the purposes to be served by their use. For example, all physical activities have some recreational value. When this quality is to be *specifically* developed, however, activities like tennis, swimming, or golf, which are high in recreational content, should be taught rather than, say, calisthenics or marching, the recreational possibilities of which are low.

Physical Fitness

Many types of physical activities develop strength, endurance, and body flexibility, essential components of physical fitness. It is true that these qualities may be developed through activities requiring little skill, such as calisthenics and running. However, these activities are not sufficiently interesting to most people for continuance as a regular habit in their daily lives. Activities requiring skill, on the other hand, when once acquired, will be practiced much more consistently and zealously. Thus, such activities as the following require skill and result in more general use: gymnastics, tumbling, wrestling, and some forms of dancing for strength, flexibility, agility, and balance; and basketball, tennis, and swimming for

---

[1] Kenneth S. Freeman, *Schools of Hellas,* 3rd ed. (London: Macmillan and Company, 1922), p. 299.

[2] Friedrich Ludwig Jahn and Ernst Eiselen, *Die Deutsche Turnkunst* (Berlin: Auf Kosten der Herausgeber, 1816), p. 315.

[3] Seward C. Staley, *The Curriculum in Sports* (*Physical Education*) (Philadelphia: W. B. Saunders Company, 1935), p. 109.

endurance and stamina. The danger with the use of sports activities in the development of physical fitness lies in their competitive aspects. Competition provides a temptation to overexert, to go the limit. Such exertion is desirable for many, but may be harmful to those not in condition and for those men and women well beyond school and college age.

Neuromuscular Coordination

The neuromuscular coordination of the individual, which includes his ability to learn new skills and finally to achieve competency in physical activities, is essential to all phases of physical education. Activities for developing such coordination, therefore, should be considered. The following factors are involved:

1. *Nerve-eye-muscle coordination:* Skills requiring the coordination of hand and eye, as in throwing at targets, goals, and so forth, and on foot and eye, as in kicking a ball.

2. *Agility:* Skills requiring rapid movement of the entire body, in different directions and in response to unexpected circumstances, as dodging in football, pivoting in basketball, and agile stunts in tumbling.

3. *Rhythm:* Skills requiring smooth, rhythmic, and relaxed motion, as in the club swing in golf, in the rhythmic movement of the dance, and in performing an "effortless" crawl stroke in swimming.

4. *Precision of movement:* Skills requiring precise performance, in which every detail must be executed with exactness, as in apparatus exercises and in diving.

5. *Speed:* Skills requiring coordination while traveling at considerable speed, as in soccer, basketball, and ice hockey.

6. *Poise:* Skills resulting in the well-poised individual, the final culmination of the entire physical being, strong, enduring, well-coordinated, and highly skilled.

Social Acceptability

American culture gives special regard to the level of motor performance attained by the adolescent boy.[4] No other single factor

---

[4] Rena R. Frabony, "An Investigation of the Relationships Between Motor Ability, Interest in Participating in Physical Activity, and Personal-Social Adjustment of Girls in Adolescence," Microcarded Master of Arts Thesis, University of California, 1956.

means so much for a boy's social status among his peers as the ability to play well. It has also been generally observed that skill in games is a contributing factor for young girls, but in lesser degree than it is for boys of the same age. As both grow older, this factor operates less and less for the girl, but if the boy lacks skill at any age, he loses status with his group. His realization of failure to establish himself socially often prevents good schoolwork or happy normal friendships.[5] Various studies have substantiated these observations.

Kuhlen and Lee [6] found that "active in games" was particularly important for the social acceptability of boys, especially during adolescent years. This trait ranked fifth among 19 traits studied at the sixth-grade level. With girls, the situation was different, as this trait ranked only eleventh for sixth-grade girls. The results of a similar experiment by Tryon [7] were in essential agreement with Kuhlen and Lee. She concluded that the seventh-grade boy who lacks skill and has a distaste for organized games is ridiculed and shunned by the group; at the twelfth grade, outstanding athletic skill can maintain the prestige of a boy even though he has few other assets. For girls, however, she found that skill in active games was tolerated by twelve-year-olds but was not particularly desirable; such skill offered a certain amount of prestige for fifteen-year-old girls who were unsuccessful in heterosexual relations. In a study of sociometric status and motor skills, Fox [8] found that the relationship of motor ability to popularity decreased as girls progressed from the fourth to the sixth grade; for boys, this relationship increased for the same grades. Frabony [9] obtained similar results with adolescent girls.

Other studies of a similar nature have been reported. Jones,[10] in

---

[5] Lois H. Meek, chairman, *The Personal-Social Development of Boys and Girls with Implications for Secondary Education* (New York: Committee on Workshops, Progressive Education Association, 1940), Part III, Sec. E.

[6] Raymond G. Kuhlen and Beatrice J. Lee, "Personality Characteristics and Social Acceptability in Adolescence," *Journal of Educational Psychology*, Vol. XXXIV, No. 6 (September 1943), p. 321.

[7] Caroline C. Tryon, *Evaluations of Adolescent Personality by Adolescents*, Monograph of the Society for Research in Child Development, Vol. IV, No. 4 (1939).

[8] Kathleen Fox, "A Sociometric Study in Child Friendships and Motor Skill, in the Intermediate Groups," Microcarded Master's Thesis, State University of Iowa, 1954.

[9] Frabony, *op. cit.*

[10] Harold E. Jones, "Physical Ability as a Factor in Social Adjustment in Adolescence," *Journal of Educational Research*, Vol. XL (December 1946), pp. 287-301.

the Berkeley Growth Studies, found that competitive athletic skills are among the chief sources of social esteem for boys in the period preceding maturity. He attributes this phenomenon not merely "to the high premium which adolescents place upon athletic efficiency, but also to the fact that strength and other aspects of physical ability are closely joined to such favorable traits as activity, aggressiveness, and leadership." Osborne's study [11] of boys at camp showed that in many cases the boy who withdrew from participation in camp activities was the boy who lacked skill in sports and who, consequently, had no secure place with boys of his own age. Sperling [12] found that a more socially desirable degree of personality development accompanies a greater degree of experience in physical education activities. Comparing ten superior and ten inferior third-grade pupils in motor proficiency, Rarick and McKee [13] concluded that children in the superior group were judged by their teachers to be active, popular, calm, resourceful, attentive, and cooperative; whereas children in the inferior group were more frequently judged as showing negative traits and were more often indicated as being shy, retiring, and tense.

Utilizing a reputation test of the "Guess Who" type, Bower [14] found that physical ability and strength are clearly related to the popularity of boys ten to thirteen years of age. He found that the salient physical characteristics of the consistently popular boy are short stature and good physical ability. Biddulph [15] reported that sophomore and junior high school boys with high athletic achievement test scores showed a significantly higher self-adjustment score on the California Test of Personality and were superior in social adjustment as indicated by teachers' ratings and sociograms. In studying the relationship of athletic competition and social adjustment

---

[11] Ernest G. Osborne, *Camping and Guidance* (New York: Association Press, 1937).

[12] Abraham P. Sperling, "The Relationship between Personality Adjustment and Achievement in Physical Education Activities," *Research Quarterly*, Vol. XIII, No. 3 (October 1942), p. 351.

[13] G. Lawrence Rarick and Robert McKee, "A Study of Twenty Third-Grade Children Exhibiting Extreme Levels of Achievement on Tests of Motor Efficiency," *Research Quarterly*, Vol. XX, No. 2 (May 1949), pp. 142-152.

[14] Philip A. Bower, "The Relation of Physical, Mental, and Personality Factors to Popularity in Adolescent Boys," Microcarded Doctor's Dissertation, University of California, 1941.

[15] Lowell G. Biddulph, "Athletic Achievement and Social Adjustment of High School Boys," *Research Quarterly*, Vol. XXV, No. 1 (March 1954), pp. 1-7.

in junior high school girls, Lareau [16] found that those girls who made the school team were deferent toward their parents, were dominant or leaders, were emotionally stable, active, and extroverted, and were popular.

The development of skill in sports and games, therefore, is essential as an entree into social participation for boys. Physical prowess is pre-eminent in establishing prestige, and, as such, becomes an important factor in an individual's feelings of confidence in himself. The situation is somewhat different for girls, since athletic ability is not so primary a source of gaining social status for them. However, it may frequently be an important secondary or contributing factor toward successful personal-social relations. The contribution of physical education to the social acceptability of boys and girls is obvious. The physical activity program should provide breadth of physical skills for all boys and girls, adapted to their age and sex. Simple fundamental skills should be taught to all children in the elementary grades and continued progressively throughout the school years, and special help should be given to those who need it.

Recreational Efficiency

Much of the skill instruction in physical education is "education through the physical," in which participation in physical activities has for its purpose the development of such qualities as strength, stamina, speed, individual and group character traits, and neuromuscular coordination. In preparing for the wise use of leisure, however, the physical educator teaches skills as ends in themselves—to be used as a part of the individual's avocation. The outcome desired is recreational efficiency, or the acquisition of skills and their use as after-school, after-graduation activities.

The way leisure hours are spent is a major social and economic concern of our society. Recreation is recognized as necessary to individual and community well-being. Dewhurst and Klafter [17] have pointed out that a host of federal, state, and local officials, businessmen, promotion men, actors, musicians, thousands of men,

---

[16] Jeanne D. Lareau, "The Relationship Between Athletic Competition and Personal and Social Adjustment in Junior High School Girls," Master of Arts Thesis, University of California, 1956.

[17] J. Frederic Dewhurst and Associates, *America's Needs and Resources: A New Survey* (New York: The Twentieth Century Fund, 1955), p. 346.

women, boys and girls who work in public and private places of amusement supply the means for recreation. Recreation is big business.

The place that recreation occupies in modern life cannot be understood without consideration of the far-reaching significance of leisure. The sudden extension of leisure is the main reason for the new demand for recreation.[18] With material wants satisfied, there is time for music and art, dramatics, arts and crafts, nature study, games and sports; recreation includes them all. Leisure provides the time for participation in such worth while activities. It has other advantages. Bowen and Mitchell[19] list three: (1) to counteract the effects of specialized work; (2) to offset the strain of modern environment; and (3) to offset the influence of harmful amusements. The prevention of delinquency was one of the main arguments advanced for the promotion of the playground movement in its early infancy. Even in total mobilization, recreation is a resource of war. "Fun, play, entertainment for workers in off-the-job hours is time gained on the job to turn out more bombers, more ships, more tanks."[20]

Recreation, itself, is a broad concept including many types of activities. Several school agencies contribute to "the wise use of leisure"; physical education is only one of these. Sports and games, however, deal with fundamental drives in the individual's character and are an important asset in the maintenance of physical fitness, an essential concomitant of recreational efficiency.

In the selection of specific physical skills for recreation, the following factors should be kept in mind:

1. *Enjoyment:* The activity should give the participant pleasure, so that he will seek opportunities to continue with it from time to time. Frequently, one's enjoyment of an activity is largely dependent upon his acquired skill in it, as he usually prefers to do that which he can do well, and avoids those activities in which he performs poorly.

---

[18] Martin H. Neumeyer and Esther S. Neumeyer, *Leisure and Recreation* (New York: A. S. Barnes and Company, 1936), p. 5.

[19] Wilbur P. Bowen and Elmer D. Mitchell, *The Theory of Organized Play* (New York: A. S. Barnes and Company, 1923), pp. 35-38.

[20] Mark A. McCloskey, *Spare Time: A War Asset for War Workers* (Washington, D. C.: United States Government Printing Office, 1943), p. 1.

2. *Companionship:* The activity should be one in which many of his friends like to participate, or one that is universally popular. Included among these activities should be some that can be played with the opposite sex.

3. *Number of participants:* The activity should preferably be one that requires only a few participants to play. The best recreational sports are those that can be played alone or with from one to three companions, such as golf, tennis, swimming, and so forth. When more players are required, as in softball and volleyball, participation suffers owing to the difficulty of getting the larger group together.

4. *Vigor:* The age, sex, and physical condition of the participant should be considered in selecting recreational activities. High-school boys and college men frequently choose vigorous sports, such as basketball, touch football, and baseball. Older men, however, require milder activities, especially those that may be adaptable in dosage, for example: nine holes of golf today, perhaps eighteen next week. On the other hand, activities requiring little physical exertion or skill, such as shuffle board, frequently are not challenging enough for the majority.

5. *Skill:* The activity should require skill to perform it satisfactorily. Individuals are more interested when they are learning and obtain greater satisfactions when they can note their own improvement and measure their own attainments.

6. *Competition:* Generally speaking, the activity should be competitive in nature. Many people, however, prefer hikes in the woods, ski trips, nature study, horseback riding, and the like, where competition is absent. Nevertheless, for most, the oppositive element in sports is one of its most intriguing aspects.

7. *Facilities:* Facilities for the activity should be generally available. Obviously, one cannot swim without water or take ski hikes without snow. The more generally accepted recreational sports are those for which facilities may be found in most communities.

CULTURAL POTENTIALITIES OF PHYSICAL EDUCATION

Culture has been defined as "training or discipline by which man's moral and intellectual nature is elevated." As indicated in Chapter 1, its application in society has been confined traditionally to classical areas of human thought: literature, philosophy, art, music, and the humanities. In this text a broader definition has been given to the culture concept, for example, the extension of "one's stock of appreciations" to include all aspects of living that will improve one's understanding and enjoyment of people and events in his civilization.

Cozens and Stumpf [21] have produced a scholarly and penetrating tome on sports in American culture. The following passage colorfully presents this cultural orientation: "Sports and physical recreation activities belong with the *arts* of humanity. Such activities have formed a basic part of all cultures, including all racial groups and all historical ages, because they are as fundamental a form of human expression as music, poetry, and painting. Every age has had its artists and its amateurs, its adherents and its enemies. While wars, systems of government, plagues and famines, have come and gone in the long record of mankind, these fundamental things have always been present in greater or lesser degree." [22] In discussing the origins of the Olympic games, Ryan [23] asks this interesting question: "What is the nature of these contests, which draw the attention and participation of men and women from all over the world every four years and which can override serious and fundamental political differences to the extent that East and West Germany can unite to send a single team?" In the ancient Olympiad, the Greek city-states shared control of the games, even when at war with each other, and would declare a "truce of the Gods" so that the contests could be held.

Aesthetic Possibilities

Down through the ages, the human body has been the subject of art masterpieces. Athletic youth has frequently been portrayed, particularly in sculpture. In all the world's history, none have equaled the Greeks in making statues of exquisitely formed athletes. In recent times, R. Tait McKenzie, physician and director of physical education at the University of Pennsylvania before his death, approached nearest to Greek achievements. Beginning with a figure

---

[21] Frederick W. Cozens and Florence S. Stumpf, *Sports in American Life* (Chicago: University of Chicago Press, 1953).

[22] *Ibid.*, p. 1.

[23] Allen J. Ryan, "The Olympic Games and the Olympic Ideals," *Journal of American Medical Association*, Vol. CLXII, No. 12 (November 17, 1956), p. 1105.

of a sprinter, whose proportions were determined from nearly a hundred sprinters, he made statue after statue of young men in various athletic activities, beautiful in form and expressing the full "joy of effort." McKenzie had a greater scope of subjects than did the Greeks centuries ago. Many athletic events today in which great grace and beauty of the human body in action are shown, such as diving, skating, pole vaulting, hurdling, and numerous other games and sports, were unknown to the Greeks. A runner in a relay race, a boxer, a shot-putter, a diver, a flight of hurdlers, and a team of football players massed for an onslaught are some of McKenzie's subjects. Whether looked upon as studies in anatomy or as charming sculptured figures embodying the vigor and beauty of youth, they are satisfying.[24]

Millions of people today witness innumerable athletic events, yet their eyes and minds are trained to see the action, the competitive aspect of the sport, and their thoughts and emotions are concerned with whether "their" team wins. An appreciation of the beauty of polished, graceful, effortless performance, for its own sake, is lost on most. Physical educators can well consider a renewal of aesthetic appreciation in presenting the various aspects of their programs to boys and girls in the school. Four factors involved in an aesthetically perfect performance are noted below:

1. *Bodily proportion:* The body should be well proportioned physically, should be carried in pleasing posture, and should be well-developed and vigorous.

2. *Rhythm:* Body movement in physical action should be graceful, poised, rhythmic; the action should be effortless in appearance and synchronized with the movement of others if involved in the same movement.

3. *Precision:* The action should be well executed; it must be technically correct in its performance.

4. *Color:* The surroundings in which the action takes place should be appropriate to the activity and, also, pleasing to the eye; unsightly objects and unhygienic conditions distract from an otherwise aesthetic performance.

---

[24] Christopher R. Hussey, *R. Tait McKenzie: A Sculptor of Youth* (Philadelphia: J. B. Lippincott Company, 1930). The February 1944 issue of the *Journal of Health and Physical Education* is devoted to McKenzie's life and works.

IMPORTANCE OF SKILLS AND APPRECIATIONS

Activities rating high in aesthetic contribution are those that require the greatest precision of movement, that show the human body to best advantage, and that necessitate a rhythmic, polished performance. Such activities as the following, therefore, are rated high in aesthetic values: various art forms of the dance, heavy apparatus, diving, track and field, fencing, skiing, archery, free exercise, skating, and tumbling.

Contemporary Interest

Sports and games have become an integral part of the great American scene. From the largest metropolitan centers to the smallest rural communities, men and women participate in athletics of all sorts; from the professional baseball, football, and boxing events to the purely amateur six-man football and basketball games of the small hamlets of the nation, men and women witness these contests. The scene is a colorful one with intense local loyalties, bands, parades, bonfires, and "million-dollar gates." Great businesses have been developed to provide the facilities, equipment, and supplies needed; the radio and television devote regular programs to sports news and conduct play-by-play broadcasts and telecasts of many of the great athletic contests over the country; the sports section in newspapers is a regular feature and special sports reporters are engaged to insure adequate and up-to-the-minute coverage; the movie news-reels devote space to reviewing the highlights of many of the outstanding contests.

Although physical educators are primarily concerned with activity and with encouraging people to participate, they also should develop good spectators. To appreciate an excellent performance, to understand the rules, to be tolerant toward the difficulties of the official's position in these contests, to converse intelligently on athletic subjects, therefore, becomes a function of the physical education program and constitutes a phase of the cultural heritage of our present-day civilization.

Activities high in the "contemporary interest" are those given the greatest coverage in the newspapers, those broadcast on the radio and televised with greatest frequency, and those which stimulate interesting conversations. Thus, baseball, football, basketball, boxing, golf, ice hockey, and track and field have the highest ratings.

321

History and Literature

As indicated above, athletes were portrayed in early Greek sculpture. Athletic contests were also described in the Greek literature of that time. For example, in Homer's *Iliad*, several athletic events were contested at the funeral of Patroclus, over which Achilles presided, including chariot races, boxing, wrestling, foot races, spear fights, weight-throwing, archery, and spear-throwing for distance. Even in Homer's story, one contestant in the chariot race fouled another, causing considerable discussion about his disqualification. Some time later, in Homer's *Odyssey*, an interesting contest took place. Odysseus, after being provoked by Leodamus: ". . . sprang and seized a discus larger than the rest and thick, heavier by not a little than those which the Phaeacians were using for themselves. This with a twist he sent from his stout hand. The stone hummed as it went; down to the ground crouched the Phaeacian oarsmen, notable men at sea, at the stone's cast. Past all the marks it flew, swift speeding from his hand."

Both ancient and medieval literary masterpieces have included descriptions of athletic events, for example: archery contests in *Robin Hood*, jousting in *Ivanhoe,* and fencing in *The Three Musketeers.* Modern literature is no exception. Many books have been written and many moving pictures have been filmed either with athletics as their background or with athletic contests occupying important places in the plot.

Dancing, also, is a part of the physical education program and occupies an important place in the cultural contributions of this field. Dancing has its roots in the very origins of civilization: portraying the customs and emotions of primitive man and civilized man alike. It has been recognized as an art form through the ages. Folk dances, taught by physical educators, also include a presentation of the origins and purposes of the dance in its native land, with a discussion of the customs of the people and a display of the costumes worn.

Under "History and Literature," activities with high ratings have their origin in antiquity, are mentioned prominently in ancient, medieval, and modern literature, and are among the early activities included in the physical education programs of the United States and other countries. Thus, the following are particularly important:

archery, track and field, dance, boxing, wrestling, fencing, and stunts and tumbling.

MEASUREMENT

As in all measurement, tests of recreational competency and of cultural appreciations are made for the purpose of determining status and measuring improvement. A large number of tests are available, many of them presented in the next chapter. Tests designed to measure knowledge of rules, techniques, and strategy of various physical education activities have been constructed; these appear in Chapter 15. Unfortunately, however, tests of cultural appreciation in physical education are comparatively undeveloped. The limited number that are available, however, also appear in Chapter 15.

SELECTED REFERENCES

Bowen, Wilbur P., and Elmer D. Mitchell, *The Theory of Organized Play.* New York: A. S. Barnes and Company, 1923.

Cozens, Frederick W., and Florence S. Stumpf, *Sports in American Life.* Chicago: University of Chicago Press, 1953.

Dewhurst and Associates, *America's Needs and Resources: A New Survey.* New York: The Twentieth Century Fund, 1955, Chapter 11.

Hussey, Christopher R., *R. Tait McKenzie: Sculptor of Youth.* Philadelphia: J. B. Lippincott Company, 1930.

McKenzie, R. Tait, *Journal of Health and Physical Education,* Vol. XV, No. 2 (February 1944).

CHAPTER FOURTEEN

Skill Tests

In discussing the importance of skills in the preceding chapter, it was pointed out that the learning of desirable skills is the very foundation of physical education. It is through the development of skills and subsequent practice in them that physical educators realize their objectives. Accomplished performance in skills provides incentive for their continuance. Without sufficient skill for satisfactory participation in physical activities, the physical benefits from vigorous strength and endurance activities, the social values from group activities and team sports, the personal-social competence from skill in any socially accepted activity, the recreational competence from activities of value for leisure time, and the appreciation of skilled performance wherever observed, are not realized. In fact, skill in physical activities is essential for the well-integrated personality. To evaluate status and progress in the acquisition of skills, therefore, is an important phase of measurement in physical education.

Actually, skill testing accomplishes three major purposes in physical education, as follows:

1. The achievement and progress made by pupils in the various activities included in the program may be determined, thus evaluating the progress of each pupil and increasing his interest in the program.

2. Pupils may be classified according to levels of ability in each activity. Groups in specific sports may also be equated for class and intramural competition.

324

3. Progress toward educational objectives may be measured. In the area of skill tests, this is especially true of the recreational objective, where the learning of specific activities becomes an end in itself. And, too, in physical education programs calling for "minimum standards" in activities high in recreational content, achievement levels may be established in terms of skill-test scores.

Well-constructed skill tests are not available for all the many activities of physical education. However, considerable progress has been made in the proper construction of such tests in several areas. A number of these tests will be presented in this chapter.

ARCHERY

The most outstanding work in this field has been done by Edith Hyde, Chairman of the Committee on Measurement of Achievement in Archery of the National Association of Directors of Physical Education for College Women.[1] In her study, she established, with the assistance of F. W. Cozens, standards of achievement for college women in the Columbia Round, a standard event used in archery competition. The shooting is in the following order:

1st range: 24 arrows shot at 50 yards
2nd range: 24 arrows shot at 40 yards
3rd range: 24 arrows shot at 30 yards
Total for 3 ranges: 72 arrows

Essential Directions for Administering and Scoring the Test

1. Standard 48-inch target faces shall be used, so placed that the center of the gold is 4 feet from the ground.
2. Arrows shall be shot in ends of 6 arrows each, one practice end only being allowed at each distance.
3. The entire round need not be completed on the same day; however, at least one distance shall be completed at each session.
4. The target values are: Gold, 9; Red, 7; Blue, 5; Black, 3; White, 1; outside of white or missing target, 0.
5. An arrow cutting two colors shall count as having hit the inner one; an arrow rebounding from, or passing through, the scoring face of the target shall count as one hit and 5 in value.

---

[1] Edith I. Hyde, "National Research Study in Archery," *Research Quarterly*, Vol. VII, No. 4 (December 1936), p. 64, and "The Measurement of Achievement in Archery," *Journal of Educational Research*, Vol. XVII, No. 9 (May 1934), p. 673.

Scoring Tables for Columbia Round [2]

The archery achievement scale, appearing in Table XLI of Appendix B, consists of three parts, as follows:

1. Scale for first Columbia Round shot by a student. Before administering this round, the beginning student should be permitted a minimum of practice, 120 arrows at each distance being suggested as sufficient.

2. Scale for total score made in the Columbia Round after an unlimited amount of practice in the event. This scale would normally be used toward the end of the archery season to determine the student's achievement in the activity.

3. Three separate scales for each of the distances included in the round, to be used during any practice period when 24 arrows are shot at one of the three distances. As this part of the scale was constructed from the final or highest Columbia Round scores, the achievement level for beginners will naturally fall relatively low on the scale.

BADMINTON

French Badminton Test. French [3] constructed a satisfactory badminton test for women (and restudied it with Stalter [4]). It contains two elements: a serve test and a clear test. Reliability coefficients ranging from .77 to .98 were obtained. For validity, a correlation of .85 was obtained in a preliminary study between the test and a combination of subjective estimates and standings in tournament play.

The Serve Test. The subject serves 20 birds at the target diagrammed below and described as follows: (a) A clothesline rope is stretched 20 inches directly above the net and parallel to it. (b) A series of four arcs is drawn within the right service court at distances of 22 inches, 30 inches, 38 inches, and 46 inches from the intersection point of the short service line and the center line (the

---

[2] Edith I. Hyde, "An Achievement Scale in Archery," *Research Quarterly*, Vol. VIII, No. 2 (May 1937), p. 109.

[3] M. Gladys Scott, "Achievement Examinations in Badminton," *Research Quarterly*, Vol. XII, No. 2 (May 1941), p. 242.

[4] Esther French and Evelyn Stalter, "Study of Skill Tests in Badminton for College Women," *Research Quarterly*, Vol. XX, No. 3 (October 1949), p. 257.

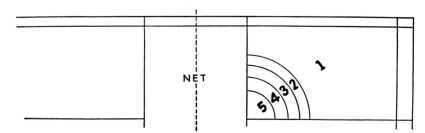

Figure 14.1. Target for the Serve Test (Badminton).

use of different-colored lines helps in scoring). *Scoring:* zero is recorded for each trial that fails to go between the rope and the net or that fails to land in the service court for the doubles game. Score each of the other birds as shown in Figure 14.1. Any bird landing on a line dividing two scoring areas shall receive the higher score. The score of the entire test is the total of 20 trials. Illegal serves shall be repeated.

The Clear Test. The subject returns a serve, attempting to score on the target shown in Figure 14.2 and described as follows: (*a*) A clothesline rope is stretched across the court 14 feet from the net and parallel to it, 8 feet from the floor. (*b*) The following floor markings are made: (1) A line across the court 2 feet nearer the net than the rear service line in the doubles game. (2) A line across the court 2 feet farther from the net than the rear service line in the singles game. The subject stands between the two square marks, X and Y, which are 2 inches square and located 11 feet from the net and 3 feet from the center line. The service shall be

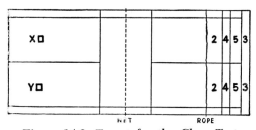

Figure 14.2. Target for the Clear Test (Badminton).

made from the intersection of the short line and the center line on the target side of the net; the bird must cross the net with enough force to carry it to the line between the two squares before it touches the floor. As soon as the bird is hit, the subject may move about as she wishes. *Scoring:* A zero is recorded for each trial that fails to go over the rope or that fails to land on the target. Score each of the

327

other birds as shown in the diagram. Any bird landing on a line dividing two scoring areas shall receive the higher score. The score on the entire test is the total of 20 trials. If the stroke is "carried" or "slung," it is considered a foul, and the trial is repeated.

The following grading plan for the badminton skill test has been proposed by the committee:

Beginners		Advanced	
A	115–145	A	170–180
B	85–114	B	110–169
C	40–84	C	55–109
D	15–39	D	25–54
Fd	0–14	Fd	0–24

A T-score scale was also presented and appears in Scott's report. This scale may be found useful in checking improvement and in motivating performance.

Lockhart-McPherson Badminton Test. Lockhart and McPherson [5] proposed a badminton test for college women, which consists of volleying a shuttlecock against a wall. While intended for college women, Mathews [6] has reported that it is equally satisfactory for college men. In the validation of the test, the originators obtained the following correlations: .71 between the test results and the evaluation of badminton playing ability by three experienced judges, and .60 between the test results and percentage of total games won in a round-robin badminton tournament. The test-retest reliability correlation for the volleying test was .90.

The following wall and court markings are needed for this test: *Wall markings:* An unobstructed wall space at least 10 feet high and 10 feet wide is needed; across this space a one-inch net line is marked 5 feet above and parallel to the floor. *Floor markings:* Two floor lines parallel to the wall are necessary; a starting line is drawn 6½ feet from the wall and a restraining line is drawn 3 feet from the wall. Other items of equipment needed are a badminton racket, shuttlecock, stop watch, and score sheets.

To start the test, the subject stands behind the starting line with a badminton racquet in one hand and a shuttlecock in the other;

[5] Aileene Lockhart and Frances A. McPherson, "The Development of a Test of Badminton Playing Ability," *Research Quarterly,* Vol. XX, No. 4 (December 1949), p. 402.

[6] Donald K. Mathews, *Measurement in Physical Education* (Philadelphia: W. B. Saunders Company, 1958), p. 158.

on the signal to start, she serves the shuttlecock against the wall above the net line. The shuttlecock is volleyed against the wall as many times as possible in 30 seconds. The score is the number of hits made on or above the net line without crossing the restraining line in making the play. If the shuttlecock is missed, the player must retrieve it and put it back in play with a serve from behind the starting line.

The score is the total number of legal hits made on or above the net line in the time allowed. T-scales for college women appear in the reference. However, any physical educator using the test may easily construct scales of his or her own in accordance with instructions in Appendix A.

BASEBALL

Wardlaw [7] suggested a regulation baseball test, consisting of the following elements: (1) control and accuracy in pitching, (2) infield throw, (3) batting, and (4) rapid throw. T-score tables were constructed for each element of the test. Validity and reliability coefficients, however, were not given.

Rodgers and Heath [8] constructed a softball test which is limited to fifth- and sixth-grade boys. The validity and reliability of the test battery, however, are low for use in classifying pupils in situations where an accurate measure of softball ability is desired, or in making important judgments concerning individual pupils, although the battery may be used to determine group ratings. The test elements include the following: (1) softball pitch for accuracy, (2) batting, (3) catching fly balls, (4) catching grounders, and (5) hit and run.

Kelson Test. Kelson [9] has proposed a baseball classification plan for boys. His subjects were 64 boys, ages 8 to 12 years, who participated in the 1951 Little League Baseball Program at Las Vegas, New Mexico. His criterion of baseball ability consisted of a composite of the following baseball qualities: seasonal batting averages and the evaluation by 12 judges of distance accuracy in throwing,

---

[7] Charles D. Wardlaw, *Fundamentals of Baseball* (New York: Charles Scribner's Sons, 1929), p. 83.

[8] Elizabeth G. Rodgers and Marjorie L. Heath, "An Experiment in the Use of Knowledge and Skill Tests in Playground Baseball," *Research Quarterly*, Vol. II, No. 4 (December 1931), p. 113.

[9] Robert E. Kelson, "Baseball Classification Plan for Boys," *Research Quarterly*, Vol. XXIV, No. 3 (October 1953), p. 304.

catching of fly balls, and fielding ground balls. A correlation of .85 was obtained between this composite criterion and the distance the boys could throw a baseball. Multiple correlations involving other tests did not appreciably increase the amount of this correlation.

Directions for administering the baseball distance throw are as follows: Lines, five feet apart, are marked off from 50 feet to 200 feet beyond a starting line. Scorers are stationed on the lines 25 feet apart. The subjects are permitted a run before throwing, but are not allowed to cross the starting line. Using Little League baseballs, the score is the best throw in feet of three trials. The following scoring plan is presented by Kelson:

Classification	Distance of Throw
Superior ability	177 feet and over
Above average ability	145 to 176 feet
Average ability	113 to 144 feet
Below average ability	80 to 112 feet
Inferior ability	79 feet and under

BASKETBALL

The number of basketball tests for both boys and girls that have been proposed exceeds that for any other athletic activity. As with skill tests for other physical education activities, the majority of these are based upon the opinions of their authors, unsubstantiated by scientific evidence.

Basketball Test for Boys

A number of fairly satisfactory basketball tests exist for use in boys' physical education programs. Edgren [10] was the first to present such a test based upon statistical analysis, although his report does not give reliability coefficients. A validity coefficient of .77, however, was obtained between the test battery and a subjective rating of the performance of players. Lehsten [11] developed a five-item basketball battery composed of dodging run, 40-foot dash, baskets per minute, wall bounce, and vertical jump. This test is well related (approximately .80) with subjective ratings of basketball ability.

---

[10] H. D. Edgren, "An Experiment in the Testing of Ability and Progress in Basketball," *Research Quarterly*, Vol. III, No. 1 (March 1932), p. 159.

[11] Nelson Lehsten, "A Measure of Basketball Skills in High School Boys," *The Physical Educator*, Vol. V, No. 5 (December 1948), p. 103.

Scale scores for the individual items and the total battery are available in the reference.

Johnson Tests. Another well-constructed basketball test was proposed by Johnson,[12] who experimented with 19 tests, checking each for validity and reliability. Two batteries of tests were finally proposed, to measure the following: (1) *basketball ability*, composed of three test items: field-goal speed test, basketball throw for accuracy, and dribble; (2) *potential basketball ability*, composed of four test items, none of which requires ball handling: footwork, jump and reach, dodging run, and Iowa Revision of the Brace Test. The battery reliability and validity for the ability test were .89 and .88, respectively; for the potential ability test, .93 and .84, respectively. Individual items on the ability test, however, had reliability coefficients ranging from .73 to .80. In securing validity, Johnson used the biserial correlation, dividing all his subjects into two groups, the "good group" and the "poor group."

A brief description of the items on the *Johnson Basketball Ability Test* follows:

1. *Field-goal speed test.* Starting close under the basket in any position he desires, the subject throws as many baskets as he can in 30 seconds. One point is given for each basket made.

2. *Basketball throw for accuracy.* The target is a series of rectangles of various sizes, arranged one inside of the other, the dimensions being as follows: 60 inches by 40 inches, 40 inches by 25 inches, and 20 inches by 10 inches. The target is hung on the wall with the length of the rectangle in a horizontal position, the bottom being 14 inches from the floor. The subject has ten trials, from a distance of 40 feet, using either the baseball or the hook pass. *Scoring:* 3 points, inner rectangle and line; 2 points, middle rectangle and line; and 1 point, outer rectangle and line.

3. *Dribble.* Four hurdles are placed in a line 6 feet apart, with a distance of 12 feet from the starting line to the first hurdle. The subject starts from one end of the starting line (which is six feet long), dribbles around through the hurdles and back to the other end of the starting line. *Scoring:* the number of zones passed in 30 seconds, as shown in Figure 14.3.

---

[12] L. William Johnson, "Objective Test in Basketball for High School Boys." Unpublished master's thesis, State University of Iowa, 1934.

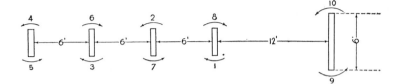

Figure 14.3. Diagram of the Zones for Dribble Test.

The three tests are scored as a battery by adding the three obtained scores. The total score range was 16 to 68, with the median at 42.

Knox Basketball Test. Robert Knox [13] has developed a basketball battery composed of speed dribble, wall bounce, dribble-shoot, and "penny-cup" tests. Reliability coefficients for various test items ranged from .58 to .90; for the total battery the coefficient was .88. The criterion for validating the test was success in making a ten-man high-school varsity basketball squad competing in an Oregon district tournament. Three divisions of basketball ability, nonplayers, substitutes, and first-team members, were compared at eight "B" league high schools composing the district organization. The tests were given to all boys in these schools during the second week after regular basketball practice had started.

The results of the study are as follows: (1) There was 89 per cent agreement between the results of the basketball test and squad membership for tournament play; and 81 per cent agreement with membership on the first team. (2) The six members of the "all-star" team achieved total scores on the test that were not reached by 95 per cent of the 254 boys included in the study. (3) Of the 24 members of the Eugene high-school basketball squad, the total scores obtained on the test agreed with the eventual selection of players taken to the Oregon State Tournament in five out of seven cases as to squad membership and five out of five cases as to membership on the first team.

Scoring of the test is accomplished by adding together directly the scores made on the four tests. The score in each instance is the number of seconds required to complete the test. The probable range of initial scores before extensive coaching and practice is

---

[13] Robert D. Knox, "Basketball Ability Tests," *Scholastic Coach,* Vol. XVII, No. 3 (March 1947), p. 45.

from 34 to 58; low scores are the better scores. Directions for administering the test items follow.

1. *Speed-dribble test:* Four chairs are placed in a straight line so that the first one is 20 feet from the starting line and the others 15 feet apart. The subject dribbles around the chairs as in the Johnson dribble test.
2. *Wall-bounce test:* The subject stands with his toes behind a line five feet from a wall. The object of the test is to ascertain how long it will take him to chest-pass (no batting) the ball against the wall and catch it 15 times.
3. *Dribble-shoot test:* From a starting line on the right side-line of the court, 65 feet from the basket, arrange three chairs directly in line with the basket, so spaced as to divide the distance into four equal segments. The subject dribbles around the obstacles; shoots until he makes a shot; and dribbles back around the obstacles to the starting line.
4. *Penny-cup test:* A 20-foot course is set up with a "signal line" eight feet from the start. Three tin cups, painted blue, white, and red, respectively, are placed five feet apart on the finish line (20-foot mark). The subject stands behind the starting line with his back to the cups and with a penny in his hand; at the signal "Go," he pivots and races toward the cups; as he crosses the "signal line," the tester calls out one of the cup colors; the subject must drop his penny into the cup so designated. The test is repeated four times, the total elapsed time representing the score.

Glines and Petersen [14] used the Knox test to equate students for basketball teams within university men's physical education service classes. The competition between equated teams was very close. They also obtained a correlation of .89 between scores on the basketball test and the total points the participants scored in competition throughout the course. Glines [15] also administered the Knox test early in the season to all boys in the high school at Hamilton City, California. Seventeen of the highest twenty boys on the test made either the varsity or junior varsity basketball teams; the five boys with the highest scores on the test eventually formed the starting lineup on the varsity team.

Boyd, McCachren, and Waglow [16] administered the Knox test to 42 candidates for the University of Florida junior varsity basketball squad. A bi-serial correlation of .96 was obtained between scores on the test and those who made and those who were eventually cut from the squad. The correlations, however, between test

---

[14] Don Glines and Kay Petersen, University of Oregon, informal report, 1956.

[15] Correspondence from Don Glines, December 9, 1956.

[16] Clifford A. Boyd, James R. McCachren, and I. F. Waglow, "Predictive Ability of a Selected Basketball Test," *Research Quarterly,* Vol. XXVI, No. 3 (October 1955), p. 364.

scores and the coach's ratings of each squad member's basketball ability were low.

Stroup Basketball Test. Stroup [17] used the scores made by competing teams as a criterion for validating his basketball skill test. The subjects were 121 students enrolled in college physical education service courses. Each time their class met, they were randomly placed on basketball teams; 82 such teams were formed throughout the study. These teams played a total of 41 ten-minute basketball games. At the end of this competition, they were given tests of goal shooting, wall passing, and dribbling. Approximately 84 per cent of the games were won by the team with the high skill score average.

Descriptions of the techniques used in administering the three items of the Stroup test are as follows:

1. *Goal shooting.* Starting at any position on the floor, the subject shoots as many baskets as possible in one minute, retrieving the ball each time himself.

2. *Wall passing.* The subject stands behind a line six feet from a wall and passes the ball against the wall as many times as possible in one minute. A pass is not counted if the ball is batted instead of caught and passed and if the subject moves over the restraining line when making a pass.

3. *Dribbling.* The subject dribbles alternately to the left and right of bottles placed in a line 15-feet apart for a 90-foot distance, circles the end bottle each time, and continues for one minute. A miss is counted if a bottle is knocked over or if the bottle is not passed on the proper side. The score is the number of bottles properly passed in the time limit.

Each subject's raw scores for the three items are converted to scale scores, which are then averaged to obtain his basketball skill score. Stroup's table for this conversion appears in Appendix B, Table XLII.

Basketball Tests for Girls

In the women's field, Young and Moser [18] have constructed a

---

[17] Francis Stroup, "Game Results as a Criterion for Validating Basketball Skill Test," *Research Quarterly*, Vol. XXVI, No. 3 (October 1955), p. 353.

[18] Genevieve Young and Helen Moser, "A Short Battery of Tests to Measure Playing Ability in Women's Basketball," *Research Quarterly*, Vol. V, No. 2 (May 1934), p. 3.

satisfactory test of basketball ability. Their battery is composed of: (1) wall-bouncing speed test, (2) accuracy throw at a moving target, (3) free jump, (4) Edgren ball handling test, and (5) bounce and shoot. The test has a validity coefficient of .86, with ratings by expert judges of each player's ability in a game situation as the criterion measure. Schwartz [19] has worked out a battery of basketball tests for high-school girls, validating them through critical analysis by experts, and has constructed scoring tables for each element of the test. Validity and reliability coefficients are not given in the report. Colvin, Glassow, and Schwartz [20] have also constructed a test which includes five items with satisfactory reliability coefficients. A validity coefficient of .66 is given for three of the tests, the best combination that the authors found.

Leilich Test. In a factor analysis study of the primary components of selected basketball tests for college women, Leilich [21] found four factors to be basic for these tests: basketball motor ability, speed, ball handling involving passing accuracy and speed, and ball handling involving accuracy in goal shooting. On the basis of this analysis, the following three tests were proposed: bounce and shoot, half-minute shooting, and push pass. Achievement scales on these tests have been constructed by the Professional Studies and Research Committee of the Midwest Association of College Teachers of Physical Education for Women.[22]

Directions for administering the three women's basketball tests are as follows:

1. *Bounce and Shoot.* Two dotted lines are drawn on the floor in a "V," with the apex at the middle of the endline under the basket and extending at 45-degree angles for 18 feet on both sides of the court. A 24-inch solid line is centered at the end of each dotted line and at right angles to them. One foot behind and 30 inches to the

---

[19] Helen Schwartz, "Knowledge and Achievement Tests in Girls' Basketball on the Senior High School Level," *Research Quarterly*, Vol. VIII, No. 1 (March 1937), p. 143.

[20] Ruth B. Glassow and Marion R. Broer, *Measuring Achievement in Physical Education* (Philadelphia: W. B. Saunders Company, 1938), p. 103.

[21] Avis Leilich, "The Primary Components of Selected Basketball Tests for College Women," Microcarded Doctoral Dissertation, Indiana University, 1952.

[22] Wilma K. Miller, Chairman, "Achievement Levels in Basketball Skills for Women Physical Education Majors," *Research Quarterly,* Vol. XXV, No. 4 (December 1954), p. 450.

outside of the 18-foot lines, 18-inch lines are drawn; at each of these, forward legs touching the line, a chair is located and a basketball is placed on it.

In taking the test, the subject starts behind the 24-inch line at the right of the basket. At the signal, she picks up the ball from the chair, bounces it once, shoots for the basket, recovers the rebound, and passes the ball to a catcher behind the chair from which she got the ball (the catcher replaces the ball on the chair). She then runs to the chair on the left side and repeats as before. This performance is continued, alternating five times on each side. Each bounce must start from behind a 24-inch line. Fouls consist of running with the ball, double bouncing, and failure to start each time at the 24-inch line. The test terminates when the subject has retrieved the ball after the tenth shot at the basket. In scoring, the subject receives two scores, as follows:

a. *Time Score:* Time is taken to the nearest tenth of a second from the starting signal until the girl has caught or retrieved the ball following the tenth attempted shot at the basket; one second is added to this time for each foul committed.

b. *Accuracy Score:* Two points are awarded for each basket made, one point for hitting the rim but not making the basket, and no point for missing both the basket and the rim.

2. *Half-Minute Shooting.* Starting at any position she chooses on the court, the subject shoots as many baskets as possible in 30 seconds. If the ball has left her hands at the end of 30 seconds, the basket counts if made. The score is the largest number of baskets made in two trials.

3. *Push-Pass.* A three-ring concentric target is drawn on the wall, with the lower edge of the outer ring 24 inches from the floor; one-half-inch lines are used and are included within the diameter of each circle. The radii for the rings are: inner ring, 10 inches; middle ring, 20 inches; outer ring, 30 inches. The contestant stands behind a restraining line 10 feet from the wall. The test consists in passing a basketball with a two-hand chest pass to the target, recovering the pass, and continuing to pass for 30 seconds. All passes must be made from behind the restraining line. The subject is scored 5, 3, and 1 for hitting within the inner, middle, and outer circles respectively. Line hits are counted for the inner circle area.

FOOTBALL

Borleske [23] has proposed a test designed to measure ability to play touch football, composed of five items, as follows: (1) forward pass for distance, (2) catching forward passes, (3) punting for distance, (4) 50-yard dash carrying the ball, and (5) zone pass defense. In constructing the test, Borleske experimented with 18 individual objective tests, obtaining a validity coefficient of .85 with the opinion of experts using a check sheet for subjectively rating performance. The battery of five tests finally selected has a correlation of .93 with the larger objective battery of which the five tests were a part. A short battery of three tests (forward pass for distance, punting for distance, and 50-yard dash with the ball) correlated .88 with the criterion.

A description of the short battery of touch football tests is given below. The omission of the pass-catching and pass-defense items simplifies the test considerably and reduces the amount of time required for its administration.

1. *Forward pass for distance.* The field is marked with lines every five yards and with markers every ten yards, so that the subjects can throw in pairs from both ends of the field. From one to six pairs of passers, depending on the width of the field, can throw together. Each passer checks the spot where the ball hits the ground when his partner throws, and estimates the distance to the nearest yard. Each participant is allowed three throws after warming up for one minute. The best throw of the three trials is counted. Each throw must be preceded by the catch of a pass from center.

2. *Punt for distance.* The punt for distance is executed in much the same way as the pass for distance described above, the punters working in pairs, each punter being allowed three trials, the punt being preceded by a pass from center. The ball must be kicked within two seconds after receiving the center pass.

3. *Running-straightaway, speed, or sprint.* The subject starts on snap of ball by center from a point five yards back of center and from a backfield three-point stance, catches the ball, and carries it by any form used in football for a distance of 50 yards, running as

---

[23] Frederick W. Cozens, "Ninth Annual Report of Committee on Curriculum Research of the College Physical Education Association: Part III," *Research Quarterly*, Vol. VIII, No. 2 (May 1937), p. 73.

fast as possible. One minute is allowed for warm-up. A T-score table appears in Table XLIII, Appendix B.

GOLF

Although the game of golf may be considered its own best test, a number of attempts have been made to measure the various elements involved, especially for indoor use. These tests usually have the added advantage of being good practice media. Two types of tests have been developed: (*a*) tests in which devices are used; (*b*) tests in which various shots are recorded for accuracy on a target.

Clevett [24] has proposed empirical indoor tests for accuracy with the brassie, midiron, mashie, and putter. Although not scientifically constructed and lacking in norms, these tests have sufficient interest and practical value to warrant brief descriptions.

1–2. *Brassie and midiron tests.* These tests are given in a cage. The target is ten feet square, marked off into 25 areas, each of which is 20 inches square, and placed 21 feet from the tee. The point values of the various squares are given in Figure 14.4 (a). Balls striking to the left of the target are scored higher than those striking to the right (for right-handed players), as Clevett maintains that a ball which strikes the right side of the target would slice, an outstanding error in golf. Each individual plays ten shots with the brassie and ten with the midiron. No preliminary practice or instruction is permitted.

3. *Mashie test.* The mashie test is designed to ascertain the individual's ability to make a short approach shot to the green. The approach is from 15 feet from the nearest edge of a target, composed of gymnasium mats, marked off into 25 areas each of which is four feet square. The point values of the various squares are given in Figure 14.4 (b). Ten shots are permitted, each being scored according to the spot where the ball lands rather than where it rolls or bounces.

4. *Putting test.* The putting test is made on smooth carpets 27 inches wide and 20 feet long, securely fastened to the floor. The putting line is 15 feet from the "hole." Forty-eight scoring areas, each nine inches square, are marked off on the carpet as shown in

[24] Melvin A. Clevett, "An Experiment in Teaching Methods of Golf," *Research Quarterly,* Vol. II, No. 4 (December 1931), p. 104.

Figure 14.4 (c). Balls that stop slightly short of the hole are considered to be lower in point value than balls that travel slightly beyond the hole, as on an irregular green such a ball often rolls into the hole. The score is counted as the point where the ball stops. Ten trials are permitted.

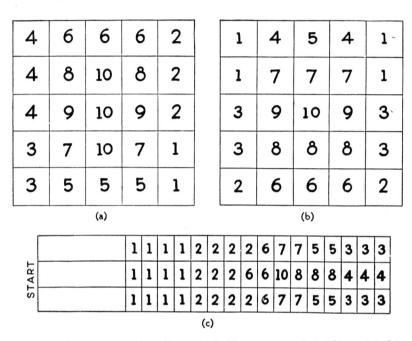

Figure 14.4. Targets for Clevett's Golf Test: Brassie-Midiron, Mashie, and Putting.

GYMNASTICS

Little work has been done in measuring general gymnastic ability, except as based upon subjective judgment. As form plays such a large part, the construction of objective tests for this activity is difficult. Zwarg,[25] however, has given excellent suggestions for judging competitive gymnastic exercises. Hunsicker and Loken [26] analyzed

[25] Leopold F. Zwarg, "Judging and Evaluation of Competitive Apparatus for Gymnastic Exercises," *Journal of Health and Physical Education*, Vol. VI, No. 1 (January 1935), p. 23.

[26] Paul Hunsicker and Newt Loken, "The Objectivity of Judging at the National Collegiate Athletic Association Gymnastic Meet," *Research Quarterly*, Vol. XXII, No. 4 (December 1951), p. 423.

the judging of the 1950 National Collegiate Athletic Association Gymnastic Meet and found that the objectivity coefficients were reasonably high. Judging on the horizontal bar was most and tumbling was least consistent.

Wettstone [27] studied the factors underlying potential ability in gymnastics and tumbling. A list of the qualities of a good gymnast was developed and tests for 15 of those gymnasts with highest ranking were devised. With 22 active gymnasts at the University of Iowa as subjects, a correlation of .79 was obtained between ratings of their abilities by gymnastic coaches and the following three elements: (1) thigh circumference divided by height; (2) strength test, consisting of chinning, dipping, and thigh flexion; and (3) the Burpee (squat-thrust) test for ten seconds. In the strength test, the three test items are added together. Thigh-flexion strength is measured by having the subject hang from stall bars and flex the leg and thigh to a horizontal position as many times as possible. The following regression equation is used to predict the subject's potential gymnastic ability, PGA (the X-numerals refer to the numbered variables above):

$$PGA = .355X_1 + .260X_2 + .035X_3 + 13.990$$

HANDBALL

Only one handball test has been subjected to statistical analysis. Cornish [28] experimented with the following test items: 30-second volley, front-wall placement, back-wall placement, power stroke, and placement-service. A correlation of .67 was obtained between a combination of the 30-second volley and the service-placement tests and a criterion measure composed of the total number of points scored by each subject minus those scored against him in playing 23 games.

RHYTHM TESTS

Several efforts have been made to measure motor rhythms and dance. For the most part, however, these have not as yet advanced

---

[27] Eugene Wettstone, "Tests for Predicting Potential Ability in Gymnastics and Tumbling," *Research Quarterly,* Vol. IX, No. 4 (December 1938), p. 115.

[28] Clayton Cornish, "A Study of Measurement of Ability in Handball," *Research Quarterly,* Vol. XX, No. 2 (May 1949), p. 215.

to the practical stage. Annett [29] obtained a low correlation of .47 between the Seashore Rhythm Test and a criterion consisting of expert judgment of skill in motor rhythm. Lemon and Sherbon,[30] after studying the Seashore Rhythm Test and others of their own device, concluded that tests of this quality more useful to physical education were possible and deserved further study. Shambaugh,[31] utilizing rather complicated procedures and a small number of subjects, developed an improved method for measuring rhythmic motor response.

Over a period of five and one-half years, Ashton [32] developed a gross motor rhythm test using simple movement initiated by the student. This test consists of three sections: directed walk, run, and skip; musical excerpts for improvisation; derived or combined dance steps, in which the step is identified but the subject initiates the movement for polka, waltz, and schottische. Rating scales for the sections of the test appear in the reference. Ashton concluded that the administration of this test had proven feasible and economical of time when varied forms of dance have to be judged without excessive staff training and with the use of only one period of class time.

In preparing a social dancing test, Waglow [33] had a record transcribed for the following rhythms: waltz, tango, slow fox trot, jitterbug, rhumba, and samba. The test consists of an evaluation of the subject's ability to perform each of the dance steps to the recorded music. The reported objectivity coefficient for the test is .79.

Benton [34] studied, not only elements of rhythm, but factors basic to dance movement techniques, including: Johnson-type tests, McCloy Physical Fitness Index, Seashore Series A Rhythm Test, Brace-

---

29 Thomas Annett, "A Study of Rhythmic Capacity and Performance in Motor Rhythm in Physical Education Majors," *Research Quarterly*, Vol. III, No. 2 (May 1932), p. 183.

30 Eloise Lemon and Elizabeth Sherbon, "A Study of Relationships of Certain Measures of Rhythmic Ability and Motor Ability in Girls and Women," *Supplement to Research Quarterly*, Vol. V, No. 1 (March 1934), p. 82.

31 Mary Effie Shambaugh, "The Objective Measurement of Success in the Teaching of Folk Dancing to University Women," *Research Quarterly*, Vol. VI, No. 1 (March 1935), p. 33.

32 Dudley Ashton, "A Gross Motor Rhythm Test," *Research Quarterly*, Vol. XXIV, No. 3 (October 1953), p. 253.

33 I. F. Waglow, "An Experiment in Social Dance Testing," *Research Quarterly*, Vol. XXIV, No. 1 (March 1953), p. 97.

34 Rachel Jane Benton, "The Measurement of Capacities for Learning Dance Movement Techniques," *Research Quarterly*, Vol. XV, No. 2 (May 1944), p. 137.

type tests, Motor Rhythm Test, and Static Balance Test. A criterion of the judgment of three dance experts, who observed the subjects on selected dance movements, was established. Multiple correlations between .77 and .93, when corrected for attenuation, were reported for five regression equations using various combinations of variables found significant in the research.

SOCCER AND SPEEDBALL

Heath and Rodgers [35] have constructed a soccer test in which validity is determined and reliability coefficients of the various test items are computed. The individual test elements consist of a dribble, a throw-in, a place kick for goal, and kicking a rolling ball. This test is designed for fifth- and sixth-grade boys. The reliability of the test battery is between .71 and .74.

Buchanan [36] developed the following speedball tests for high-school girls: lift of ball to others, throwing and catching, kick-ups, dribbling, and passing. Validity coefficients for the various tests range from .57 to .88 against a criterion of combined teacher ratings of playing ability. Reliability coefficients are high; T-scales for each test are available. A short battery consisting of the throwing and catching test plus three times the passing test is suggested for use, if testing time is limited. A complete description of the test appears in the Scott and French textbook.

McDonald Volleying Soccer Test. McDonald [37] studied the use of volleying a soccer ball against a backboard as a test of general soccer ability. With college men as subjects, he obtained the following correlations between scores on the test and the ratings of playing ability by their coaches: .94 for varsity players, .63 for junior varsity players, .76 for freshman varsity players, and .85 for the combined groups.

The backboard for the test is 30 feet wide and 11½ feet high. A restraining line is drawn nine feet from the backboard and parallel to it. Three soccer balls are used: one is placed on the restrain-

---

[35] Marjorie L. Heath and Elizabeth G. Rodgers, "A Study in the Use of Knowledge and Skill Tests in Soccer," *Research Quarterly*, Vol. III, No. 4 (December 1932), p. 33.

[36] M. Gladys Scott and Esther French, *Evaluation in Physical Education* (St. Louis: C. V. Mosby Company, 1950), pp. 120-129.

[37] Lloyd G. McDonald, "The Construction of a Kicking Skill Test as an Index of General Soccer Ability," Unpublished Master's Thesis, Springfield College, 1951.

ing line; the other two are located nine feet behind this line in the center of the area. The test consists of kicking the soccer ball against the backboard as many times as possible in 30 seconds. Any type kicks may be used; both ground balls and fly balls which hit the backboard count. To count, however, all balls must be kicked from the ground with the supporting leg behind the restraining line. Rebounds may be retrieved in any manner, including use of the hands. If a ball is out of control, the subject may play one of the spare balls, but must bring the ball by use of hands or feet to a position at the restraining line before kicking against the backboard (no penalty other than the lost time in getting the ball in position to kick). The score is the number of legal kicks in the time period; the best of four trials is recorded.

SWIMMING

A large number of tests have been proposed for testing swimming ability. Many of these have been empirically established to measure various levels of swimming ability: beginner, intermediate, and advanced. Cureton [38] has done a great deal of work in this area; his studies were among the early attempts at a scientific foundation for swimming.

Hewitt's Scales. Hewitt has done some excellent and very practical work in the construction of swimming achievement scales for men in the armed forces, for college men, and for high-school boys and girls. The test items for the various groups are as follows:

1. *High-school boys and girls:* [39] time for the 25-yard flutter kick while holding a regulation water polo ball; time for the 50-yard crawl; and number of strokes to cover 25 yards each with the elementary back, side, and breast strokes (glide and relaxation tests).

2. *College men:* [40] time for 20- and 25-yard underwater swims; distance covered during 15-minute swim for endurance; time for 25- and 50-yard swims each with the crawl, breast, and back-crawl strokes; and number of strokes to cover 50 yards each with the ele-

---

[38] Thomas K. Cureton, *How to Teach Swimming and Diving* (New York: Association Press, 1934).

[39] Jack E. Hewitt, "Achievement Scales for High School Swimming," *Research Quarterly*, Vol. XX, No. 2 (May 1949), p. 170.

[40] Jack E. Hewitt, "Swimming Achievement Scales for College Men," *Research Quarterly*, Vol. XIX, No. 4 (December 1948), p. 282.

mentary back, side, and breast strokes (glide and relaxation tests).

3. *Men in the armed forces:* [41] time for the 20- and 25-yard underwater swims; distance covered during 15-minute swim for endurance; and number of strokes to cover 50 yards each with elementary back, side, and breast strokes (glide and relaxation tests).

The reliability of the tests at the college and high-school levels was checked with entirely satisfactory results. The coefficients for the various tests ranged from .89 to .95. At these levels, too, criteria of over-all swimming ability were established, consisting in each situation of the total accomplishment in all events. Short batteries of swimming tests to be used for classification purposes were then determined. For college men, the 25-yard or 50-yard crawl plus the three gliding strokes correlated .87 with the criterion; for high-school boys and girls, the side-stroke gliding test correlated .94 with the total score.

Fox Swimming Power Test. An objective test of swimming power for the front crawl and side strokes has been developed by Fox.[42] The reliability coefficients for the two tests are .95 and .97 respectively. T-scores were prepared, based on the performance of college women ranging in ability from beginning to advanced swimmers. These norms appear in Table XLIV, Appendix B. According to the author, the test promises to be as effective for the elementary back, back crawl, and breast strokes. Directions for administering the test follow.

A rope approximately 20 feet longer than the width of the pool is tied at one end to some firm object two feet from one end of the pool; the other end remains free directly across the pool. A weight is suspended from the rope at a point half way across the pool, so that the rope will drop when the free end is released. Starting at the position of the rope, the deck of the pool is marked off in 5-foot intervals with adhesive or masking tape; distances from the start may be marked on these with waterproof material.

In taking the test, the rope is pulled taut enough so that it is about a foot under water at the point the subject is to start. The swimmer assumes the appropriate floating position for the stroke

---

[41] Jack E. Hewitt, "Achievement Scales for Wartime Swimming," *Research Quarterly,* Vol. XIV, No. 4 (December 1943), p. 391.

[42] Margaret G. Fox, "Swimming Power Test," *Research Quarterly,* Vol. XXVIII, No. 3 (October 1957), p. 233.

(i.e., side float for side stroke, face float for crawl stroke), and rests her feet on the rope with the malleoli at rope level. At the start, the rope is dropped; the swimmer takes five complete strokes with glides. The distance covered for the side stroke is measured from the rope to the position of the ankles at the beginning of the recovery of the legs for the sixth stroke. For the crawl stroke, the distance traversed by the swimmer is measured by noting where the ankles are at the moment the fingers enter the water to begin the sixth arm cycle. The distance measurement is made to the nearest foot from the five-foot distance markers on the deck.

TENNIS

Dyer Backboard Test. A backboard volleying test of general tennis ability has been constructed by Dyer.[43] Thus, the test does not analyze the various strokes and elements of the game. It has been used extensively as a classification device for tennis and as a means of determining the progress being made in the game as a whole. The test consists merely of volleying a tennis ball as rapidly as possible against a backboard. Directions for administering the test are as follows:

1. A backboard or wall, approximately 10 feet in height, and allowing about 15 feet in width for each person taking the test at one time, is used. A line three inches in width, to represent the net, is drawn across the backboard so that the top line is three feet from the floor.

2. A restraining line, five feet from the base of the wall, is drawn on the floor.

3. Two balls and a racquet are provided for each subject taking the test at one time. A box containing extra balls, about 12 inches long, 9 inches wide, and 3 inches deep,, is provided and placed on the floor at the junction of the restraining line and the left side-line for right-handed players, and at the right for left-handed players.

4. In starting the test, the subject drops the ball and lets it hit the floor once, then plays it against the wall as rapidly as possible

---

[43] Joanna T. Dyer, "The Backboard Test of Tennis Ability," *Supplement to the Research Quarterly,* Vol. VI, No. 1 (March 1935), p. 63, and "Revision of Backboard Test of Tennis Ability," *Research Quarterly,* Vol. IX, No. 1 (March 1938), p. 25.

for 30 seconds. There is no limit to the number of times the ball may bounce before it is hit. Also, with the exception of the start and when a new ball is put into play, the ball need not touch the floor before being played. Any stroke or combination of strokes may be used, but all balls must be played from behind the restraining line. The line may be crossed to retrieve balls, but any hits made while in such a position do not count. Any number of balls may be used. If the subject loses control of the ball, she may use the second that was supplied to her, after which, if necessary, she may take other balls from the box.

5. Each ball striking the wall on or above the net line before the end of the 30 seconds counts as a hit and scores one point. Three trials are given, the final score being the sum of the scores on the three trials.

6. For efficient administration of the test, divide the group into units of four players each, numbered from one to four. Their duties are as follows:

a. No. 1 takes the test.
b. No. 2 counts the number of balls that strike the wall on or above the net line.
c. No. 3 checks the number of violations at the restraining line.
d. No. 4 collects and returns all balls to the box.
e. After each person in the entire group has had one trial, the test is repeated in the same order, until everyone has had three trials in all.

7. Scoring tables for the Dyer test have been computed and appear in Table XLV of Appendix B. T-score and percentile rank norms for this test as applied to women physical education students have been prepared by Miller, and will be found in her reference.[44]

Dyer reported a correlation of .92 between scores on her test and the relative positions of the subjects following round-robin play, in which each match consisted of 20 points (the probable equivalent of three or four games). Fox [45] obtained a correlation of .53 between scores of college women beginning players on the Dyer test and subjective ratings of their ability to execute the forehand drive,

---

[44] Wilma K. Miller, "Achievement Levels in Tennis Knowledge and Skill for Women Physical Education Major Students," *Research Quarterly,* Vol. XXIV, No. 1 (March 1953), p. 81.

[45] Katharine Fox, "A Study of the Validity of the Dyer Backboard Test and the Miller Forehand-Backhand Test for Beginning Tennis Players," *Research Quarterly,* Vol. XXIV, No. 1 (March 1953), p. 1.

the backhand drive, and the serve. Using a restraining line of 28 feet (instead of five feet), Koski [46] obtained correlation coefficients ranging from .51 to .68 between wall rally results and tournament play, with college men as subjects. He also constructed norms for beginning and intermediate levels of tennis ability.

An accurate account of the use of the Dyer Tennis Test in a field situation was kept by Leon Doleva, when faced with coaching and instructing tennis at Williston Academy.[47] Sixty boys were tested and arranged into three groups: the first squad was considered the varsity and had twelve boys; the other two groups had twenty-four boys each. Ladder tournaments within each group were organized, and an opportunity was provided for boys to change from one group to the other on the basis of tennis merit. Certain of the results were reported as follows: the six boys with the highest test scores became the first six players on the school team and were never displaced; the number one man on the test became the number one man on the team; and only two members from the intermediate group were able to advance to the first squad.

Broer-Miller Test. Broer and Miller [48] designed a test to measure the ability of college women to place forehand and backhand drives into the backcourt area. One regulation net is used, with a rope stretched four feet above the top of the net. Special tennis court markings are needed, as illustrated in Figure 14.5.

In taking this test, the subject stands behind the baseline, bounces the ball to herself, and attempts to hit it into the back 9 feet of the opposite court. Fourteen trials are taken each with forehand and with backhand strokes. Each ball is scored 2-4-6-8-6-4-2, depending upon the area in which it lands, as shown in Figure 14.5. Balls that go over the rope score one-half the value of that area in which they land. If the player misses the ball in attempting to strike it, it is considered a trial. "Let" balls are taken over.

Broer and Miller obtained a reliability coefficient for this test of .80 for both beginning and intermediate tennis players. The validity of the test was determined by correlating the ratings given the

---

[46] Arthur Koski, "A Tennis Wall Rally Test for College Men," mimeographed report.

[47] Clayton T. Shay, "An Application of the Dyer Tennis Test," *Journal of Health and Physical Education,* Vol. XX, No. 4 (April 1949), p. 273.

[48] Marion R. Broer and Donna Mae Miller, "Achievement Tests for Beginning and Intermediate Tennis," *Research Quarterly,* Vol. XXI, No. 3 (October 1950), p. 303.

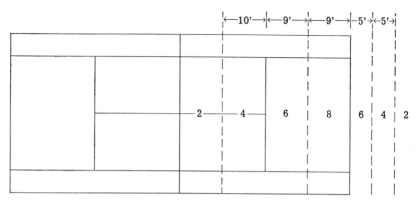

Figure 14.5. Court Markings for Forehand-Backhand Drive Test.

subject by various judges with the subject's performance on the test. For the intermediate group, this correlation was .85; for the beginning group, it was .61. Fox [49] reported a correlation of .69 between the Dyer and Broer-Miller tests, with college women as subjects.

TABLE TENNIS

A table-tennis test, patterned after the Dyer tennis test procedure, has been constructed by Mott and Lockhart.[50] For the test, a table-tennis table is needed, hinged in the middle and arranged so that one-half of it is propped against a post or wall above and perpendicular to the playing surface, so as to serve as a backboard. A chalk line is marked on the perpendicular half of the table, six inches above the playing surface of the table; a kitchen match box is thumbtacked to the edge of the table and even to its end (place on the right side for right-handed players; on the left side for left-handed players). A stop watch, table-tennis racket, and three table-tennis balls are also necessary.

The testing procedure is as follows: At the signal "Go," the player drops a ball to the table and rallies it against the perpendicular table surface as many times as possible in 30 seconds. Any number of bounces on the playing surface are permitted. If the player loses control of the ball, another may be taken from the match box, dropped to the playing surface, and played. Hits on the perpendicu-

[49] Katharine Fox, *op. cit.*

[50] Jane A. Mott and Aileen Lockhart, "Table Tennis Backboard Test," *Journal of Health and Physical Education,* Vol. XVII, No. 9 (November 1946), p. 550.

lar surface do not count if the ball is volleyed, the player puts her free hand on the table during or immediately preceding a hit, or the ball strikes the perpendicular surface below the chalk line. The test score is the best score of three trials.

A reliability coefficient of .90 for the table-tennis backboard test with college women as subjects was obtained. A validity coefficient of .84 is also reported, but the criterion is not given. T-scales for college women were constructed and appear in Appendix B, Table XLVI.

VOLLEYBALL

The items usually found in volleyball tests include the following: serving, return over net, volleying, passing, spiking or killing, set-up, and playing out of the net. French and Cooper [51] experimented with four test elements: repeated volleys, serving, set-up and pass, and recovery from net. They found that the best combination of measures for girls in Grades 9 to 12 was the serving test and repeated volleys. The validity coefficient of this combination, with ratings of volleyball ability as the criterion, was found to be .81. Bassett, Glassow, and Locke [52] studied the reliability and validity of two volleyball test items, serving and volleying, with college women. Reliability of the serving test was .84, and of the volleyball test, .89. Validity coefficients, using the composite ratings of three judges as criterion, were .79 for the serving test and .51 for the volleying test.

Russell-Lange Volleyball Test. Russell and Lange [53] studied the two test items recommended by French and Cooper, serving and repeated volleys, as applied to girls in Grades 7, 8, and 9. They concluded that these tests, with slight modifications, were adequate for use with girls in the junior high school. Validity and reliability ratings were about the same as those reported by French and Cooper.

Brief descriptions of the serving and volleying tests as given by Russell and Lange are as follows:

Serving Test. The subject serves ten times in a legal manner into

---

[51] Esther L. French and Bernice I. Cooper, "Achievement Tests in Volleyball for High School Girls," *Research Quarterly,* Vol. VIII, No. 2 (May 1937), p. 150.

[52] Gladys Bassett, Ruth Glassow, and Mabel Locke, "Studies in Testing Volleyball Skills," *Research Quarterly,* Vol. VIII, No. 4 (December 1937), p. 60.

[53] Naomi Russell and Elizabeth Lange, "Achievement Tests in Volleyball for High School Girls," *Research Quarterly,* Vol. XI, No. 4 (December 1940), p. 33.

a target on the court across the net. "Let" serves are repeated. Special court markings, as shown in Figure 14.6: (1) Chalk line across court 5 feet inside and parallel to end line. (2) Chalk line across

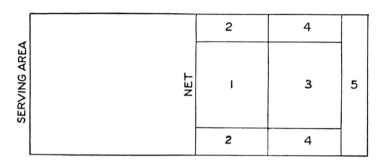

Figure 14.6. Diagram of the Zones for the Serving Test.

court parallel to and 12½ feet from the line under the net. (3) Chalk lines 5 feet inside and parallel to each side line, extending from line under the net to line (1). Each serve is scored according to the value of the target area in which the ball lands, as shown in the diagram. A ball landing on a line separating two areas is given the highest value. A ball landing on a side or the end line scores the value of the area adjacent. Trials in which foot faults occur score zero. (This test is identical with the one proposed by French and Cooper.)

Volleying Test. In this test, the subject volleys as rapidly as possible against a wall. Special court markings are as follows: (1) A line 10 feet long marked on the wall at net height, 7 feet 6 inches from the floor. (2) A line on the floor opposite the wall marking, 10 feet long and 3 feet from the wall. The subject starts the volley from behind the 3-foot line, with an underhand movement tosses the ball to the wall, and then volleys the ball repeatedly against the wall above the net line for 30 seconds. The ball may be set up as many times as desired or necessary; it may be caught and re-started with a toss as at the beginning. If the ball gets out of control, it must be retrieved by the subject and put into play at the 3-foot line as at the beginning. The score consists of the number of times the ball is clearly batted (not tossed) from behind the 3-foot line to the wall above or on the net line. The best score of three trials should be recorded. Rest periods between trials should be allowed. (In the French-Cooper volleying test, each trial is for 15 seconds and a total of 10 trials is completed by each subject, the score for the test being the sum of the five best trials.) Russell and Lange have also provided scoring tables for these two tests applied to junior-high-school girls, as shown in Table XLVII, Appendix B.

Brady Volleyball Test. A volleying test has been proposed by Brady[54] as a measure of general volleyball playing ability for college men. In this test, a simple target is marked on a smooth side wall, consisting of a horizontal chalk line 5 feet long and 11 feet 6 inches from the floor; vertical lines are extended upward toward the ceiling at the ends of the horizontal line. In the test, the subject stands where he wishes and throws the ball against the wall; he then volleys it as many times as possible in one minute. Only legal volleys are counted, i.e., they must be volleys, not thrown balls, and they must hit the wall within the boundaries of the target. If the ball is caught or gets out of control, it is started again as at the beginning of the test.

A reliability coefficient of .93 was found between repeated tests by the subjects during the same testing period. For validity, a co-efficient of .86 is reported between scores on the test and the combined subjective judgment of four qualified observers.

ACHIEVEMENT SCALES

The Cozens Scales

Cozens and associates have developed a large number of achievement scales covering all school levels, elementary grades through college, for both boys and girls. In each instance, the pupil is classified according to the Cozens Classification Index. Scoring scales for the same events are given separately for each of the classifications. The scales are based upon the six-sigma score procedure with special corrections devised for events found to give skewed distributions. The various achievement reports with a summary of the events included are given below.

1. N. P. Neilson and Frederick W. Cozens, *Achievement Scales in Physical Education Activities for Boys and Girls in Elementary and Junior High Schools* (New York: A. S. Barnes and Company, 1934).

---

[54] George F. Brady, "Preliminary Investigations of Volleyball Playing Ability," *Research Quarterly*, Vol. XVI, No. 1 (March 1945), p. 14.

Thirty-three events for boys and 20 for girls are included: track-and-field type, strength items (boys only), and skills of baseball, basketball, and soccer.

2. Frederick W. Cozens, Hazel J. Cubberly, and N. P. Neilson, *Achievement Scales in Physical Education Activities for Secondary School Girls and College Women* (New York: A. S. Barnes and Company, 1937). Scales for baseball, basketball, running and soccer test items are included for college women, senior-high-school girls, and junior-high-school girls. The junior-high-school girls also have scales for jumping and hopping events. For college women and senior-high-school girls, scales for test items in field hockey, speedball, swimming, and volleyball are available. In addition the college women's series contains scales in archery and tennis events.

3. Frederick W. Cozens, Martin H. Trieb, and N. P. Neilson, *Physical Achievement Scales for Boys in Secondary Schools* (New York: A. S. Barnes and Company, 1936). Forty-five scales are presented of the following types: baseball, basketball, football, gymnastics, strength, track and field (runs, jumps, hurdles, shot-put), and walking.

4. Frederick W. Cozens, *Achievement Scales in Physical Education Activities for College Men* (Philadelphia: Lea and Febiger, 1936). These scales are for 35 tests of essentially the same types as for high-school boys, but with a different selection of events.

The McCloy Scales

McCloy [55] has also prepared some fifty scoring tables for boys and young men involving running, walking, jumping, vaulting, weight-throwing, and strength events. The classification for participation in these events is based on his classification indices as appropriate to the age level involved.

TESTS OF GENERAL SPORTS SKILLS

Attempts have been made to develop test batteries which will sample skills in a number of sports. Two of these will be described below.

---

[55] C. H. McCloy, *The Measurement of Athletic Power* (New York: A. S. Barnes and Company, 1932).

Johnson Test of General Sports Skills

Johnson [56] constructed a test battery to measure skills of college men in the five sports of basketball, soccer, softball, touch football, and volleyball. Twenty-five test items, selected as basic skills of the five sports, were utilized as a criterion measure. A multiple correlation of .91 was obtained between the following five items and the criterion.

1. *Football pass for distance:* same as in the Borleske tests.
2. *Basketball dribble:* same as in the Johnson and Knox tests.
3. *Volleyball volleying test:* same as in the Brady test.
4. *Softball throw for distance:* Best of three distance throws with a 12-inch softball. A run is permitted.
5. *Soccer repeated volleys:* An outline 15 feet long and 10 feet high is drawn on a wall. A floor area 30 feet square is also marked out; a restraining line is drawn 5 feet from the wall. Six assistants are placed around the floor area (two on each side and two across the back line), who stop the ball when about to leave the area and place it on the line where it would have crossed. The test is for the subject to kick the ball against the wall as many times as possible in one minute. The score is the number of balls which strike within the target or on the line outlining the target.

The subject's total score is calculated from the following regression equation: 2.8 (Basketball Dribble) + .6 (Soccer Repeated Volley) + 1.1 (Softball Distance Throw) + 1.0 (Touch Football Distance Pass) + .4 (Volleyball Volleying).

The following norms indicate the student's general sports skill rating:

Score	Rating
370 – up	Excellent
287 – 369	Good
203 – 286	Average
121 – 202	Poor
120 – below	Inferior

---

[56] Kenneth P. Johnson, "A Measure of General Sports Skill of College Men," Microcarded Doctoral Dissertation, Indiana University, 1956.

Adams Sport-Type Motor Educability Test

From a study of the literature, Adams [57] concluded that there are two types of motor educability, stunt-type and sport-type, and that these are not highly related. From a study of 49 "sport-type" learning tests, he selected four, which had a multiple correlation of .79 with the total group of tests. The subjects were college men. These tests were as follows:

1. *Wall Volley Test.* The subject stands three feet from a wall and volleys a volleyball above a line drawn on the wall 10½ feet above the floor. The score on each trial is the number of consecutive volleys up to 10. The total score is the sum of scores on 7 trials.

2. *Lying Tennis Ball Catch.* The subject lies flat on his back, holding a tennis ball. He throws the ball 6 feet or higher in the air and catches it in either hand, while remaining in the lying position. The score is the number of successful attempts in 10 trials.

3. *Ball Bounce Test.* The subject stands in the middle of a 6-foot circle and attempts to volley a volleyball on the top end of a bat. The score on each trial is the number of consecutive volleys up to 10. The total score is the sum of scores on 10 trials.

4. *Basketball Shooting Test.* The subject makes 20 free throws from the foul line. The score is the number of baskets made.

The following regression equation is a rounded-off version of the one presented by Adams:

Sport Educability Score = 7.2 (Wall Volley) + 17.3 (Tennis Ball Catch) + 2.7 (Ball Bounce) + 19.2 (Foul Shooting).

SELECTED REFERENCES

Adams, Arthur R., "A Test Construction Study of Sport-Type Motor Educability Test for College Men," Microcarded Doctoral Dissertation, Louisiana State University, 1954.

Clevett, Melvin A., "An Experiment in Teaching Methods of Golf," *Research Quarterly*, Vol. II, No. 4 (December 1931), p. 104.

Cozens, Frederick W., "Ninth Annual Report of Committee on Curriculum Research of the College Physical Education Association: Part III," *Research Quarterly*, Vol. VIII, No. 2 (May 1937), p. 73.

Cureton, Thomas K., *How to Teach Swimming and Diving.* New York: Association Press, 1934.

---

[57] Arthur R. Adams, "A Test Construction Study of Sport-Type Motor Educability Test for College Men," Microcarded Doctoral Dissertation, Louisiana State University, 1954.

Glassow, Ruth B., and Marion R. Broer, *Measuring Achievement in Physical Education*. Philadelphia: W. B. Saunders Company, 1938.

Hyde, Edith I., "An Achievement Scale in Archery," *Research Quarterly*, Vol. VIII, No. 2 (May 1937), p. 109.

Leilich, Avis, "The Primary Components of Selected Basketball Tests for College Women," Microcarded Doctoral Dissertation, Indiana University, 1952.

Russell, Naomi, and Elizabeth Lange, "Achievement Tests in Volleyball for Junior High School Girls," *Research Quarterly*, Vol. XI, No. 4 (December 1940), p. 33.

Scott, M. Gladys, "Achievement Examinations in Badminton," *Research Quarterly*, Vol. XII, No. 2 (May 1941), p. 242.

CHAPTER FIFTEEN

Knowledge Tests

In connection with the teaching of the various activities included in the physical education program, it is important to give pupils instruction not only in the skills involved, but in various types of information, such as the rules governing the activity, the requirements of the performers, the general strategy of the game (when competitive sports are taught), the history of the activity, and its general value to the pupil. Although not now generally used, knowledge tests can and should be employed more extensively in this phase of the program. Such tests may also be utilized in teaching physiology and hygiene. Although it was not until about 1930 that objective written tests began to appear in physical education, indications are that measurement of this sort will occupy an increasingly important place in the future. Details describing the construction of knowledge tests appear in Chapter 2.

Objective knowledge tests have at least three important purposes in physical education:

1. To discover the pupil's level of knowledge at the beginning of a course of instruction. This initial information permits the instructor to eliminate those phases of the course already familiar to the class and to concentrate his attention on less well known parts.

2. To determine the degree to which pupils have grasped the subject matter presented. This is the typical use of such tests in the academic classroom.

3. To motivate learning. Objective knowledge tests given from

time to time acquaint students with their level of ability and with their rate of progress, which may thus motivate further effort.

Physical Education Activities

Comprehensive Tests for College Women

Several comprehensive tests, designed to sample knowledge in a number of physical activities have been constructed for use with college women. Certain of these will be described below.

Hennis knowledge tests. Knowledge tests suitable for use in the college women's instructional program for badminton, basketball, bowling, field hockey, softball, tennis, and volleyball were constructed by Hennis.[1] Preliminary to the construction of the tests, an analysis of textbooks and printed source material for each sport was made. Based largely on this analysis, checklists were prepared and sent to various types of colleges and universities throughout the United States; the item content for these tests was determined from the replies. An item analysis was made for each test following the administration of the tests at 44 institutions. Reliability coefficients for the different tests range from .72 to .81.

The revised forms of the tests contain from 33 to 37 items. In general, the types of course content sampled include the following: history of the sport, equipment, etiquette, skills and techniques, playing strategy, team tactics, and rules and scoring. Percentile norms for the tests were constructed based upon test results from a large number of women students at many colleges and universities. The tests and norms do not appear in the reference; however, any qualified instructor may obtain information concerning the availability of the tests by writing the author.[2]

Knowledge tests by French. French [3] constructed extensive knowledge tests for college women physical education majors in the following activities: badminton, basketball, body mechanics, canoeing, field hockey, folk dancing, golf, rhythms, soccer, softball, stunts

---

[1] Gail M. Hennis, "Construction of Knowledge Tests in Selected Physical Education Activities for College Women," *Research Quarterly,* Vol. XXVII, No. 3 (October 1956), p. 301.

[2] Dr. Gail M. Hennis, Woman's College of the University of North Carolina, Greensboro, North Carolina.

[3] Esther French, "The Construction of Knowledge Tests in Selected Professional Courses in Physical Education," *Research Quarterly,* Vol. XIV, No. 4 (December 1943), p. 406.

and tumbling, swimming, track and field, volleyball, and recreational sports (aerial darts, bowling, deck tennis, handball, shuffle board, table tennis, and tetherball). Two forms of the test are available, a long form and a short form. The reliabilities of the tests for the long form are from .70 to .88; for the short form, they range from .62 to .88. From 21 to 26 questions compose the various tests. Norms are available for the short forms.

University of Minnesota tests. Catherine Snell and her associates [4] in the Department of Physical Education for Women at the University of Minnesota have set up a comprehensive program of multiple-choice knowledge tests covering ten physical activities and hygiene. These tests underwent three revisions before being published. The number of questions in each of the activity areas was reduced from 70 to 45, and in hygiene from 180 to 85, by the elimination of those found to be ambiguous, those answered correctly by everyone taking the examination, and those answered incorrectly by everyone taking the examination. Expert opinion was the criterion used for establishing validity. In each examination, the correlation of chance halves, odd-numbered items versus even-numbered items, was computed to give the reliability coefficient for half the examination. The Spearman-Brown Prophecy Formula was used to determine the reliability coefficient of the whole examination.

The knowledge tests included in the Minnesota program are of the multiple-choice type. The activity areas included are as follows: archery, baseball, basketball, fundamentals, golf, hockey, riding, soccer, tennis, and volleyball. The reliability coefficients range from .51 for riding to .92 for hockey. The tests appear in the references.

Scott's Tests for College Women

The Central Association of Physical Education for College Women, through its Research Committee with M. Gladys Scott of the State University of Iowa as chairman, has constructed physical education knowledge tests for college women. The purposes of this project are to develop tests that are superior to those that individual teachers have time to prepare, that will serve as an ade-

---

[4] Catherine Snell, "Physical Education Knowledge Tests," *Research Quarterly,* Vol. VI, No. 3 (October 1935), p. 78; and Vol. VII, No. 3 (May 1936), p. 77.

quate measure of comprehension in the respective activities, and that will provide a pattern for the construction of other test items and examinations. The Committee also felt that their work would encourage teachers of physical education to emphasize knowledge and understanding of physical education activities as well as the learning of skills.

Knowledge tests for three different physical education activities were completed. These are: swimming,[5] tennis,[6] and badminton.[7] In each instance, the test battery consisted of multiple-choice and true-false statements. The procedures used in constructing the tests were very similar, the steps being as follows:

1. *Preparation of experimental form.* Questionnaires concerning the content included and the teaching procedures used in presenting each of the activities to physical education classes were sent to a large number of college teachers in the central district. From the replies received, the members of the Committee for each sport suggested questions for the experimental form of the tests. These statements were then submitted to a number of teachers of women students participating in the separate activities; the final experimental batteries were prepared from the criticisms made by these people.

2. *Revision of experimental form.* The experimental form for each of the tests was sent to a number of colleges and universities and there administered to women participating in the respective activities. Following this, the results were tabulated and analyzed, the various test items revised, and the final test battery determined. In one instance, swimming, the revised test form was again submitted to women in some twelve institutions and again revised. Test items were retained on the following bases:

(*a*) Index of discrimination. The index of discrimination was used as the measure of validity for each individual item included in the test. This index is much easier to compute than is the critical ratio, and it may be used when the subjects are heterogeneous. The formula is: $M_{\text{rights}} - M_{\text{wrongs}}$, in which "$M_{\text{rights}}$" is the total score

[5] M. Gladys Scott, "Achievement Examinations for Elementary and Intermediate Swimming Classes," *Research Quarterly*, Vol. XI, No. 2 (May 1940), p. 100.

[6] M. Gladys Scott, "Achievement Examinations for Elementary and Intermediate Tennis Classes," *Research Quarterly*, Vol. XII, No. 1 (March 1941), p. 40.

[7] M. Gladys Scott, "Achievement Examinations in Badminton," *Research Quarterly*, Vol. XII, No. 2 (May 1941), p. 242.

of all cases answering the item correctly, and "M_{wrongs}" the total score of those answering the item incorrectly. The minimum difference considered significant was arbitrarily selected and varied somewhat for the different tests. The following were chosen: elementary swimming, 6.5; intermediate swimming, 5.5; badminton, 4.0 (although all items between 4.0 and 6.0 were starred with the recommendation that they be eliminated if the test battery is shortened); and tennis, 5.0.

(b) Difficulty rating. The difficulty rating of each test item is the percentage of subjects who passed the item. The easiest item—those with difficulty ratings over 95—were omitted. In general, the tests for all three activities are overbalanced on the easy end.

(c) Elimination of choices. Choices in the multiple-choice items that were never selected by the experimental subjects were eliminated. This fact accounts for an uneven number of choices among the questions of this type.

3. *Reliability.* The reliability of the test batteries was computed by correlating the odd-numbered items against the even-numbered items and the full test length determined by use of the Spearman-Brown Prophecy Formula. The results are as follows:

Test	r
Swimming:	
Elementary test	.89
Intermediate test	.88
Tennis:	
Elementary test	.87
Intermediate test	.78
Badminton	.72–.79

For each test, scoring tables based on letter grades were prepared for the tests. These follow a percentage distribution based roughly upon equal segments of the normal probability curve. In Scott's reports, the complete knowledge tests are given, together with scoring keys and tables.

The Hemphill Knowledge Tests for Boys [8]

Fay Hemphill has constructed a number of knowledge tests in various physical activities for secondary-school boys. The phases of the program included in his study are:

---

[8] Fay Hemphill, "Information Tests in Health and Physical Education for High School Boys," *Research Quarterly*, Vol. III, No. 4 (December 1932), p. 83.

1. Major athletic activities: football, basketball, and baseball.
2. Minor sports: soccer, volleyball, handball, and tennis.
3. Health related to physical education.
4. Self-defense: boxing and wrestling.
5. Recreational sports: golf, hiking, fishing and hunting, swimming, boating and canoeing, riding and horsemanship, camping and picnicking, and horseshoes.

The material for the tests was taken from the following two sources: (a) tests of information in health and physical education that had been used in previous tests; and (b) statements of leading authorities who had written books on the activities. The validity of the selection of test items was also checked by ratings of the importance of techniques and methods obtained from coaches and other experts in the activities; these ratings were correlated with the average number of pages devoted to each by several leading authors. The rank-order correlation corrected was .72.

Badminton

In addition to the Scott tests mentioned above, two other badminton knowledge tests have been constructed for use with college women.

Phillips test. In a test constructed by Marjorie Phillips,[9] the questions consist of multiple-choice and true-false types. Validity was based upon three criteria: (1) questions were constructed from a table of specifications developed from course outlines, texts, statements of objectives, and opinions of fourteen experienced badminton teachers; (2) indices of discrimination were computed; and (3) the Votaw curve applied to upper and lower halves was used. Reliability of the test as determined by the Kuder-Richardson techniques is .92, when corrected for guessing. Percentile and T-scales are available for beginners and intermediates.

University of Washington test. A committee of the Women's Physical Education Department, University of Washington, chaired by Katharine Fox, has constructed a beginning badminton knowledge test.[10] The test consists of 106 questions of different types, in-

---

[9] Marjorie Phillips, "Standardization of a Badminton Knowledge Test for College Women," *Research Quarterly*, Vol. XVII, No. 1 (March 1946), p. 48.

[10] Katharine Fox, "Beginning Badminton Written Examination," *Research Quarterly*, Vol. XXIV, No. 2 (May 1953), p. 135.

cluding multiple true-false, true-false, and identification. The questions test the student's knowledge of strokes and techniques, rules and scoring, strategy and terminology. In constructing the test, the usual procedures for obtaining curricular validity and item validity were followed. Reliability for the test is .90, as determined by use of the split-halves method and application of the Spearman-Brown prophecy formula. The test questions and scoring table appear in the reference.

Basketball

Basketball knowledge tests appearing in published reports are largely confined to the women's game. Schwartz [11] reports an extensive investigation for high-school girls, validity being secured by submitting the test to 54 experts for criticism and by trial with 50 girls. The final test contains 50 true-false, 15 completion, 20 multiple-choice, and 15 pictorial questions, making a total of 100 test items covering rules, team play, strategy, fundamental techniques, and positions of players with their duties. No reliability coefficients or scoring tables are reported. In the report by Schwartz, all the knowledge tests but the 15 pictorial questions are given; the scoring key, however, is omitted. The pictorial part of the test constitutes an interesting development, consisting of stick men pictures and diagrams illustrating a choice of possible plays or positions from which the correct selection is to be indicated.

In addition to the test by Schwartz and the one by Snell previously described, Schleman [12] reports an examination for girls' basketball officials which, while not validated, is unique. The test consists of setting up in a scrimmage actual situations that must be recognized by the subject taking the test. Periods of one and one-half minutes are played with a deliberately planned foul or violation being committed during each. The official calls all violations but the ones designated, and it is up to the subject to catch the omissions.

Golf

Murphy has carefully constructed a golf knowledge test that has

[11] Helen Schwartz, "Knowledge and Achievement Tests in Girls' Basketball on the Senior High School Level," *Research Quarterly*, Vol. VIII, No. 1 (March 1937).
[12] Helen B. Schleman, "A Written-Practical Basketball Officiating Test," *Journal of Health and Physical Education*, Vol. III, No. 3 (March 1932), p. 37.

considerable merit.[13] The test items were selected from six of the leading texts and twelve articles on golf; the final selection was based upon their frequency of use. The complete test consists of 50 true-false, 13 completion, and 30 matching statements. Reliability for the battery is .86, computed by applying the Spearman-Brown formula to the correlation between chance halves. A satisfactory degree of accuracy is thus indicated. In a second study, Murphy presented a T-score table for the test.

A golf knowledge test was constructed by Waglow and Rehling [14] for use in physical education service courses for college men. The test consists of 100 true-false statements. Curricular validity was based on an analysis of prominent books on golf. The reported reliability of the test is .82, by the split-half method and use of the Spearman-Brown prophecy formula. The test questions and T-score standards are included in the reference.

Gymnastics

Gershon [15] developed a knowledge test of apparatus gymnastics for college men in professional physical education. Curricular validity was obtained from a review of textbooks, courses of study, and periodical literature dealing with gymnastics; a checklist from this analysis was submitted to a jury of "educators" to obtain their estimates of the contribution of the subject matter to a course in apparatus gymnastics.

An experimental test was administered to 586 college men in professional physical education at 21 colleges and universities. Item analysis data obtained from this administration resulted in a revised test of 100 items. National norms were established from the results of testing 940 professional students in 40 colleges and universities representing various sections of the United States.

The major areas included in this apparatus gymnastics knowledge test are as follows: apparatus activities, mechanical principles and coaching hints, health and safety, nomenclature, learning and mo-

---

[13] Mary Agnes Murphy, "Criteria for Judging a Golf Knowledge Test," *Research Quarterly*, Vol. IV, No. 4 (December 1933), p. 81, and "Grading Student Achievement in Golf Knowledge," *Research Quarterly*, Vol. V, No. 1 (March 1934), p. 83.

[14] I. F. Waglow and C. H. Rehling, "A Golf Knowledge Test," *Research Quarterly*, Vol. XXIV, No. 4 (December 1953), p. 463.

[15] Ernest Gershon, "Apparatus Gymnastics Knowledge Test for College Men in Professional Physical Education," *Research Quarterly*, Vol. XXVIII, No. 4 (December 1957), p. 332.

tivation, competitions and exhibitions, general education values, selection and care of equipment, and history. A copy of the test, test directions, and evaluation schedules may be obtained from the author [16] by any qualified instructor of college men in professional physical education.

Handball

Phillips [17] has presented a knowledge test of handball, as a part of his text in this sport, but has not subjected it to statistical analysis. The test consists of 50 true-false statements divided into two parts: Part I, rules and glossary; Part II, fundamental techniques.

Field Hockey

Kelly and Brown [18] have constructed an objective written examination on field hockey, designed for use with women majoring in physical education who are prospective teachers, coaches, and umpires of field hockey. This test consists of 88 multiple-response questions, designed to test the following four major areas: rules, techniques, coaching procedures, and officiating. A copy of the test questions may be obtained from one of the authors.[19] Validity of the test was established by item analysis, by comparisons of scores made by expert, major, service, and lay groups, and by correlation of test scores with extent of field hockey experience and with instructor's ratings of the competence of major students to teach field hockey. The reliability coefficient for the test is between .79 and .89.

Deitz and Freck have suggested a field hockey test,[20] composed of 77 true-false and completion statements. The test was formulated from the author's teaching experience, no validity or reliability coefficients being reported.

Ice Hockey

Harriett Brown has presented a brief test, composed of 18 ques-

---

[16] Dr. Ernest Gershon, Wisconsin State College, LaCrosse, Wisconsin.

[17] Bernath E. Phillips, *Fundamental Handball*. New York: A. S. Barnes and Company, 1937.

[18] Ellen D. Kelly and Jane E. Brown, "The Construction of a Field Hockey Test for Women Physical Education Majors," *Research Quarterly*, Vol. XXIII, No. 3 (October 1952), p. 322.

[19] Dr. Ellen D. Kelly, Professor and Head, Department of Health and Physical Education for Women, Illinois State Normal University, Normal, Illinois.

[20] Dorothea Deitz and Beryl Freck, "Hockey Knowledge Tests for Girls," *Journal of Health and Physical Education*, Vol. XI, No. 6 (June 1940), p. 366.

tions and true-false statements, based upon the rules for girls' ice hockey.[21] No attempt was made to validate the test or to determine reliability for it.

Soccer

In conjunction with their soccer skill tests, reported in the preceding chapter, Heath and Rodgers have set up a knowledge test for fifth- and sixth-grade boys consisting of 100 true-false statements dealing with playing regulations and game situations.[22] Validity for the test is claimed on the basis of: (1) the "choice of material suitable for the test" and (2) differences of accomplishments between Grades V and VI. The coefficient of reliability of the test, determined by Spearman's formula for the correlation between chance halves, was .90, which indicates an adequate degree of accuracy. T-scales for the fifth and sixth grades are also provided.

Softball

As in their knowledge test for soccer, Rodgers and Heath have set up an examination in softball for fifth- and sixth-grade boys consisting of 100 true-false statements on game rules and game maneuvers.[23] The reliability coefficient for the test was .89, utilizing the method of correlation of chance halves corrected by Spearman's formula. The questions and a T-scale table appear in the report.

A softball test for determining the extent of knowledge of college men in service courses was developed by Waglow and Stephens.[24] The test consists of 60 true-false statements, 25 completion items, 10 ball-in-play or dead-ball situations, and 5 fair-or-foul questions. Curricular validity was based on the softball course as taught at the University of Florida. The value of various items in the test were determined by computing difficulty ratings and indices of discrimination. The reliability of the test is .78. The test questions appear in the reference.

---

[21] Harriett M. Brown, "The Game of Ice Hockey," *Journal of Health and Physical Education*, Vol. VI, No. 1 (January 1935), p. 28.

[22] Marjorie L. Heath and Elizabeth G. Rodgers, "A Study in the Use of Knowledge and Skill Tests in Soccer," *Research Quarterly*, Vol. III, No. 4 (December 1932), p. 33.

[23] Elizabeth G. Rodgers and Marjorie L. Heath, "An Experiment in the Use of Knowledge and Skill Tests in Playground Baseball," *Research Quarterly*, Vol. II, No. 4 (December 1931), p. 113.

[24] I. F. Waglow and Foy Stephens, "A Softball Knowledge Test," *Research Quarterly*, Vol. XXVI, No. 2 (May 1955), p. 234.

Tennis

Hewitt test. An excellent tennis written test has been constructed by Hewitt.[25] His examination consists of two forms of 50 questions each, covering: the history of tennis, equipment necessary, rules of the game, playing situations, and fundamentals. Self-correlation for half the test by the Spearman-Brown Prophecy Formula is .95, thus indicating very satisfactory reliability. It also correlates .81 with the Minnesota Tennis Knowledge Test. Either form of the test may be given with satisfactory results.

Hewitt reports correlations of .94 with Dyer's Backboard Test of Tennis Ability and of .89 with months of playing experience. These findings were not verified by comparable studies made by Scott with college women. Her correlations were as follows:

> .38, Dyer's Test and Scott's Written Test—elementary group.[26]
> .18, Dyer's Test and Scott's Written Test—intermediate group.[27]
> .31, Dyer's Test and Hewitt's Written Test—early season.[26]
> .29, Dyer's Test and Hewitt's Written Test—end of season.[27]

Scott concludes from her studies reported above and from others of a similar nature that there is a consistent low relationship between tennis skill and tennis information for college women. The Hewitt tennis knowledge test has been copyrighted by the author and may be secured, together with scoring keys and tables, from him.[28]

University of Washington test. A committee of the Women's Physical Education Department, University of Washington, developed a knowledge test, which is associated with their tennis test described in the preceding chapter.[29] Five test forms are used: multiple true-false, true-false, completion, matching, and identification. Knowledge of the following phases of tennis are tested: position, timing and footwork; fundamental and advanced strokes; strategy and court position; history and events; equipment and court markings; rules and scoring. Item validity was determined from the performances of the upper and lower thirds of the sub-

---

[25] Jack E. Hewitt, "Comprehensive Tennis Knowledge Test," *Research Quarterly,* Vol. VIII, No. 3 (October 1937), p. 74.

[26] M. Gladys Scott, *op. cit.,* March 1941.

[27] Personal correspondence, August 4, 1942.

[28] Jack Hewitt, Director of Physical Education, University of California, Riverside, California.

[29] Marion R. Broer and Donna M. Miller, "Achievement Tests for Beginning and Intermediate Tennis," *Research Quarterly,* Vol. XXI, No. 3 (October 1950), p. 303.

jects on the total test. The reliability of the test for the beginning group was .82, for the intermediate group .92, and for the two groups combined .86. The examination questions are included in the reference.

Miller knowledge test. Wilma Miller's knowledge test [30] is associated with her tennis skill test described in the preceding chapter. This test is designed for use with college women who are majors in physical education. One hundred true-false, multiple response, and multiple-choice questions compose this test, designed to sample the following types of information: history, rules, equipment and facilities, technics and strokes, strategy and tactics, tournaments, terminology, and etiquette. Curricular validity was established through analyses of textbooks, courses of study, and the judgment of competent persons. Statistical validity of the test was determined by use of the Votaw formula, using the highest-scoring and lowest-scoring 27 per cents of the distribution of the scores of 381 students. Reliability of the test is .90. Qualified instructors may secure a copy of the test by writing the author.

Volleyball

Langston [31] constructed and standardized a test to measure the volleyball knowledge of men majoring in physical education and who have completed their course of instruction in this sport. The test is composed of 100 statements: Part I consists of 70 true-false questions; Part II consists of 30 multiple-choice questions. The phases of volleyball tested are history, pass, set-up, spike, net recovery, block, service, offensive strategy, defensive strategy, rules, and officiating. Curricular validity was accomplished through analysis of published material followed by the judgment of competent volleyball instructors. The usual item validity and discrimination analyses were employed. The questions were coded for IBM scoring. Qualified teachers may secure a copy of this test, directions, and scoring key from the author.[32]

---

[30] Wilma K. Miller, "Achievement Levels in Tennis Knowledge and Skill for Women Physical Education Major Students," *Research Quarterly*, Vol. XXIV, No. 1 (March 1953), p. 81. Author's Address: Northern Illinois State Teachers College, DeKalb, Illinois.

[31] Dewey F. Langston, "Standardization of a Volleyball Knowledge Test for College Men Physical Education Majors," *Research Quarterly*, Vol. XXVI, No. 1 (March 1955), p. 60.

[32] Dr. Dewey F. Langston, Eastern New Mexico University, Portales, New Mexico.

HEALTH EDUCATION TESTS [33]

There are a number of health education tests on the market. Most of these are confined to tests of information rather than behavior. It is true that proper and correct health knowledge and understanding are essential. However, if this knowledge is not translated into appropriate conduct, the health teacher's effort is only partially effective.

Byrd Health Attitude Scale [34]

The Byrd Health Attitude Test consists of 100 statements which the pupil answers by underlining his attitude in terms of five responses, as follows: "Strongly agree," "Agree," "Undecided," "Disagree," and "Strongly disagree." Numerical ratings of 1 to 5 are assigned to the responses for each statement, with 5 being the most desirable response in each instance. Thus, the minimum score on the test is 100 and the maximum 500.

This scale was selected after experimental trials and two revisions from an original list of 400 items. The entire original list was administered in two parts to 1,727 high-school, junior-college, and university students. The 100 statements finally selected were those showing the greatest discrimination between the students who scored in the highest 10 per cent and those in the lowest 10 per cent. Critical ratios of these selected items and reliability for the test, however, are not given.

On the whole, the test items are well stated. The answers to a few questions seem to be quite obvious, such as: "Diseased adenoids should be left undisturbed." This test can be used to best advantage in health counseling. In using it for this purpose, the counselor should check on the way the various questions are answered and follow-up on those which indicate faulty health practices and attitudes.

---

[33] Appreciation is expressed to Franklin B. Haar, Professor of Health Education, University of Oregon, for his assistance in the selection and evaluation of health education tests included in this text.

[34] Oliver E. Byrd, *Byrd Health Attitude Scale*. Stanford University, Calif.: Stanford University Press, 1940.

Byrd Personal Health Inventory [35]

This inventory is intended to be used as a permanent part of the school health records for each pupil. It provides for information about the pupil's family history, personal health problems, social history, disease history, immunizations, operations, accidents, after school or summer work, nutrition, organ and system review, and health habits. The inventory should be filled in by the pupil or parent upon the pupil's entrance to the school and should be reviewed by the physician at the time of the school medical examination. It should also be accessible to the school nurse, or to teachers who desire a better understanding of the health problems of students in their classrooms. Health instructors may use the form as a means of individualizing health education. The inventory should be completed by the student on the high school and college levels, and by a parent on the elementary level.

As a whole, the inventory is well organized and clear in meaning. The section on "health habits" is inadequate. It contains one question on sleeping habits, and five on drinking alcohol, smoking tobacco, drinking tea and coffee, and using drugs. No manual of directions for the use and interpretations of the information obtained on the inventory is available.

Kilander Health Knowledge Test [36]

The *Kilander Health Knowledge Test* has gone through four editions between 1936 and 1954. It is designed for use with high-school seniors and college freshmen, and consists of one form of 100 multiple-choice questions. The questions included in the test were selected from all major areas of health education: nutrition, safety and first aid, community hygiene and sanitation, mental and social hygiene, common errors and superstitions, and the general field of health practices. The test itself has been carefully constructed and is the result of preliminary experimentation with 150 items given to several thousand high-school and college students and teachers. Reliability coefficients by the split-half method are: college freshmen, .80; high-school seniors, .83. Percentile tables for

---

[35] Oliver E. Byrd, *Personal Health Inventory*. Stanford: Stanford University Press, 1947.

[36] H. F. Kilander, *Kilander Health Education Test*, 4th Edition. East Orange, N. J.: 33 Colonial Terrace, 1954.

both college freshmen and high-school seniors are given in the manual. Norms are now based on over 100,000 individual scores. This test has been used extensively in graduate research studies in health education.

Shaw-Troyer Health Education Test [37]

The Shaw-Troyer *Health Education Test* is intended primarily for Grade 7 through college, although it may be used for the upper elementary grades as well. Part I of the test contains 60 multiple-choice questions pertaining to basic health knowledge; Part II presents four broad problems, with 40 true-false questions to explain the student's application of his health knowledge to these problems. The following topics are sampled by the test: health status; personal appearance; foods and nutrition; play and recreation; dental health; care of the special senses; temperance; mental health; social health; heating; lighting; and ventilation; child care; home care of the sick; community health protection, disease prevention and control; safety and first aid. Two equivalent forms of the test are available.

Curricular validity for the Shaw-Troyer test was based on an analysis of textbooks, syllabi, bulletins, and other health education materials. The test items were checked and approved by experts in nutrition, public health, and medicine, and by teachers of health, biology, and physical education. An item analysis was made, utilizing the range 10 to 90 per cent. Reliability of the test is reported at .90. Percentile norms based on several thousand cases are available.

Dearborn College Health Knowledge Test [38]

This test consists of 100 multiple choice items related to the following health areas: social and biological background, nutrition and diet, excretion and cleanliness, exercise and body mechanics, fatigue and rest, mental hygiene, reproduction and heredity, prevention and control of disease, hygiene of environment, and use of medical care. The scope, content, and emphasis were determined

---

[37] John H. Shaw and Maurice E. Troyer, *Health Education Test: Knowledge and Application*, rev. ed. Rockville Center, N. Y.: Acorn Publishing Company, 1956; "The Development of a New Test in Health Education," *Journal of School Health*, October, 1947.

[38] Terry H. Dearborn, *College Health Education Test*. Stanford: Stanford University Press, 1950.

by detailed analysis of authoritative statements, published tests, ten standard college textbooks, and a poll of the recommendations of a representative group of health educators. The selected test items were checked for scientific accuracy by physicians, health education specialists, and experts in the sciences related to health. A mean correlation of .75 was obtained between scores made on the test and the final grades of students in hygiene courses at several institutions. The coefficient of reliability for the test is .89.

Bridges Health Education Test for College Freshmen [39]

Bridges' test consists of 100 multiple choice questions, selected from the following health areas: nutrition, emotional health, exercise and rest, narcotics and stimulants, body functions, social health, community health, personal health, family living, sense organs, occupational health, home nursing, and current health. Curricular validity was secured for the test by textbook analysis and submission of the questions to a jury of experts. The reliability coefficient reported for the test is .83.

Mayshark Health and Safety Attitude Scale [40]

Mayshark developed two equivalent forms of a health and safety attitude scale for the seventh grade; each form contains 60 situation-response, multiple-choice items. The health areas covered are anatomy and physiology, personal hygiene, foods, emergency health procedures, environmental hygiene, diseases, and mental hygiene. Attitudes included in the test were selected from an analysis of 15 or more state courses of study in health and physical education. All words used in the test were checked against the Thorndike and Lorge word list to ensure their appropriateness for the seventh-grade child. The reliabilities reported were .94 for Form A and .93 for Form B. This investigator obtained a statistically significant difference between the health attitudes of seventh-grade boys and girls, as determined by the results from his test.

Health and Safety Misconceptions

An instrument to determine the health and safety misconceptions

---

[39] A. Frank Bridges, *Health Knowledge Test for College Freshmen*. Rockville Center, N. Y.: Acorn Publishing Company, 1956.

[40] Cyrus Mayshark, "A Health and Safety Attitude Scale for the Seventh Grade," *Research Quarterly*, Vol. XXVII, No. 1 (March 1956), p. 52.

among fifth- and sixth-grade children has been constructed by Dzenowagis and Irwin.[41] The instrument was used to determine the prevalence of 216 misconceptions among 2,210 fifth-grade children and 1,881 sixth-grade children in six urban and suburban communities in Eastern Massachusetts. The original list of misconceptions were obtained from the following sources: previous studies of health misconceptions; published books and articles on this subject; information obtained from various students, teachers, and physicians; press, magazine, radio, and other forms of advertising which stated or implied health misconceptions. The validity of these statements were checked by authorities in health and safety education.

The entire list of misconceptions, with the frequency of responses for the two grades, is included in the reference. This list is divided into four tables, based on the degree of severity of the misconceptions, as follows: extremely harmful, 35 statements; very harmful, 59 statements; moderately harmful, 88 statements; slightly harmful, 34 statements. On the basis of their results, the investigators recommended that fifth- and sixth-grade teachers identify the harmful health and safety misconceptions of their pupils as a partial basis for the selection and organization of subject matter and experiences in the area of health and safety.

Health Practice Inventory

Johns and Juhnke [42] have developed a health practice inventory, which may be used for senior high school and college students and adult groups of both sexes. The test consists of 100 multiple-choice questions, chosen from practices in the following health education areas: personal health; nutrition; dental health; physical activity and recreation; rest, sleep, and relaxation; prevention and control of chronic disease; stimulants and depressants; mental, family, consumer, and community health; safety education. The reliability of the test is around .85. This form is especially useful for health counseling, as it brings together a great deal of information concerning the individual's health practices.

---

[41] Joseph G. Dzenowagis and Leslie W. Irwin, "Prevalence of Certain Harmful Health and Safety Misconceptions Among Fifth- and Sixth-Grade Children," *Research Quarterly*, Vol. 25, No. 2 (May 1954), p. 150.

[42] Edward B. Johns and Warren L. Juhnke, *Health Practice Inventory*, rev. ed. Stanford: Stanford University Press, 1952.

Sex Knowledge Inventory

McHugh [43] has constructed an inventory-type test, designed to discover basic factual information and attitudes about human sex relations. Form Y of the inventory deals largely with sex physiology and hygiene. Form X covers information on a wide variety of sexual topics in a competent manner; this form is designed for use with marriage counseling and is intended for this purpose only. In this latter respect, however, care should be exercised not to place too much reliance on this inventory as the only means of obtaining pertinent information relative to the individual's sex knowledge and adjustment to sexual problems.

SCALE FOR CULTURAL APPRECIATIONS

Practically no effort to measure cultural appreciations has been made in physical education. However, a New York State committee of some years ago, composed of C. L. Brownell, H. F. Mace, M. F. Krebs, E. A. Bauer, and Carl G. Chamberlain, prepared a scale of "social efficiency and cultural appreciations." Although the scale is highly subjective and un-normed, it is given below in somewhat modified form as an example of a practical first step toward measurement in this area.[44]

1. Does the pupil appreciate music and rhythm?
   Does he play a musical instrument?
   Does he sing?
   Does he attend concerts?
   Does he dance?
   Does he enjoy watching others dance?
   Does he have a graceful body rhythm in his daily activities?

2. Does the pupil appreciate nature?
   Does he hike out of doors?
   Does he enjoy the woods, the sky, the fields and streams?
   Can he recognize birds, animals, flowers, or trees?
   Does he enjoy the beauties of nature—sunsets, landscapes, etc.?

3. Does the pupil appreciate personality?
   Does he respect others?

---

[43] Geolo McHugh, *Sex Knowledge Inventory: Experimental Edition*. Durham, N. C.: Family Life Publications, 1950.

[44] Frederick Rand Rogers, *Fundamental Administration Measures in Physical Education*, pp. 76-79. Newton, Mass.: Pleiades Company, 1932.

Does he regard the interests of others?
Does he like cheerfulness?

4. Is the pupil able to enjoy freedom and not abuse it?
Does he respect law and order?
Does he control his emotions?
Does he express his opinions at the proper time and place? or
Does he abuse his privileges?

5. Does the pupil understand the physical laws of nature?
Does he appreciate the force of gravity?
Does he understand momentum?
Does he understand to a reasonable degree the basic principle of heat, light, electricity, mechanics, and sound?

6. Does the pupil enjoy life?
Is he happy when doing something creative?
Does he like to work?
Does he like to play?
Is he interested in everything that happens?

7. Does the pupil appreciate discriminations?
Can he discriminate between good and bad choices?
Does he appreciate good choice of recreation?
Does he appreciate the right kind of friends?

8. Does the pupil appreciate beauty?
Does he admire a beautiful body?
Does he enjoy a beautiful poem?
Does he appreciate beauty in music?
Does he love beauty in art?
Does he appreciate beauty in speech?

9. Does the pupil appreciate physical vigor?
Does he keep himself fit?
Has he a strong physique?
Does he appreciate abundant vitality in himself and others?

Note: Each of the above questions is answered "Usually," "Often," "Occasionally," "Seldom."

a. No. marked *Usually* .... × 3 = ...
b. No. marked *Often* .... × 2 = ...
c. No. marked *Occasionally* .... × 1 = ...
Rating—(Add last numbers on lines *a*, *b*, and *c*) ....

Selected References

Rogers, Frederick Rand, *Fundamental Measures in Physical Education*. Newton, Mass.: Pleiades Company, 1932.

Scott, M. Gladys, and Esther French, *Evaluation in Physical Education*. St. Louis: C. V. Mosby Company, 1950, Chapter VII.

PART FIVE

Administrative Problems

CHAPTER SIXTEEN

Measurement Programs

Measurement programs are not easy to conduct. They require hard work and close attention to detail. These factors, coupled with the usual heavy load of physical educators, make the problem of inaugurating and conducting such programs especially difficult. Many directors and teachers, however, are attempting it, even in small schools, feeling that the benefits derived by the pupils in increased physical fitness, social efficiency, cultural attainments, and recreational competency, and by themselves in professional growth, are well worth the effort and attendant sacrifices.

An efficient measurement program, however, depends upon a balanced teaching and administrative load for the physical educator, administrative adjustments in scheduling pupils for classes, and an adequate budget for meeting the costs entailed. Over-worked personnel, haphazard scheduling of classes, and lack of funds are not conducive to effective physical education programs. In many instances, nevertheless, these conditions are accepted at the start, in the belief that a thorough demonstration of the value of the program will convince administrative authorities, boards of education, and the community that the program is needed and will result in the necessary adjustments to guarantee its effective functioning.

This chapter considers problems arising in conducting a well-rounded measurement program in the schools. Many of those discussed are not particularly pressing if the physical educator is content to use tests for classification purposes, for motivation, and for determining program results. Meeting individual needs, however, seriously complicates the situation. It is assumed herein that meeting such needs is a primary function of physical education and should be basic in measurement considerations.

Inaugurating Measurement Programs

In many instances in schools throughout the country, physical education tests have been administered and the results stored away, no use at all being made of them. Tests have been given in some instances and then filed without even being scored. All too frequently, pupils taking these tests have not been informed of their own scores. This is educational malpractice and has caused many school administrators to look with suspicion on physical education tests as a waste of time. Those who test should be obliged to follow through; to utilize the test results in making physical education an essential force in the lives of the boys and girls in the school.

When conditions are other than ideal, the best advice that can be given the physical educator in inaugurating a measurement program is to proceed slowly and to do a thorough job of each step as it comes up. This means, first of all, thorough and accurate testing; then, thorough study of individuals with special physical, social, or recreational needs; and, finally, thorough treatment by physical educators, physicians, and others. No halfway measures should be considered acceptable.

It is better judgment, therefore, to start with only as many pupils as can be conveniently and efficiently handled, rather than to include the entire school in the program at once. This procedure has several advantages, as follows:

1. Time enough can be taken by the physical educator for a complete follow-up of each pupil included in the measurement program.

2. An opportunity is provided to try out procedures and to routinize desirable ones with a few cases, rather than to become confused with a great many.

3. Successful accomplishments with a few pupils can frequently be used to convince administrative superiors of the necessity for measurement.

4. Measurement programs are more apt to be attempted on this basis, the physical educator having more confidence in his ability to handle them without becoming so deeply involved that the task becomes hopeless.

5. Efficient programs, needed assistance, necessary supplies, equipment, and facilities, and desirable arrangements may logically be expected as outcomes of such a procedure if it is properly handled and the results effectively presented.

There are two principal ways of inaugurating measurement programs when the physical educator wishes to make a small beginning and to do an effective piece of work.

First, test only junior-high-school grades and select from these grades as many cases for intensive follow-up work as can be satisfactorily handled. Judgment should be exercised in the selection of these individuals in order to get those most in need of this service and those most likely to benefit from it. For meeting individual physical needs, it will be helpful, in making this selection, to choose a larger group of "likely candidates," selecting for follow-up work those cases that seem to have the greatest possibilities.

A complete follow-up program should be conducted for these pupils only; others may be added from time to time as progress is made. If possible, these pupils should be scheduled for the same physical education class, so that their programs can be efficiently conducted. Additional pupils may be included in these classes also, but should be given regular programs only, until such time as the physical educator may have an opportunity to put them through routine studies. The seventh to tenth grades only should be included in this method, as the amount of follow-up work that can be attempted in any school is limited at the start and should be concentrated in the lower grades of the secondary school, thus allowing several years in which to follow the individual cases.

Second, test one grade only the first year, and concentrate all the follow-up work on this group. A new grade may be added each year. If the lowest grades in the secondary school participate at first and the entering grade is added each semester or each year, the entire junior and senior high school will be included in the program within a period of three to five years, depending upon the rapidity with which the program is developed.

ADMINISTRATIVE ADJUSTMENTS

The physical educator who plans to adopt a measurement program for his school must have an opportunity to supervise case studies, to survey health habits, to interview pupils concerning their psycho-social relationships and other problems, and to conduct classes designed to meet the needs of the individuals. The school administrator who sincerely approves and seriously supports such a program should be ready and willing to provide the necessary time and assistance as rapidly as the needs are demonstrated. In the main, two administrative adjustments should be made if the program is to be conducted effectively and efficiently: (1) Extra-class time should be arranged for the physical educator to devote to case-study supervision and pupil interviews. (2) Pupils should be scheduled for fitness classes at periods during the week designated for development and relaxation work. Following are a number of suggestions that may prove helpful in arranging for these administrative adjustments.

The Physical Educator's Time

To expect the physical educator to undertake a measurement program on a comprehensive scale when his teaching assignments are already extensive and possibly greater than he should normally be expected to fulfill is unreasonable. The school should expect to pay for this service and should provide sufficient personnel for its administration. The following suggestions for providing this assistance may be considered.

1. In many small school systems today, where the physical educator is required to teach academic subjects and to perform study-hall duty, relief from these responsibilities would allow him needed extra time for the measurement program.

2. Several phases of the physical education program could be handled by other faculty members under the supervision of the physical educator, thus releasing him for additional work with pupils in need of special care. Certain academic teachers could either be paid extra for assisting with the intramural and noon-hour programs or for coaching interscholastic teams, for example, or, when faculty members are engaged, such duties may be included in their service contracts.

380

3. A number of institutions train teachers of physical education who are also prepared and may be certified to teach in an academic field, such as mathematics, history, science, or social studies. If certain academic teachers are carrying exceptionally heavy loads, or if the principal needs relief from teaching duties because of an expanding school program, they may be relieved and the physical educator provided with the help he should have by the addition to the faculty of a combination physical education—academic subject man or woman.

4. In the larger schools, the need will soon be felt for the addition of full-time physical education men and women. These individuals should be selected for their understanding of and ability to conduct measurement and corrective programs.

Individual programs should be provided, eventually, for pupils of low fitness before any others are scheduled and, if necessary, to the exclusion of others. For, to neglect the unfit while developing the fit is unreasonable, and may even overdevelop the fit. Indeed, the traditional program actually performs this malfunction. A reversal of procedure would serve to correct the balance and will pay the school system unexpected dividends in public approval and the gratitude of many parents.

Scheduling Pupils for Classes

The scheduling of those in need of developmental, postural, or relaxation programs for the same physical education classes is an essential administrative adjustment if best results are to be obtained in meeting individual physical fitness needs. It permits the physical educator to concentrate his attention on the individual needs of the pupils in the class to the exclusion of other responsibilities. In small schools, this is not an easy task. Neverthelesss, if two or three periods can be set aside for this work, the majority of pupils may be accommodated if their academic programs are carefully studied. It is essential, however, for the principal or scheduling officer to have during the summer the physical education classification of each pupil in the school. In order to supply this information, *the annual tests must be conducted in the spring.*

When there are physical education teachers for both boys and girls in the school, two methods of scheduling for physical education

381

are possible, depending on whether or not a special exercise room is available.

(1) *With a special exercise room:* Boys may be scheduled for physical fitness work in the special exercise room while the regular girls' classes are being held in the gymnasium; and the girls in the same manner when the boys are in the gymnasium. While specially constructed special exercise rooms are to be preferred, vacant classrooms, or even storage rooms, have been equipped and utilized for this purpose. In large schools, where there are separate gymnasiums, and corrective rooms for both boys and girls, and where staff members are assigned to corrective work only, the matter of scheduling students for these special classes is a comparatively simple one.

(2) *Without a special exercise room:* Boys and girls may be scheduled for individual classes at the same period, and the gymnasium divided for class work. This procedure has proved successful in several schools. The physical education teachers can thus concentrate their efforts on the special needs of their pupils. Time for case studies, posture correction, and interviews is also possible: the boys' physical education teacher doing this work while regular girls' classes are in progress; and the girl's director, while the boys are in classes.

Where there is only a boys' physical education teacher in the school, definite periods should be set aside for physical fitness work only. Of course, in many situations, ideal arrangements are, for the time being, impossible, and in such instances the next best thing should be done. Following are several suggested makeshifts, arranged in preferential order: (1) The physical educator may hold both physical fitness and regular physical education classes simultaneously, and attempt to shuttle back and forth between the two groups. The use of well-trained pupil leaders is a great help in this situation. (2) Only one day each week may be set aside for individual work. (3) The pupils in each physical education class who need developmental and remedial programs may be noted and singled out for special work during regular class. (4) The physical fitness program may be conducted either during the school's activity period or as an after-school class.

Medical Examinations

Medical examinations should precede the administration of strenuous physical tests. Pupils subject to hernia, or those with cardiac defects, or those recovering from recent accidents, illnesses, or operations should be exempt from such testing. Others who in the opinion of the physician might be harmed by the tests should not take them. Generally speaking, however, it is safe for any individual who is able to participate in the regular physical education program of the school to take activity tests. If there is any doubt in individual cases, however, the subject should be excused until a careful check can be made.

Testing Personnel

"Many hands make light work" is a truism so far as the administration of testing programs is concerned. Three ways of handling the personnel problem follow:

1. *Staff, faculty, and students.* The use of student leaders as testers has been advocated frequently and has considerable merit. Students can be utilized in recording and in scoring tests, with little more than the proper directions; but in the actual giving of tests, they should be well trained and carefully supervised. In initiating student testing, it is advisable to utilize underclassmen as much as possible, thus providing experienced testers for a number of years. The physical education staff may also be augmented by using the services of other members of the faculty.

2. *"Trading works."* A common practice in many rural areas during the summer months is to "trade works" in order to get the threshing done, one farmer helping all those neighbors who have assisted him. This idea may well be utilized in conducting measurement programs, the physical directors of four or five nearby schools "trading works" with each other, and doing the testing in each of the schools on successive days. The cost of testing apparatus might also be shared in the same manner. This practice has now been adopted successfully in several situations. In one instance, a county athletic association purchased strength-testing equipment for the use of its member schools.

3. *Teacher-training students.* School systems located near teachers colleges or professional schools often have opportunities to develop cooperative educational projects. Such projects are mutually beneficial; for the school system, they can play a vital part in the educational curriculum by providing services that might otherwise be difficult to obtain; for the teacher in training, they can provide practical experiences in thinking through professional problems and applying appropriate procedures in local situations. Such projects may include, but need not be limited to, the administration and scoring of tests. A number of teacher-training institutions have adopted this practice as a regular procedure in their training and service programs.

Time for Testing

Various authorities have agreed that the total amount of program time spent in testing should not exceed 10 per cent annually. In some schools, it may be necessary, at least in the beginning, to cut the amount of teacher and pupil testing time to an absolute minimum. The following suggestions, based upon a reduction of the number to be tested each year, may prove helpful to those faced with this problem:

1. *Gradual beginning.* This procedure coincides with the suggestions made above for physical educators who wish to make a small beginning with their measurement work and to broaden out as time goes on. If the pupils in only one or two grades were tested the first year, and a new grade added annually or oftener, the amount of testing required would be kept small and provisions would be made for expansion from year to year.

2. *Alternate testing.* Instead of testing every pupil in the school each year, pupils may be tested every second year. For example, the seventh, ninth, and eleventh grades may be tested annually. Referred cases, of course, should be tested oftener.

3. *Retests.* Considerable time can be saved each year by retesting only those pupils who were found to have deficiencies at the time of the preceding tests, thus testing the entire student body once a year only.

Economy of Testing Time

Frequently, the use of certain tests has been condemned on the ground that they are excessively time-consuming in their administration. In some instances this criticism is justified. However, before the physical educator abandons desirable tests for this reason, he should study ways and means for their economical administration in order to satisfy himself that the test cannot be given in a reasonable length of time. The application of good administration to all testing projects should be followed as a matter of course. But physical educators should remember that academic teachers test almost constantly. There are daily quizzes, weekly papers, monthly formal examinations, quarterly reviews, semester "finals." In some subjects as much as 50 per cent of the program is test-taking. For taking good tests is positively developmental; for example, a high-jumping test is excellent practice. Similarly, a PFI test is strength-developing. A test of information in hygiene serves to fix facts in mind. And so on.

Strength testing. As an example of efficient test administration, the procedure for administering and scoring the Physical Fitness Index tests at the rate of 50 per hour and faster is described in Chapter 8.

Track and field testing. Individual timing in track events is obviously a slow process. An economical procedure for timing dashes, in which the participants run at full speed for the entire distance, is to record the distances they can run in a set time, rather than record the times they can run a set distance. In the selected dash, the track would be marked off in two-yard zones, beginning at the finish and working back toward the start to the point that the slowest runner is sure to reach. As many runners as there are lanes are started, an observer being assigned to each one. When the finish gun or whistle is sounded (in 10 seconds for 100 yards and in 6 seconds for 60 yards, for example), each observer spots the zone reached by his runner. The distance for each may then be corrected into time for the entire distance or scored directly in points, depending upon the scoring system used.

Shuttle runs, as in the "potato" race, may be timed in a similar manner. Six lines, two yards apart, are drawn on the floor or ground. The runners shuttle forward and back for a set time, say 12 seconds, and the distance traveled by the end of the time is noted by an observer. The zones are numbered 1, 2, 3, 4, and 5 going forward; and 6, 7, 8, 9, and 10 when returning. Thus, three round trips and four zones would be recorded as 34. Swimming events may be handled by using a similar scheme.

Zones for the standing broad jump, at two-inch intervals, can also be used to reduce testing time, the jumper taking three consecutive jumps, of which the best is recorded. Markings in this instance would be two inches apart and the tester would estimate the distance between markers. The shot-put and various other throws may be administered in a similar manner, utilizing arcs drawn at convenient intervals with the center of the throwing circle as the center of the arc. In the shot-put, these arcs may be one foot apart, beginning at a distance that can be exceeded by the poorest performer and continuing beyond the distance expected from the best performer. In the case of the discus throw or the basketball throw, these marks may be from five to ten feet apart, the judge estimating the distance between arcs at which the object lands.

In this type of marking, it is usually most economical to have the markings made from both ends of the testing area, as was done with the football punt and pass for distance in Borleske's touch football test. Thus, the football is punted or passed from the second line, making it unnecessary to return it for each subject.

In such events as the high jump and pole vault, the most effective way to reduce the amount of time required is to increase the number of standards and jumping pits. Some time can be saved, however, by utilizing the following procedures: (1) Permit the subject to choose the height at which he wishes to start. (2) Permit each subject to jump once at each height, but to continue to jump after he has knocked the bar off. Record the best height cleared.[1]

Posture testing. Considerable time can be saved in testing posture by utilizing rough subjective screening tests to select those pupils who will be given complete posture examinations. In such screenings, each pupil is quickly inspected by the examiner, who decides subjectively whether or not he should be included in the posture corrective program. Those so selected should then be given either a detailed objective test, like the Cureton, the Wickens-Kiphuth, or the Wellesley test, or a careful subjective test, like that proposed by Phelps and Kiphuth.

Skill tests. Each skill test proposed for use in physical education

---

[1] In the track and field tests devised by McCloy, the methods of scoring described in this section were utilized to a large extent.

should be studied individually for ways in which it can be economically administered. As these tests vary so greatly in their testing requirements, set methods to be applied in all situations cannot be given.

Routine Procedures

There are a number of routine procedures that should be followed in the administration of any testing program if efficiency is to be achieved. Among these procedures are the following:

1. Plan, if possible, to have pupils report for testing in a continuous, unbroken procession. Stops, starts, and waits in the testing process cause losses of time and should be avoided. The physical educator, however, should utilize pupils assigned to his physical education classes first; study halls, second. He should disrupt classroom schedules last, and then only if necessary.

2. Have all necessary testing equipment set up and organized for the efficient administration of the tests to be given. All floor or field markings required should also be made before the testing time. Careful planning in this respect is essential if tests are to be given quickly and with a minimum of confusion. The physical educator should set down on paper the complete layout of and details for the testing. He should exercise as much care in this respect as he customarily gives to planning track meets and other athletic events.[2]

3. Provide for the required number of qualified examining and recording assistants. Assistants who are to help with the testing, whether they be pupils or other staff and faculty members, should be carefully instructed in their duties and in the testing techniques they are to perform. Nothing should be left to chance, as it is better not to test at all than to permit unqualified testers to assist. In fact, it is best to have a testing staff in which all members are qualified to take charge of any testing station and carry on in an efficient manner. Written instructions covering all phases of the testing might logically be prepared and at least one organization meeting held so that a complete understanding of the entire process may be given all testers.

---

[2] John F. Bovard, F. W. Cozens, and E. Patricia Hagman, *Tests and Measurements in Physical Education*, 3rd ed. rev. (Philadelphia: W. B. Saunders Company, 1949), Chap. 9.

4. Give students a short explanation of the reason for the test at the outset so that they will understand in general what it is they are striving to do and what outcomes they may expect. This procedure is of considerable help in securing the full cooperation of pupils and in obtaining an all-out effort on their part in taking the tests. The use of visual aids, such as photographs, motion pictures, lantern slides, or filmstrips, would be particularly valuable in motivating the measurement program.

5. Inform pupils of the results of their own tests. Too often pupils are not given the results they have obtained on a test. Not only should this information be told to the pupils, but a complete interpretation of what the scores mean should also be given. For the most part, such information and such explanations should be made privately, in order to protect the pupil psychologically. Such information constitutes the best form of motivation possible, and provides an excellent opportunity for improving the pupil's understanding of physical education.

A Lesson from Field-Testing Conditions

As a project of the Eastern District Research Council, American Association for Health, Physical Education, and Recreation, Appleton [3] conducted a field trial of physical performance tests, in order to establish national norms for entering college students. Two batteries of six items each, a total of 12 tests, were administered at 17 colleges and universities. Each institution was requested to follow a common set of directions. Similar data were collected by the physical education staff at the United States Military Academy under controlled testing conditions. These data were obtained from six training centers throughout the country by testers trained at the Academy.

The data from each college were compared with the West Point results and with those from the other institutions. Consistency was evident in the West Point data, but was definitely lacking in the colleges. Critical ratios between the means of the various institutions for the different tests were found to range from +8 to −20, as the most extensive difference, and from +5 to −5, as the smallest

---

[3] Lloyd O. Appleton, *The Practicability of Standardized Procedures for Physical Performance Tests* (West Point: Office of Physical Education, United States Military Academy, April 15, 1949), (mimeographed).

difference. It was concluded that the differences between colleges were due, not to differences in the degree of ability, but rather to the testing conditions.

The final observation made by Appleton can well be applied to all physical educators engaged in testing boys and girls in their programs: Motivation, proper interpretation of written procedures, and extreme care by scorers are very important factors in the administration of tests; every care should be taken to see to it that these factors are properly accomplished if comparable results are to be obtained at different institutions and under varying testing situations.

PRESENTATION OF RESULTS (METHODS)

An essential finale of measurement programs is the preparation of a report of testing results and the progress made in conducting these programs. Such reports might logically include statements of the nature, objectives, and scope of the program; nontechnical descriptions of the tests used; interpretations of the significance of test scores; explanations of the use made of the test results and follow-up procedures; and reports of pupils' progress in terms of average improvement, significant case-study data, and other pertinent findings resulting from the program.

In the preparation of these reports, it is necessary to make various tabulations and to prepare significant graphs that may be used in effectively portraying the results obtained. The final selection of tabulations and graphs to be used in the report will depend primarily upon two factors, as follows: (1) the essential ideas to be stressed, that is, the actual results obtained, or the method of arriving at the results; (2) the interests and abilities of the group for whom the report is prepared, that is, whether laymen or technically trained personnel.

The sole object of presenting tabular materials and graphs is, of course, to portray basic facts in condensed form so that outstanding points to be stressed will be evident to those for whom the report is prepared. However, much of the effectiveness of such presentations has been destroyed because tabular materials have often been presented in such form that they could not be read and interpreted with ease. In order to aid in improving these reports, therefore, the following suggestions for the preparation of tabulations and graphs are given.

Construction of Tables

Various points to keep in mind in constructing tables are as follows:

1. Emphasize only one significant fact in each table.
2. Avoid crowded tables.
3. Place each table on a single page, if possible.
4. Arrange tabulations in a logical manner.
5. Space columns of figures so that they may be easily read.
6. Construct the tables so that they may be read from left to right.
7. Arrange the points to be compared so that comparison can be made easily.
8. Rule tables as follows:

   a. Double horizontal line at top of the table.

   b. Single vertical lines to set off the main divisions of the table.

   c. Single horizontal and vertical lines to mark off minor sub-divisions.

   d. Vertical lines to separate columns of figures.

   e. Omit lines at both right and left margins.

   f. Use either a double space after every fifth row of figures, or rows of dots extended from the items to the first column of figures.

   g. Horizontal column at bottom of the table.

9. Align right-hand digits in columns of figures, except when decimal points are used. Decimal points must always be aligned.
10. Label the table in sufficient detail so that it may be read and understood without supplementary explanation. Use a single phrase and avoid the use of unnecessary words.

Graphic Exhibits

A graphic exhibit is usually more easily interpreted than a tabular exhibit. As a general rule, each tabular exhibit, especially if it contains several long columns of figures, should be accompanied by a graphic presentation of the same data. The vivid portrayal of test data and their easier understanding by the public make the use of this device especially effective in reporting the results of measurement programs. Points to keep in mind in the logical construction of graphs are as follows:

1. Select the type of graph that will best show the points to be emphasized.

2. Emphasize only one significant point in each graph.

3. Arrange the graph so that it may be read from left to right.

4. As a general rule, show the zero line on the graph. If the nature of the data is such that the presentation of the zero line gives the graph a long-drawn-out and unbalanced appearance, show the zero line and then place at a small distance above it two wavy lines extending horizontally across the body of the graph and indicating a break in it.

5. Place the scale line at the left, except in especially wide graphs, when it may be placed on both sides.

6. Distinguish clearly the line of the graph from other rulings on the graph.

7. Construct graphs that are pleasing in appearance, well spaced and well proportioned, and centered on the page.

8. Title the graph as clearly and completely as possible, using a single phrase and avoiding unnecessary words.

9. As a rule, place the title of the graph below the body of the graph and designate it as a figure with arabic numerals, that is, "Figure 2."

PRESENTING THE RESULTS OF TESTING

Test scores and other evaluative data should be tabulated and prepared for presentation to school administrators, boards of education, pupils and parents, and the public as justification for the continued support of physical education. Such data may be used for the following purposes:

1. To portray the results of the physical education program *in general.*

2. To justify *particular phases* of the program.

3. To prove the worth of a *change in methodology.*

4. To indicate the need for *expanded* programs.

5. To show the necessity for *redirected* programs.

In certain instances, a series of tables or graphs will be necessary to support completely the conclusions reached. For example, it is very doubtful whether one can portray the results of the entire physical education program in one table and still maintain clarity. Proving the worth of a *particular phase* of the program, however, may be done with one table, as shown in the next section of this chapter.

Following are several illustrations of the use of tabular presentation.

Justification of Particular Phases of the Program

To induce boys to participate in a wide variety of physical education skills, a decathlon was conducted at the Melrose, Massachusetts, High School during the winter and spring of 1936-1937.[4] Twenty events were scheduled, with points awarded for each of 35 levels of performance. No other pressure was exerted to encourage boys to participate. All but ten boys in the school participated in one or more events—641 boys in all. The total number of activity participations was 4,064—an average of nearly six and a half different events for each boy. Of considerable significance was the half-mile: 299 boys ran in this event—a real record of participation.[5]

Table VI reports the events included in the decathlon and the number of participants in each event.

Need for Expanded Program

In determining the swimming ability of undergraduate students at the University of Illinois, Cureton administered tests to 621 men classified as the "basic group" by his Motor Fitness Test.[6] Fifty-nine per cent, or 368 men, could not pass the 100-yard test in the pool; 84 per cent could not swim 440 yards; only 3 per cent of this basic group could qualify for live-saving. The results of this testing appear in Table VII.

---

[4] Frederick Rand Rogers, *An Admirable New England High School Physical Education Program* (Newton, Mass.: Pleiades Company, April 18, 1938), p. 16.

[5] For a method of tabulating intramural participation, see H. Harrison Clarke, "The Use of Intramural Participation Statistics," *Research Quarterly*, Vol. VI, No. 3 (October 1935), p. 27.

[6] Thomas K. Cureton, "The Unfitness of Young Men in Motor Fitness," *Journal of the American Medical Association*, Vol. CXXIII (September 11, 1943), p. 69.

TABLE VI

NUMBER OF PARTICIPANTS IN MELROSE HIGH SCHOOL 1936-37 DECATHLON

Events	Participants
1. 100 Yards	319
2. 50 Yards	292
3. High Jump	73
4. Running Broad Jump	190
5. Shot-Put	245
6. Half-Mile	299
7. Hop-Step-Jump	253
8. Standing Broad-Jump	202
9. Fence Vault	34
10. Snap-Under-Bar	227
11. 5-Potato-Race	155
12. 8-Potato-Race	175
13. Half-Lever	33
14. Pull-Ups	158
15. Push-Ups	148
16. Rope-Climb	152
17. Free Throws	371
18. Baskets (one minute)	372
19. Football-Punt	178
20. Football-Pass	188
Total	4064

TABLE VII

SWIMMING CLASSIFICATION OF "BASIC GROUP"
UNIVERSITY OF ILLINOIS MEN

	Classification	Number	Per Cent
NS	Unable to swim 75 feet after jumping into deep water feet first (nonswimmers)	235	37.84
PS	Unable to swim 100 yards, any way at all (poor swimmers)	133	21.42
AS	Able to swim 100 yards but unable to demonstrate crawl, back crawl, breast and side stroke 75 feet each (average swimmers)	159	25.60
SS	Able to swim 440 yards and demonstrate four strokes as named (superior swimmers)	73	11.76
LS	Qualified in life-saving with one or more of the national life-saving organizations (life-savers)	21	3.38
		621	100.00

Worth of a Change in Methodology

In experimenting with methods of equating groups for basketball competition, Oestreich recorded the number of games won, lost, and tied (at the close of regular playing time) for teams equated on the basis of *strength indices* and for teams arranged by the "choose-up sides" method.[7] In Table VIII, three groups appear as follows: (1) Initial League: a preliminary trial with teams equated by strength indices. (2) Berry League: four teams equated by Strength Index scores. (3) Pick-up League: three teams organized by choosing sides.

TABLE VIII

COMPARATIVE SCORES OF BASKETBALL GAMES PLAYED BY DIFFERENTLY
ORGANIZED TEAMS AND LEAGUES

Point Difference in Score	Initial League	Berry League	Pick-up League
0— 4	61%	72%	44 %
5— 9	28%	20%	28 %
10—14	11%	4%	17 %
15—19		4%	
20—24			5.5%
25—29			5.5%
Total	100%	100%	100 %
Median Difference	3.5 points	3.4 points	6 points

Eighteen games were played by teams in the Initial League and 26 by those in the Berry League. The results of the two leagues were comparable: the median point differences in scores were 3.5 and 3.4 points, respectively. In the Pick-up League, the median point difference was 6 points.

COOPERATIVE MEASUREMENT PROJECTS

The formulation and conduct of measurement programs are difficult functions. They require complete rethinking and re-evaluation of physical education. Numerous problems appear—to be solved eventually in respect to peculiar local set-ups. In many instances, follow-up procedures—the use of test results—have not been well considered and need to be studied carefully, tried out locally, and

---

[7] Harry G. Oestreich, "Strength Testing Program Applied to Y. M. C. A. Organization and Administration," *Supplement to the Research Quarterly*, Vol. VI, No. 1 (March 1935), p. 197.

adopted, modified, or rejected according to the results of this trial in actual school situations. Also, many physical educators hesitate to take the plunge into measurement because of lack of time due to heavy schedules and large classes. If truly interested in measurement, such individuals need encouragement and assistance in planning their local programs.

For these reasons, a cooperative measurement project, in which not only physical directors, but also administrative officers assist each other, would be of great value. Such a project involves an organization of physical educators who are convinced of the value of and the need for measurement and who reside in the same geographical area. The organization need not be especially formal in its construction, although it is desirable to designate one individual to act as chairman and to assume responsibility for the necessary administrative work entailed. A secretary would also be helpful in recording the minutes of all meetings held and in preparing reports on the results of the project. Furthermore, the number of individuals included in the organization need not be large. It is undoubtedly much better to have only a few physical educators who are seriously interested in and committed to measurement, than to have a large number, many of whom may be lacking in enthusiasm and inclined to discourage and discredit much of the work attempted. And finally, a few principals and a superintendent or two should be induced to attend regularly. Two measurement projects of this sort will be described briefly below.

Central New York State Project [8]

A cooperative measurement project was organized in March 1939 by a number of schools in central New York State and continued to function for several years. The purpose of the project originally was to try out in actual school situations procedures for meeting the physical fitness objective in physical education with special reference to:

1. Measurement—the use of physical fitness test data, case study, and follow-up procedures, with emphasis on pupil program adjustment and general program organization pursuant thereto.

---

[8] C. R. Robbins, "Central New York Demonstration," *School Activities*, Vol. XI, No. 7 (March 1940), p. 296.

2. Recording—ways and means of simplifying procedures and eliminating inefficiency in physical education record-keeping.

3. Reporting—the development of simple and efficient reports that would be useful in informing school authorities concerning the nature, scope, problems, and progress of this program and that would also be used to inform the public regarding the physical education program and results.

As the project developed, consideration was also given to measurement and follow-up procedures for meeting other objectives of physical education. It was felt necessary at the start, however, to concentrate on a single area of measurement rather than to chance the failure of the project by attempting too much. Emphasis was placed upon the thoroughness with which these programs could be conducted.

The Measurement Project proved successful. Not only did the physical educators participating receive considerable encouragement and assistance, but the pupils in the schools benefited greatly, as was indicated by improved individual test scores and by higher school averages. In terms of the test used in this particular project, which was the Rogers Physical Fitness Index, the following significant results were obtained:

1. The median PFI score for the nine schools included in the 1941-42 tabulation was 112, an increase of 15 points over the scores recorded for the year preceding the inauguration of the Project. In the tabulation for the final year, 1,569 boys were included.

2. All nine of the schools had median PFI's above 100 in 1941-42. In 1938-39, only two of the six schools then reporting had median PFI's above 100.

3. At Hamilton and Waterville, there were only a few boys with PFI's below 100.

4. At Warners, the median score had reached 112. Following a year's change in program and dropping of the testing work, the median PFI decreased eight points, to 104.

Average increases of 12 to 15 PFI points per year were typically reported for boys selected for special follow-up work. In one school, the average annual increase over a three-year period was 19.5 points, an improvement of 25 per cent in physical power and strength (during a fourth year, the average increase was 25 points), results that cannot fail to be very significant for the present and future well-being of these individuals.

A check on Army and Navy Examination statistics at Waterville, N. Y., where an outstanding physical fitness program was in operation for a number of years, shows that of the first 58 graduates of the school examined prior to the outbreak of World War II, when acceptance standards were high, only two were rejected, and these two were subsequently accepted. At North Syracuse, N. Y., of 265 graduates of the school examined for draft or enlistment up to eleven months after Pearl Harbor, only five were rejected and these five for the following reasons: two, organic heart defects; one, post-infantile paralysis; one, postoperative condition; and one, severe automobile accident. None of these conditions could have been corrected by a school physical education program. A similar situation prevailed at Hamilton, N. Y.

Oregon Pilot Physical Fitness Project [9]

During the academic year, 1954-55, the Oregon Association for Health, Physical Education, and Recreation carried out a pilot physical fitness project, through a Central Physical Fitness Committee. The following three basic premises for creating an effective physical fitness program for boys and girls in Oregon schools were adopted:

1. The program should be directed toward boys and girls who are subpar in fundamental physical fitness elements.

2. The program should be based upon the identification of such individuals through the use of valid tests.

3. The program should be designed to meet the individual needs of each low fitness individual.

Eleven high schools in different parts of the state agreed to participate in the project. Testing teams from the University of Oregon and Southern Oregon College assisted in the establishment of the pilot programs. Initially, one day was spent in each school, at which time approximately 100 boys and girls, preferably from the sophomore class, were given the Physical Fitness Index (PFI) test. At this visit, too, clinics were conducted to train testers and seminars

---

[9] H. Harrison Clarke, "Oregon Pilot Physical Fitness Project," *The Physical Educator*, Vol. XIV, No. 2 (May 1957), p. 55.

were held to consider appropriate follow-up procedures for those with low scores, as applied to the local situation.

Three months later, the testing teams returned to the schools to re-test the same students, so as to evaluate the progress made. At this time, the local physical educators were able to help with the testing; assistance was also provided by the faculty and physical education major students of other colleges and universities when the testing was done in their respective areas of the state. Thus, the following additional colleges participated: Oregon State College, Willamette University, Portland State College, and Lewis and Clark College.

The results of this pilot project, as indicated by the test scores, were as follows:

1. The median PFI for the boys in all schools was 108 at the time of the final test; this was a gain of 10 points over the initial tests. The highest median for a single school was 120 at Roseburg, up 18 points over the first test; the median at Medford was 118, a gain of 15 points. Only one school had a median PFI for boys below 100 at the close of the project.

2. The girls' median PFI reached 106 on the re-tests, a substantial gain of 13 points. The highest median was 118 at Coos Bay, an increase for this school of 22 points. The girls in only one school re-tested below median 100. It was generally agreed that the girls displayed some hesitancy in taking the tests the first time; however, this had mostly disappeared on the re-tests, the girls showing much greater interest and effort.

In the high scoring and/or large-gain schools, special attention in physical education was given to the low-scoring boys and girls. In several instances, all pupils below 90 were given individual exercise assignments. Time was provided during the regular physical education class period to practice their special exercises; daily homework with the exercises was encouraged. The nature of the individual programs was vigorous body-building activity, including conditioning and progressive-resistance exercises, apparatus and tumbling, and track work. Careful orientation was provided these pupils on the PFI test, the meaning of each individual's score, and the activity program to follow.

In the low-scoring schools with small gains, very little time was spent in helping individual pupils. The special conditioning activities and the differentiation of class activities found in the high-scoring schools were not in evidence. At two such schools, both boys and girls were in health education classes for six weeks after the first tests were administered; and the following six weeks were devoted to preparation for a physical education exhibition. Thus, only a very few class periods of vigorous physical activity were possible between tests.

SELECTED REFERENCES

Clarke, H. Harrison, "Oregon Pilot Physical Fitness Project," *The Physical Educator*, Vol. XIV, No. 2 (May 1957), p. 55.
———, "Physical Fitness Testing for the Professional Physical Educator," *The Physical Educator*, Vol. XII, No. 1 (March 1955), p. 23.
Robbins, C. R., "Central New York Demonstration," *School Activities*, Vol. XI, No. 7 (March 1940), p. 296.

CHAPTER SEVENTEEN

Application of Measurement

As has been stressed throughout the text, the *use* of test results in physical education is fundamental. Test results may be used to present important facts to school administrators, boards of education, and the public. This was considered in the preceding chapter. Test results may also be used to motivate boys and girls to greater efforts and for continued practice of desirable habits of exercise, heathful living, and desirable social conduct. This is essential in conducting health and physical education programs.

Tests, however, are essentially the *means of measurement*. They should not constitute the program itself. Testing is a particular phase of administration, as tests should be used to obtain essential information about pupils so that programs can be planned effectively and conducted efficiently. The follow-up procedures constitute "the program" and are of greatest importance to the physical educator as a teacher. To study the *application* of this function of measurement is the purpose of the present chapter.

INDIVIDUALS DIFFER

Individuals differ in their mental, physical, and social make-up. Some have great intelligence and learn quickly; others are slow in their mental processes and have difficulty in keeping up with schoolwork. Some are "alive" physically; others are weak and unfit. Some are capable of being great athletes; others will always be mediocre and below average. Some get along well with people and are liked and respected by their peers; others are obnoxious and unsportsmanlike in their social relationships. Some learn physical skills with great facility; others will probably always be a bit awkward and clumsy at sports and games. As a consequence of these observations, each child, as far as possible, should be treated differently in school programs. The old emphasis in education passed every child through the same educative process. The new emphasis adapts the educational program to the individual's capacities and needs—and necessarily after those capacities and needs have been determined by examinations, tests, and analyses by teachers. Such a program brings out and develops the inherent ability of the boy and girl in the school.

Procedures necessary for adapting physical education programs to the capabilities of boys and girls and to meet their individual needs follow. These procedures are definitely related to the various objectives of physical education as discussed in Chapters 3, 10, and 13. Particular consideration is given to physical fitness, social adjustment, homogeneous grouping, and sports and athletic activities.

PHYSICAL FITNESS NEEDS

In meeting individual physical fitness needs, pupils with special deficiencies must first be discovered through examinations and tests. The best tests, of course, should be selected (preferably those that have proved practicably usable in school), so that physically unfit students may be selected for study and treatment. Such a selection of tests might logically include the following types:

1. Medical examination and various sensory tests: Pupils with serious conditions who, in the opinion of physicians, should receive a modified physical education program, should be discovered.

2. Posture and foot tests: Pupils with remedial postural and foot defects may be selected for special exercise prescriptions.

3. Tests of body build: Somatotyping, or other methods of assaying body build, will furnish an important framework of reference for interpreting many test scores and for understanding those limitations and expectations traceable to body type and structure.

4. Nutrition tests: Especially for younger children, a determination of nutritional status is especially important for understanding growth demands.

401

5. Tests of general physical condition: To discover those pupils whose general fitness either is below par or is declining is the most fundamental phase of physical fitness testing. These tests should be ones that physical educators are trained to administer and the results of which they are competent to interpret.

After pupils with special needs have been discovered, it is then necessary to assign specific reasons for each pupil's lack of fitness. Only then may successful individual programs be established. This type of physical education, consequently, is an individual program for physical educators; its essence is the determination of "causes of causes" of deficiencies, followed by the amelioration of these prime causes. That this individual *causal* approach to the improvement of physical fitness is effective has been convincingly demonstrated in a number of actual school situations. The program outlined below for both boys and girls is the result of many years of trial, with subsequent modification based upon experience in many public schools scattered throughout the country. This program, therefore, not only is based upon theoretical considerations but has withstood the acid test of actual practical trial in schools.

In the program described, the following tests were used to evaluate physical fitness: medical examination, Snellen vision test, audiometer test, Phelps and Kiphuth posture appraisal scheme, foot inspection and footprint angle, and the Rogers Physical Fitness Index. It should be clear, however, that the techniques, devices, and procedures described are not limited to use with these particular tests, but may be applicable to any proper tests that detect individuals who are sub-par physically. Also, the program was used successfully with both boys and girls.

Case Studies

If individual physical fitness needs are to be met successfully and effectively, no effort should be spared to find the underlying or basic or originating cause of low physical fitness. Persevering analysis and reasoning and conscientious attention to detail are required in dealing with each case. The first step in this process is to conduct case studies of pupils in the low-fitness group, after which routings of pupils for treatment programs should be made.

A case-study form is a convenient instrument for recording pertinent data relative to individual studies. A form used successfully for this purpose appears in Figure 17.1.

Academic record. In studying individual pupils, it is important to record from time to time statements of the pupil's academic status. Frequently, his scholastic work fluctuates with his physical fitness. It should be suggested to the school administrator, also, that physical fitness test scores be included on the academic report card of each pupil, as they are often of significant help to the principal, the classroom teacher, and the parents in understanding the cause of sharp deviations in schoolwork, and will secure the active co-operation of all the school personnel in the physical fitness problems of pupils.

Weight record. It is helpful to know the percentage that a pupil's weight is above or below normal in those cases that are diagnosed by the physician or by other methods as either undernourished or obese. The search for a cause of low physical fitness, however, cannot end with this observation, as the questions must immediately be raised: What causes undernourishment? What causes obesity? Is the reason glandular malfunction, dietary problems, organic drains, lack of exercise, or what? A weight record also indicates changes in weight, as an additional index of progress—or lack of it, as the case may be—in treating the pupil.

Mechanical or functional impairment. The physical educator, in administering physical fitness tests, should be on the alert to discover defects causing mechanical or functional impairment that may account for lack of ability in taking the test. *These obstacles should be noted on the test card, opposite any tests particularly affected, for future reference and investigation.* Any slight injuries or minor ailments, such as blisters on the hand, or colds, should also be noted on the record, as these may be significant factors in low fitness scores, and such pupils should be retested at a later date when the condition has been corrected or relieved.

Recent illnesses, accidents, and operations. Probably the school physician will not consider it advisable for individuals with histories of recent illnesses, accidents, or operations to take strenuous physical fitness tests. However, in the case of individuals who have recovered sufficiently to take the tests, these factors may be a cause of low physical fitness and should be recorded, together with the physician's recommendation.

Medical examination. As a medical examination has usually been given each pupil prior to the administration of physical fitness tests, it is advisable to include on the case-study form a brief summary of

Case-Study Data Sheet

I. *Physical Objective Test Data*

Date of Test									
Strength Index									
Normal Strength Index									
Physical Fitness Index									
PFI Deviation from proportional									

II. *Somatotype:* ....

III. *Academic Status*

                    Intelligence quotient: ....

Scholastic Record:

   1. Date: .... Record:..

   2. Date: .... Record: ....

   3. Date: .... Record: :..

IV. *Individual PFI - Somatotype - I.Q. Synthesis:*

V. *Weight Record*

Date									
Height									
Weight									
Per Cent Above or Below Normal									
Gain or loss in weight									

VI. *Mechanical and Functional Impairment*

VII. *Medical Examination*

	Date	Summary of Findings	Physician
Examination prior to Physical Fitness Test			
Re-Examination			
Re-Examination			

VIII. *Recent Illnesses, Accidents, and Operations*

Date	Condition	Physician's Recommendation

Figure 17.1. Clarke Case-Study Form for Students with Low Physical Fitness Indices.

the physician's findings. This procedure will later help the physical educator in better understanding his low-fitness pupils and in planning or recommending appropriate steps for individual programs.

IX. *Faulty Health Habits*

Date	Faulty Habits	Recommendations	Interviewer

X. *Social Adjustment*

XI. *Posture Appraisal*

XII. *Nurse's Report*
(Indicate economic status of family)

XIII. *Physical Fitness Council*
(Give date and summary of suggestions)

XIV. *Clinical or Other Services*
(Give date and explanation of services)

XV. *Treatment and Results*

XVI. *Summary of Case*

Figure 17.1. (continued)

The health-habit survey. Each low-fitness pupil should answer a health-habit questionnaire designed to reveal conditions that may affect his physical fitness. Usually, this questionnaire cannot be made complete enough to cover all contingencies without becoming bulky and unwieldy. It should, however, include questions concerning the most significant health practices, those that most frequently affect the physical fitness of school children, such as: living conditions, fatigue, emotional states, dietary practices, amount of work, play, and sleep, nature of hobbies, amount of physical exercise, frequency of minor ailments (headaches, colds, constipation), parental health, and so forth. The health-habit questionnaire accompanying the case-study form has been used with success; it appears in Figure 17.2.

Health Guidance

Individual conferences, based upon the replies to the questionnaire and the information contained on the case-study form, should then be held. In each conference, the physical educator should be alert for openings that will lead him to the prime cause or causes of the pupil's low physical fitness. These causes should then be followed up energetically by discussing possible remedies with the pupil. Such conferences should be held with pupils even if the questionnaires reveal no conditions that might account for their low physical fitness, since in talking with them and checking over their answers, the physical educator may discover leads that might prove significant. As the individual case-study develops, additional conferences should be held whenever they will be helpful.

Referment

If, from the individual conferences, it appears that the advice of other specialists, such as the physician, psychiatrist, or school psychologist, is needed, an appointment should be made for the pupil. Such referment will be advisable when the physical educator *suspects* physical defects, organic lesions, or personality maladjustments as the cause of low physical fitness. He should be particularly alert to refer pupils whose case studies reveal extreme obesity with the possibility of glandular malfunction; marked underweight with a history of uncorrected physical defects or with obscure reasons for the condition; personality maladjustment with concomitant

406

emotional disturbances with which the physical educator does not feel competent to deal; case studies that reveal the presence of un-corrected physical defects that may result in organic drains affecting the general fitness of the whole organism; any other conditions with indistinguishable causes.

The results of such consultations, together with detailed recommendations, should be confidentially transmitted in writing directly to the physical educator. These recommendations are essential, as the physical educator should depend entirely upon the judgment of specialists in those areas in which they alone are qualified, *and should refuse to draw conclusions from diagnoses unless accompanied by specific recommendations.* The assistance of the school nurse may also be essential in visits to the homes in those cases where parental cooperation is needed.

Developmental Programs

In the majority of cases, the treatment of low-fitness pupils will be concentrated in the physical activity program and in the modification of health habits. Pupils assigned to developmental programs should be scheduled for daily physical education classes. If his physical condition warrants it, a decision which should be reached after reviewing his case-study data, the low-fitness individual should attend the regular physical education classes twice each week and the developmental classes during the other three days. This procedure has two advantages: (1) Pupils do not feel that they have been set aside and classified as "unfit," "queer," "cripples," and so forth. They have an opportunity to take part in the regular classwork and to show their ability to be one of the larger group. (2) Low-fitness pupils need to learn the skills and to benefit from the social development of the regular classwork. It is easier for the physical educator, as it saves his time, and it is just as effective for the pupil to adopt this procedure. During the extra-class periods, therefore, the activities can be concentrated on only one purpose—the development of physical fitness—and the program can be built around meeting the individual health needs of its members.

Special Exercises

Many low-fitness pupils may also need special exercises in addition to the regular developmental activities. Those with postural

Health-Habit Questionnaire
(Second Revision)

Name: ....   Grade: .... Date: ....
     (Print last name first)

Instructions: Please answer as carefully and accurately as you can each of the following questions concerning your health habits. You are asked for this information in order that your physical education teacher may help you to improve your physical condition. Your answers will be kept confidential.

1. How many hours do you sleep each night?........................ Is your sleep restful?....................................

   Do you sleep with your windows open at night?.......... Are you warm at night (especially in the winter)?......

2. Are you usually rested and refreshed in the morning?................................. Drowsy?............................

   Are you sleepy during the day?................................ In class?............... When studying?......................

   Do you take a nap during the day?........................,........ How often?................. For how long?......................

   Do you work and play without being more than comfortably tired mentally or physically at bed time?.....Fatigued?....

   Do you get to sleep easily at night?................................. If not, why?..

3. Are your living conditions congenial?.....Depressing?.....Do you have a room for yourself?.....Bed for yourself?.....

4. Are you often "on edge", nervous, or jittery?........................ Is it difficult for you to relax?...................

   Are you subject to worries?.......... Moods?.......... Usually cheerful?.......... Are you really happy?............

5. How far do you live from school?............................ How do you get to school?...................................

   What time do you leave in the morning?........................ When, home at night?...................................

   How much time do you usually study at home each school day?..

   How much time do you usually work at outside employment (or chores) each school day?...........................

   What do you do?...

6. Do you have a hobby?.......... What is it?..

   How many hours per day of physical activity do you usually get outside of school hours?.......What do you do?.......

   What organizations do you belong to?...

   What social activities do you participate in with mixed groups (boys and girls)?.............. How often?..........

   What extra-curricular school activities do you take part in?...

   What do you do with your spare time?...

   ....

7. Please check (X) the frequency with which you have the following?

	Never	Seldom	Occasionally	Often
a. Headaches				
b. Colds				
c. Sore throat				
d. Ear ache				
e. Indigestion				
f. Bad breath				
g. Coated tongue (bad taste)				
h. Pimples or skin eruptions				
i. Boils				
j. Twitching face and eyelids				
k. Eye strain				
l. Sinus infections				
m. Foot trouble				
n. Joint pains				

Do you wear glasses?.......... If so, when were they last tested?.............. Do you hear well?...................

Figure 17.2. Clarke Health-Habit Questionnaire.

8. Do you eat three meals a day regularly?......Is your appetite good?......Do you eat at the school cafeteria at noon?....

Carry your lunch?.......... Go home for lunch?.......... What do you usually eat at noon?...........................

....

Do you eat between meals? (Check) Never .... Seldom .... Often .... Usually ....

What do you eat between meals?...

9. How often do you usually eat each of the following kinds of food (check):

	Very Seldom	Once Each Week	Three Times Each Week	Once Each Day	Twice Each Day	Three Times Each Day
a. Meat (including fish and eggs)						
b. Green vegetables (spinach, cabbage, lettuce, etc.)						
c. Other vegetables (carrots, peas, beans, beets, etc.)						
d. Potatoes						
e. Rice, Macaroni						
f. Pie, cake, pastry						
g. Candy, sweets						
h. Fresh fruit						
i. Salads						
j. Oranges, tomatoes						
k. Dried fruits (prunes, apricots, figs, etc.)						
l. Cereals						
m. Pork						
n. Fried foods						
o. Whole wheat foods						

10. How many glasses of water do you usually drink daily?........How many glasses of milk?......Tea?......Coffee?..

11. Are you troubled with constipation?......................... What do you do to correct it?................................

12. Do you smoke?............... If so, how much daily?..

Do you drink alcoholic beverages? .... If so, what?..................... How often?........... How much?........

13. How often do you visit the dentist?................... How often do you usually clean your teeth?......................

14. Have you been vaccinated?............ Immunized for diphtheria?..................... Typhoid?...........................

What other immunizations?..

15. Are your parents healthy and physically fit?............... If not, what is the reason?...................................

What is the physical stature of your father? Tall .... Medium .... Short ....

Fat .... Average .... Thin ....

What is the physical stature of your mother? Tall .... Medium .... Short ....

Fat .... Average .... Thin ....

16. Do you desire to be strong and physically fit (boys)?......... Do you wish to be attractive (girls)?................

Are you satisfied with your present physical condition?...

If your *Physical Fitness Index* is low, can you account for it?.............. How?..

....

Summary of Interview: ....

Produced by
Fred Medart Products, Inc.
St. Louis, Mo.

Figure 17.2. (continued)

defects, foot weaknesses, or obesity will benefit from activities to improve these particular conditions. In training for posture, exercises are necessary to strengthen certain groups of muscles and to stretch others so that the individual may assume and maintain the proper position with ease. The general strength and fitness of the individual, however, are extremely important.

Relaxation Program

All individuals with low physical fitness should be carefully observed for general fatigue and hypertension. Certain questions on the Health-Habit Questionnaire are designed definitely to bring out fatigue-hypertension relationships. These questions should be checked carefully and the pupil observed in his class and school activities for symptoms of this condition. Hypertensed individuals are likely to exhibit signs of being "on edge," nervous, or jittery. The causes of this condition should be sought; such factors as lack of sleep, overwork, nervous constitution, emotional stimulation in school and out, muscular tensions, pain, participation in too many activities, and the like, are the most common. Elimination of the cause is again an important factor in treatment.

Social Adjustment

Social maladjustment is frequently found in low-fitness individuals. Which is cause and which effect is difficult to determine. Obviously, however, both situations need remedying. In meeting individual needs, the usual study of causes should be conducted and the contributing conditions eliminated if satisfactory results are to be obtained. In serious situations, pupils should be referred to specialists trained in psychiatry for special advice and possible treatment. Supplementary tests of social adjustment may be used to assist in discovering low-fitness students who are maladjusted.

Complete Case Studies

As a general rule, low-fitness pupils should be retested at intervals of from four to six weeks in order to reveal the progress—or retrogression—being made by each pupil. If fair improvement is recorded, the physical educator may well feel that his program is effective. However, it is necessary to restudy cases of pupils who fail to register advances on retests. At this point, complete case studies are necessary, beginning with rechecks on health habits and including

410

careful re-examination by the school physician, who may wish to include certain supplementary tests not included in routine school examinations, such as X-rays, basal metabolisms, and so forth. In extreme cases, a conference with other school officials, such as the principal, the physician, the nurse, the guidance director, the home economics teacher, and the classroom teacher, may be desirable in order to exhaust all possible leads in finding the cause of the pupil's low physical fitness.

Abundant experience with physical fitness programs indicates that physical defects or organic lesions are often causes of low physical fitness. Therefore, the need for detecting the presence of such abnormalities in low-fitness pupils is an essential phase of individual physical fitness work. This step is especially important for those individuals who have failed to improve after participating in the initial programs planned for them. Such pupils should be sent to the school physician for careful and thorough re-examination. From time to time, additional check-ups may be desirable in certain individual cases. And, too, the school physician may wish to consult with the family physician concerning the family and personal history of each low-fitness case. The school physician, however, is an indispensable medical advisor and consultant in the physical fitness program, since through him procedures may be routinized and a sympathetic attitude toward and understanding of the medical needs of the program engendered.

Physical Fitness Council

The formation of a Physical Fitness Council to assist with the follow-up of low-fitness cases when needed is a wise procedure. The personnel of this Council varies with the individual under consideration, being called together to help and advise on individual cases. Its membership should be drawn from those school officials who are connected with the health and physical education program and those whose work brings them into intimate contact with a majority of the pupils in the school, especially with the pupils being studied. Thus, membership might well include the principal, the physician, the nurse, the guidance director, the home economics teacher, and the physical educator. The classroom or home-room teacher should also be invited to meet with the Council when the case involves one of his or her students.

Role of the School Nurse

An efficient and sympathetic school nurse is of great value in following up cases of low physical fitness. Her work is with the everyday health problems of all pupils. These functions carry her into the homes, where she learns of living conditions and the social and economic status of parents. She has an intimate contact with all phases of the health work in the school and becomes an invaluable ally to the physical educator in conducting the physical fitness program, once she understands his methods and aims—and perceives his reliance upon her and the school physician. Following individual interviews with low-fitness pupils, consultation with the school nurse is helpful in further search for the cause of low fitness. In many instances she will suggest promising leads and may help with them. Such assistance will be of great help in home contacts, particularly when parental cooperation is necessary. It may be advisable for her to make special home visits in order to discuss the correction of physical defects or organic conditions. Parental cooperation also is often necessary in order to modify the health habits of pupils, especially those practices involving changes in diet, hours of rest, amount of outside work, and so forth. It is often advisable, too, to know the socio-economic status of the parents, in order to evaluate their willingness and ability to pay for the correction of physical defects. Those and other services that may be suggested as fitness programs develop are natural functions of the school nurse, the performance of which are essential factors in the development of a successful physical fitness program.

SOCIAL ADJUSTMENT

Will lessons in team play and willingness to sacrifice one's personal advantages for the good of the team result in better citizenship? Will good sportsmanship on the athletic field be reflected in good business ethics? Will the ability to face difficult situations and the necessity to fight through to the very end be reflected in life situations requiring the individual to face odds and not give in—to stand for the right against ridicule—to fight on when the going becomes difficult? Will the ability to accept adverse decisions from officials in athletic contests result in ability to accept adverse decisions from classroom teachers and from other duly constituted authorities?

These are realistic questions in the development of social efficiency as applied to physical education. Physical educators may develop desirable social characteristics in boys and girls as they apply to their own activities, *but* do these same qualities carry over into life situations? The problem of transfer of training is, therefore, a vital one—one that is too frequently neglected in the school.

Transfer of character traits takes place when the individual is able to generalize concerning them. When problems are similar in nature and method of solution, transfer will take place provided the similarities are recognized by the pupil. If he experiences a number of situations that have common elements throughout, he may be brought to generalize. To be most effective, generalizations should be those of the pupil himself. Too frequently they are the teacher's, and as such are imposed upon the pupil. Under these conditions they may remain relatively meaningless, and there may be little transfer.

Some method, therefore, must be used that will cause learnings in the physical education field to have a wider sphere of influence. The common elements in the various types of situations covered by the same general trait-name must be utilized in order that their applications may be recognized. For example, the trait "courtesy" covers many different situations. It connotes courtesy in athletics (sportsmanship), in the schoolroom, in business, within one's own family, with one's own group, and with outside individuals and groups. The pupil must be guided in forming generalizations concerning this and other traits. The entire school may very logically cooperate in this effort, using physical education experiences as the bases upon which transfer takes place.

It should be pointed out, however, that there is danger in over-emphasizing traits in the development of social efficiency. Attention may be centered upon self, and the act and its consequences obscured. Also, situations will arise in which desirable traits are opposed to each other and the individual must make a choice, sacrificing one virtue for another. Here a total situation must be evaluated and the best decision made. The trait-conditioned person may be in severe conflict with himself and thus unable to do this easily and efficiently. Trait conditioning may develop a conformative rather than a creative society. The total-situation approach, with well-established general principles as guides upon which to base decisions, and with the will to act for the greatest good of the greatest

413

number over the greatest period of time, is the only sound answer to this problem.

Selection of Social Tests

In the selection of tests to measure social efficiency, the physical educator may logically consider such instruments related to his field as the Blanchard Behavior Rating Scale, the Cowell Social Behavior Trend Index, the Cowell Acceptance Evaluation, or a sociometric questionnaire. However, he may also use the various character and personality tests constructed in education and psychology, provided the traits measured in these tests conform to the traits developed through the physical activity program. The latter selection of tests has value in securing the transfer of social traits from physical education to school and life situations. The aim of the physical educator thus is directed toward life problems rather than toward the limited field of conduct and relationships in sports and athletics only. A consideration of both types of tests appears Chapter 11.

Meeting Individual Needs

Once those individuals with social problems are discovered, either through general observation or by objective measurement, the physical educator should take such steps as are necessary to assist these pupils in making proper adjustments. The general approach is very similar to the one outlined above for meeting individual physical fitness needs: a determination of "causes" through case-study and interview techniques, instigating appropriate remedies for removing such causes, and including in individual physical education programs the types of activities that will best develop the boy or girl socially.

Causes of social maladjustment will vary considerably from the conditions sought in studying low physical fitness. A partial list of such causes is as follows: [1]

1. Peculiarities or differences in student's physique, including physical weakness, defects, or extreme variations in body structure, facial features, or skin color, may cause him to avoid other students

---

[1] E. G. Williamson, *How To Counsel Students* (New York: McGraw-Hill Book Company, Inc., 1939), Chap. 7.

or to seek compensation through antisocial bids for attention.

2. Unhealthy mental attitudes, such as feelings of inferiority and inadequacy, are often caused by undesirable parental and school relationships, financial insecurity, and marked deviations from other pupils in dress, speech, popularity, and success.

3. Oversolicitous parents, who may shield pupils from all difficulties and harshness and who may dominate and restrict their activities, may cause submissiveness, selfishness, aggressiveness, and domineering social habits and inability to meet new situations.

4. Attitude of teachers who emphasize mistakes and blunders of their pupils and try to be clever and witty at their expense, or who tactlessly and bluntly belittle their achievements and ability to achieve, frequently produces feelings of inferiority, resentment, lack of interest, truancy, and ineffective efforts to achieve.

5. Inability to achieve in the academic field may result in attempts to compensate for this failure by assuming an attitude of bravado, destructiveness, and bullying to hide the pupil's sensitiveness and thwarted desire for social approval, or to adopt phantasy, romancing, or boasting, or to seek companionship in groups where his talents will be appreciated.

6. Physical aspects of the home, such as appearance, location, comfort, and cultural resources, often arouse feelings of inferiority, shame, rebellion, and frustration and cause students to avoid social contacts.

7. Awkwardness in students clumsy in movement and deficient in motor skills results in social unacceptability among their peers, especially during adolescence.

8. Insufficient social experiences of the right type result in social maladjustment when the individual attempts to establish new relationships.

9. Poor recreational experiences may result in social difficulties and other personality defects.

It is extremely difficult to get at the underlying causes of social maladjustment in many instances, partly because pupils are inclined to hide these facts from others, partly because these causes may be so obscure and involved with extraneous factors that the student may feel fully justified in attributing his difficulty to some source far removed from the real one, and partly because the student may be entirely ignorant of the causes of his difficulty. The physical educator needs to gain experience in the use of counseling procedures, and may wish to confer with psychologists, psychiatrists, or the regular guidance personnel in the school.

The remedy, of course, should fit the cause. General procedures for meeting the social objective in physical education are discussed in Chapter 10.

Homogeneous Grouping

The values and purposes of homogeneous grouping in physical education are given in Chapter 10; tests for equating groups on the basis of general physical abilities are presented in Chapter 12; and tests of specific activities in physical education, which may be used for such grouping on the basis of individual sport skills, appear in Chapter 14. The present section will consider methods of securing homogeneity.

Homogeneous grouping can be secured on the basis of only one quality at a time. Several measures of unlike traits when combined into a single rating tend to destroy homogeneity rather than to provide it. For example, the following individuals are not comparable:

	PFI	I. Q.	Total
Pupil A	125	75	200
Pupil B	75	125	200
Pupil C	100	100	200

Here are three boys, A, B, and C, with equal total scores. Are they homogeneous in any quality disclosed? One is physically strong, another is not; one is intelligent, another is not; the third is average in both qualities.

The proper method for securing homogeneity on a multiple basis is first to divide the group on one basis, and then to divide the new groups on a second basis. If three bases for differentiation are used, the subdivision should be redivided, making eight different groups. For example, if the divisions are on the basis of grade in school, Physical Fitness Index, and Strength Index, the groupings are illustrated in Figure 17.3.

Usually, too, groupings are most effective when the subdivisions

416

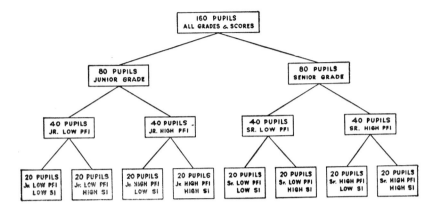

Figure 17.3. Chart for Securing Homogeneity on Multi-Variable Bases.[2]

are limited to a comparatively narrow range. Cox and DuBois,[3] for example, have reported several years of experimentation in equating secondary-school groups with the Strength Index. They recommend a 200-point range for each division of teams.

It is highly significant to note Cox and DuBois' reasons for their recommendation of a 200-point range. They found that, if 300-point ranges in SI are permitted within any single division, the strongest boys in each division almost always win, whereas the weakest almost never win in track and field events. Reducing the spread to 200 points for junior-high-school boys seems to guarantee a more equitable distribution of winning and losing experiences: an ideal teaching and learning adjustment. Judgment, however, should be used in working out these classifications; for, when the groups to be divided into teams or squads are small, levels must be determined by the number to be included on each team. For regular classwork in physical education, squads of 12 pupils each are most convenient, as this number will serve for two basketball teams within the group or a single baseball, soccer, touch football, or track team.

When the divisions have been determined, the next step is to form teams within each level. To do this, the most satisfactory method is to *match* the scores. That is, it is necessary not only to

---

[2] Adapted from: Frederick Rand Rogers, *Fundamental Administrative Measures in Physical Education* (Newton, Mass.: Pleiades Co., 1932), p. 66.

[3] Walter A. Cox and Kenneth B. DuBois, "Equating Opponents in Intramural Track and Field Activities," *Supplement to the Research Quarterly*, Vol. VI, No. 1 (March 1935), p. 219.

have the total scores of competing teams equal, but to have the variability of the pupils alike as well. Thus, if John has an SI of 1522 and is placed on Team *A*, Henry, who is on Team *B*, should have approximately the same Strength Index.

This principle for equating groups for physical activities applies not only to the Strength Index but equally well to any other test used for this purpose, whether it be Larson's, McCloy's, Cozens', and so forth; or whether it be on the basis of individual test scores, such as in basketball, soccer, or softball.

Sport and Athletic Skills

Diagnostic analyses and remedial processes can be applied to any trait that can be evaluated or measured. Such procedures have been discussed above in relation to physical fitness and social adjustment. They may also be used in relation to sport and athletic skills. In fact, the diagnosis of skill difficulties and the application of remedial measures are everyday practices of the physical education teacher; they are as nearly second nature to him as anything he does. True, these processes are largely subjective as the physical educator watches the performance of his pupils and makes criticisms and suggestions as to how the skill may best be accomplished or be improved to the point of perfection. In teaching exercises on the apparatus, stunts in tumbling, or fundamentals of game skills, the physical educator is continually alert to correct and improve the performance of his pupils; in coaching athletic teams, the coach must be eternally vigilant to improve his players' performance if the team is to be successful in competition. These are essential functions of the physical educator.

Objective skill testing, however, is little used in physical education for diagnostic and remedial purposes. Track and field is very highly objective, as times and distances become essential data in appraising the performance of the competitors. The athletic team is also objectively tested on the day of a game, when it competes in actual contest with opponents of similar abilities. The day-by-day work of the physical educator, nevertheless, is of a more subjective nature. Objective testing, the function of this text, may be an aid to him, but will undoubtedly never replace his judgment in diagnosing and suggesting remedies for the improvement of skill.

In fact, the present status of skill testing in physical education does not lend it readily to diagnostic procedures. The various skill tests presented in Chapter 14 are usable more for the general evaluation of physical education activities than for a complete analysis of the activity. In diagnosing athletic ability, McCloy's batteries of general motor capacity and general motor ability, discussed in Chapter 12, are pioneering attempts in this field and indicate the possibilities of this type of testing.

Selected References

Carpenter, Aileen, "The Future of Tests and Measurements in the Elementary Schools," *Journal of Health and Physical Education,* Vol. XV, No. 9 (November 1944), p. 479.

Clarke, H. Harrison, *Development of the Sub-Strength Individual.* St. Louis: Fred Medart Products, Inc.

Jacobson, Edmund, *Progressive Relaxation,* 2nd ed. Chicago: University of Chicago Press, 1938.

Rathbone, Josephine, *Corrective Physical Education.* 2d ed. rev. Philadelphia: W. B. Saunders Company, 1939.

Rogers, Frederick Rand, *Fundamental Administrative Measures in Physical Education.* Newton, Mass.: Pleiades Co., 1932.

Williamson, E. G., *How to Counsel Students.* New York: McGraw-Hill Book Company, Inc., 1939, chap. 7.

Appendix

Elements of Statistics

An understanding of the elements of statistics is essential to the physical educator who wishes to be completely trained in the fundamentals of his profession, and is indispensable to the individual who desires to be competent in the field of measurement. Such an understanding has definite advantages, as follows:

1. It is necessary in order to be able to read intelligently much of the published material in the field of health and physical education, since the use of statistical terms has become quite common in certain of our magazines, especially the *Research Quarterly*. For example, nearly four decades ago, 49 different statistical terms were used in the four 1930 issues of the *Quarterly*, 50 in 1931, and 34 in 1932. As time has passed, this use of statistical terms in physical education scientific literature has increased and has kept pace with changing statistical concepts. To understand these articles and to evaluate these researches is impossible without an understanding of statistical concepts.

2. It is essential in order to construct scientifically a test in physical education. The ability, therefore, to interpret and to evaluate tests is dependent upon a knowledge of statistics. With such an understanding, the physical educator is in a position to evaluate tests—to determine for himself whether they are good or bad—without depending upon the opinions of others.

3. It is beyond question that the use of certain statistical procedures is helpful in the treatment of test data. Thus, frequency tables,

percentiles, quartiles, and medians have a direct application in assembling and interpreting test scores; the mean and the standard deviation are invaluable to those interested in equating teams.

4. Finally, the ability to use statistics is a requirement for those interested in solving experimental problems and in conducting many types of research. Although the following presentation of the elements of statistics is not designed to make expert statisticians, this aspect of the work may appeal to a certain few with special interests of a scientific nature.

No attempt is made in this chapter to give a complete exposition of all statistical concepts the physical educator will encounter in his study of tests and measurements. An understanding of the elementary, basic, concepts only are included. The material is such as might logically be included in a first course in tests and measurements and is needed in order to evaluate the tests appearing in the text.

THE FREQUENCY TABLE

As statistics is a quantitative technique, dealing with large numbers of test scores, the first task is to organize the data. This is accomplished by assembling the scores into groups or classes, thus constructing a frequency table. As an illustration of this technique, the following 62 weights are given in pounds:

120	104	94	76	79	113	103
102	97	156*	115	98	139	92
119	129	93	102	116	75	84
90	75	81	109	122	59	137
79	54	116	91	67	68	72
141	131	100	147	64	60	105
83	57	89	85	110	110	108
42*	100	100	77	80	130	100
125	49	112	120	105	97	

The procedures in constructing the frequency table fall into four main heads:

First, the range of scores must be found in order to determine the distance over which the scores are spread. In the data given above, these two scores are starred, 156 being the highest and 42 the lowest; the range, therefore, is 114. In other words, all the weights fall between 156 and 42, a distance of 114 pounds.

Second, the number of groups, or step intervals, (SI) must be determined. To arrive at this number, there is only a general rule to follow: the number of steps should be between 10 and 20, the final selection depending upon the range and the number of scores. With a few cases, or with a small or moderate range, the number of step intervals should be nearer 10; while with many cases, or a moderate or large range, the number should be nearer 20. In the figures above there are what might be considered a few cases and a moderate range; therefore, approximately 12 step intervals should be selected. With a range, therefore, of 114, and a decision to use approximately 12 step intervals, each step would consist of 10 pounds.

Third, the step intervals should be in tabular form, with the largest scores at the top and the smallest at the bottom. The limits of the top "step" should be such as to include the highest score. Instead of using the highest score as the upper limit of this step, however, it is always easier and just as satisfactory to use a multiple of the size of the step selected, which in this case is 10.

Thus, as 156 is the highest score, the top step should be the interval 150-159. Each of the following 10 scores are included: 150, 151, 152, 153, 154, 155, 156, 157, 158, and 159. Scores of 149.5 to 150.4 are considered 150; scores of 158.5 to 159.4, 159. Thus, this step actually extends from 149.5 to 159.4.

All step intervals, then, should be arranged in tabular form, beginning with the step 150-159 and continuing down until the lowest step includes the smallest score, 42.

Finally, each weight score should be placed in its proper step interval. For example, the first score, 120, goes in the step 120-129; the second, 102, in 100-109; and so on until all the scores are placed, each indicated by a check mark opposite the proper step interval. The number of scores in each step is then designated with the appropriate figure. This column is known as the "frequency column" and is indicated by the letter "*f*." The total of the frequency column, indicated by the "*N*," should equal 62, the original number of weights. The details concerning this procedure are illustrated in Table IX.

MEASURES OF CENTRAL TENDENCY

A measure of central tendency is a single score that represents all the scores in a distribution. If one asked the accomplishment of a class on an examination, the answer would not be that John received 85; Mary, 75; Jack, 82; and so on until all the individual scores had been enumerated. This would be both meaningless and confusing, as one would still wonder how well the class had performed. Instead, the answer would probably be: "The average of the class was 82," or whatever the average may have been. The answer, thus, is in terms of central tendency—a single score representing all the scores.

There are three measures of central tendency in common use, as follows: (1) the mode, (2) the median, and (3) the mean.

The Mode

The mode is the score or measure that appears most frequently. When scores are ungrouped, but arranged in order from high to low, it is a very simple matter to determine the score appearing the greatest number of times. For example, in the 62 weights, 100 appears four times, the largest number for any single score, and consequently is the mode.

From grouped scores, however, it is impossible to determine the most frequent score, but one can tell the step interval in which the largest number of scores lies. In the data illustrated in Table IX, 12 scores, the largest number in any one step, appear in the interval 100-109. When it is necessary to represent a step interval by a single score, which is true in this case, the mid-point is taken. Thus, the mode is 104.5.

To find the mid-point of a step interval, add one-half the size of the step to its lower limit. In the illustration, the size of the step is 10, one-half of which is 5, which, added to the lower limit, 99.5, makes the answer 104.5.[1]

A more reliable method of obtaining the mode from the frequency distribution is to compute it from the following formula:

$$\text{Mode} = 3\,(\text{Median}) - 2\,(\text{Mean}).$$

The Median

The median is the mid-point in a distribution, that point above which and below which lie 50 per cent of the scores. When scores are ungrouped but arranged in order from high to low, it is quite

---

[1] This mid-point is taken when the test scores have been recorded to the nearest unit; it would be 105, if the scores had been recorded to the last unit.

easy to find the center, or middle score. For example, in the following five scores: 18, 17, 15, 12, and 9, the middle score is 15.

With scores grouped in a frequency table, this process is not so simple. One can, however, count up the frequency column from the bottom and find in which group the median lies. Then, by a process of interpolation, the exact point can be found. This process is illustrated in Table IX, where the 62 weights again appear in a frequency table.

With 62 scores, the mid-point is at the 31st score:

$$\frac{N}{2} = \frac{62}{2} = 31.$$

TABLE IX

CALCULATION OF THE MODE, MEDIAN, AND MEAN FROM DATA GROUPED INTO A FREQUENCY TABLE

Scores		f	d	fd
150–159	/	1	5	5
140–140	//	2	4	8
130–139	////	4	3	12
120–129	++++	5	2	10
110–119	++++ ///	8	1	8
				(+43)
100–109	++++ ++++ //	12	0	0
90–99	++++ ///	8	(30) −1	−8
80–89	++++ /	6	−2	−12
70–79	++++ //	7	−3	−21
60–69	////	4	−4	−16
50–59	///	3	−5	−15
40–49	//	2	−6	−12
				(−84)
		$N = 62$		−41

(1) Mode falls in class-interval 100–109, or at 104.5 (the mid-point).

(2) Median $= \dfrac{N}{2} = \dfrac{62}{2} = 31.$

Median $= 99.5 + \frac{1}{12} \times 10 = 100.33.$

(3) Mean (Short method): $GA + \left(\dfrac{\Sigma fd}{N} \times SI \right)$

$GA = 104.5 \qquad 104.5 + \left(\dfrac{-41}{62} \times 10 \right) =$

$\dfrac{\Sigma fd}{N} = \dfrac{-41}{62} \qquad 104.5 + (-6.61) = 97.89.$

Counting off from the small end of the frequency column, there are 30 scores below the step 100-109. Thus, the point 99.5, the lower limit of the step, is reached, the 31st score being somewhere above this point. With 30 scores gone, therefore, one more is needed to reach the middle. As there are 12 scores in the step interval, $\frac{1}{12}$ of it should be taken, or $\frac{1}{12}$ of 10, the size of the step, equals .83. Adding this amount to 99.5 gives the median: 100.33.

The Mean (Short Method)

The *mean* may best be defined as the *average*, for both terms are used interchangeably. In arithmetic, the average is the sum of the scores divided by their number

$$\text{Ave.} = \frac{\Sigma(s)}{N},$$

in which Σ means *summation* and N is the number of scores.

A short method of determining the mean, when the scores are grouped in a frequency table, is to guess an average and then apply a correction, thus: GA + C. The guessed average (GA) is taken from the mid-point of the step selected, and the correction is in terms of the deviation of the scores in step intervals from this guessed average. The formula is developed as follows:

$$\text{Mean} = \text{GA} + \text{C}$$

$$\text{C} = \text{c} \times \text{SI}$$

$$\text{c} = \frac{\Sigma fd}{N}$$

or,

$$\text{Mean} = \text{GA} + \left(\frac{\Sigma fd}{N} \times \text{SI} \right)$$

In the sample problem given in Table IX, the guessed average is selected at the 100-109 step. As the mid-point of the step is used, the GA equals 104.5. The only guide in choosing the guessed average is to select it somewhere near the center of the distribution, as this saves work.

The next step in computing the mean is to determine the deviation of the different mid-points from the one guessed. The mid-point of the step 110-119 deviates 10 points, or 1 step interval, from the guessed average, the 1 being used to indicate the deviation. Each mid-point above is 1 point farther removed, so in the "*d*" column the deviations are: 1, 2, 3, 4, and 5. These are positive deviations, as they represent values greater than the guessed average. Below the guessed average, the same situation exists, except that the deviations are negative, as the values are less than the guessed average.

Since there are more values in some steps than there are in others, it is necessary to take this fact into consideration, which is done by multiplying the number of scores contained in each step ("*f*" column) by the deviation of the step from the guessed average ("*d*" column). Thus: $f \times d = fd$. The sum of this final column (the "*fd*" column) must then be computed. As there are positive and negative values in the column, they must be added separately and their difference determined. In the problem (Table IX), the sum of the positive values is 43 and that of the negative values 84. Thus the sum of the column is -41. Substitution in the formula may now be completed.

$$\text{Mean} = \text{GA} + \left(\frac{\Sigma fd}{N} \times \text{SI} \right)$$

$$\text{Mean} = 104.5 + \left(\frac{-41}{62} \times 10 \right) = 97.89.$$

By experimenting with several guessed averages, the student will find that the same answer is obtained each time. It will readily be seen that, if the guessed average is low, a preponderance of positive values in the "*fd*" column will pull it up to the proper point. The reverse is true if the guessed average is high, for negative values will pull it down.

The Use of the Mode, Median, and Mean

The *mode* is a rough measure and may be quite inaccurate as a measure of central tendency, especially if a small group of scores is involved, as is true in the present case. The larger the number of cases and the more symmetrical (normal) the distribution, however, the more reliable it becomes as a measure of central tendency. Aside from its use as a measure of central tendncy, it also has value in indicating the greatest concentration of scores.

The *median* may be computed quickly and easily, and is not affected by extreme scores in the distribution. If one wishes to avoid the influence of extremely high or extremely low scores on the measure of central tendency, the median should be used. It should also be used when the distribution is truncated, *i.e.*, cut off at the top or bottom.

The *mean* is the most reliable of the measures of central tendency, and is the one used when advanced work in statistics is to be done. Each score in the distribution has equal weight, that is, equal to its full value, in determining the central tendency, as extreme scores at either end of the distribution affect this measure.

QUARTILES AND PERCENTILES

The use of quartiles and percentiles is valuable in making test scores meaningful and in describing the results achieved by a class or group of individuals that has been tested. It is impossible to know how well one has done on a test unless his score is shown in relationship to others taking the same test. For example, simply giving a score of 150 on an examination is meaningless. If, however, the 30th percentile score is 150, it is immediately known that this individual has exceeded 30 per cent of those taking the test but is below the score achieved by 70 per cent. Percentiles, also, are of considerable value in comparing the standing of different individuals in a number of tests. For example, how does a score of 11 seconds in the 100-yard dash compare with a score of 16 feet in the broad jump? If 11 seconds is at the 75th percentile point and 18 feet is at the 65th percentile, the comparison becomes clear.

The quartiles are of use, also, in dividing or sectioning grades or classes into quarters, based, of course, upon test results; or in determining division points for the lower 25 per cent, the middle 50 per cent, and the upper 25 per cent.

The Quartiles

The 25th percentile, or Q_1, is the first quarter or quartile point: the point below which lie 25 per cent of the scores and above which lie 75 per cent. Similarly, the 75th percentile, or Q_3, is the third quarter or quartile point: the point below which lie 75 per cent of the scores and above which lie 25 per cent. The median, by way of comparison, is the 50th percentile, or Q_2.

The method of calculating the quartiles is similar to the procedure

430

followed in locating the median, except that different points are to be found. In finding the median, it was the middle score or 50 per cent point. In finding Q_1, however, it is the one-fourth, or 25 per cent point; with Q_3, it is the three-fourths, or 75 per cent point. If the scores are ungrouped, counting up the necessary number of cases is all that is required. With grouped scores, however, it is necessary to interpolate, as was done in finding the median.

Table X illustrates the calculation of Q_1 and Q_3 for the distribution of the 62 weights. With 62 scores, the one-fourth point is at 15.5:

$$\frac{N}{4} = \frac{62}{4} = 15.5.$$

Counting up from the bottom of the frequency column, there are 9 scores below the step 70-79. The lower limit of that step, or 69.5, is thus reached, score number 15.5 lying somewhere within the step. With 9 scores gone, therefore, 6.5 more are needed. As there are 7 scores in the step interval, 6.5/7 of it is taken. The size of the step is 10, so:

$$\frac{6.5}{7} \times 10 = 9.29.$$

Adding this amount to 69.5, Q_1 equals 78.79.

In like manner: Q_3 is found by counting off three-fourths of the scores from the small end of the distribution. Three-fourths of $N = 46.5$:

$$\frac{3N}{4} = \frac{3 \times 62}{4} = 46.5.$$

There are 42 scores below the step 110-119. Therefore, 4.5 additional scores are needed. As there are 8 scores in the step:

$$\frac{4.5}{8} \times 10 = 5.63.$$

Adding this amount to 109.5, the beginning of the step, makes Q_3 115.13.

The Percentiles

It is frequently very useful to know, in addition to the median and the quartiles, the ten decile points in the distribution, that is,

10th, 20th, 30th, 40th, and the like percentile points. The method of calculating these points is similar to that used for finding the median and the quartiles except that again different points are found. For example, the 10th percentile is found by counting off one-tenth, and the 20th percentile by counting off two-tenths (one-fifth) of the scores from the small end of the distribution, rather than one-fourth, one-half, and three-fourths, as was true with Q_1, median, and Q_3, respectively.

Table X illustrates the method used in calculating the percentiles in the distribution of the 62 weights. The 10th percentile (P_{10}) is located by finding one-tenth of 62 ($N/10$), or 6.2, and counting this number of scores from the small end of the distribution. Thus, the 10th percentile is 62.5. In like manner, the 20th percentile (P_{20}), which is two-tenths of 62 ($2N/10$), or 12.4, is found by counting 12.4 scores from the small end of the distribution, and is located at 74.36. When percentile scores result in fractions, the score is usually taken at the nearest whole number. Thus, in the above examples, the deciles are 63 and 74, respectively.

The 0 and 100th percentiles are the lowest and highest scores in the distribution. Thus, in the original data from which the frequency table was constructed, the lowest score was 42 and the highest 156. Therefore, the 0 percentile falls at 42 and the 100th at 156.

A cumulative frequency column (marked "*Cum. f*") appears in Table X. The scores in this column were obtained by adding the scores serially, beginning with the lowest score and continuing to the largest. This column is of assistance in locating the desired point when counting for any particular percentile. For example, P_{80} is 49.6 scores:

$$\frac{4N}{5} = \frac{4 \times 62}{5} = 49.6$$

from the beginning of the distribution; hence, it is clear from the "*Cum. f's*" that there are 42 scores below the step 110-119, and that the lower limit of that step (109.5) has been reached.

MEASURES OF VARIABILITY

Measures of central tendency indicate typical performance for a group or for test scores as a whole. The next step is to consider the variability of these scores, that is, of the scatter or spread of the

TABLE X

CALCULATION OF QUARTILES AND DECILES (PERCENTILES) FROM DATA GROUPED
INTO A FREQUENCY TABLE
(Data from Table X)

Scores	f	Cum f		Quartiles
150–159	1	62		$Q_1 = 78.79$
140–149	2	61		$Q_3 = 115.13$
130–139	4	59		
120–129	5	55		Deciles Table
110–119	8	50		P_{100} 156
100–109	12	42		P_{90} 132
90– 99	8	30		P_{80} 119
80– 89	6	22		P_{70} 111
70– 79	7	16		P_{60} 106
60– 69	4	9		P_{50} 100
50– 59	3	5		P_{40} 93
40– 49	2	2		P_{30} 84
	$N = 62$			P_{20} 74
				P_{10} 63
				P_0 42

Calculation of Deciles

$$P_{10} = \frac{N}{10} = 6.2 \qquad 59.5 + \frac{1.2}{4} \times 10 = 63$$

$$P_{20} = \frac{2N}{10} = 12.4 \qquad 69.5 + \frac{3.4}{7} \times 10 = 74$$

$$P_{30} = \frac{3N}{10} = 18.6 \qquad 79.5 + \frac{2.6}{6} \times 10 = 84$$

$$P_{40} = \frac{4N}{10} = 24.8 \qquad 89.5 + \frac{2.8}{8} \times 10 = 93$$

$$P_{50} = \frac{5N}{10} = 31.0 \qquad 99.5 + \frac{1}{12} \times 10 = 100$$

$$P_{60} = \frac{6N}{10} = 37.2 \qquad 99.5 + \frac{7.2}{12} \times 10 = 106$$

$$P_{70} = \frac{7N}{10} = 43.4 \qquad 109.5 + \frac{1.4}{8} \times 10 = 111$$

$$P_{80} = \frac{8N}{10} = 49.6 \qquad 109.5 + \frac{7.6}{8} \times 10 = 119$$

$$P_{90} = \frac{9N}{10} = 55.8 \qquad 129.5 + \frac{.8}{4} \times 10 = 132$$

Calculation of Quartiles

$$Q_1 = \frac{N}{4}, \text{ or } \frac{62}{4} = 15.5$$

$$69.5 + \frac{6.5}{7} \times 10 = 78.79$$

$$Q_3 = \frac{3N}{4} \text{ or } \frac{3 \times 62}{4} = 46.5$$

$$109.5 + \frac{4.5}{8} \times 10 = 115.13$$

scores around the measure of central tendency. In order to show the usefulness of a measure of variability, consider the *strength indices* of the following two groups of high-school boys arranged for competition with each other:

Group *A*: Average SI = 1500
Group *B*: Average SI = 1500

As far as can be determined from the data at hand, these two groups are alike in so far as the quality being measured is concerned. Suppose, however, that the highest SI in Group A is 2500 and the lowest is 500; in Group B the highest is 2000 and the lowest 1000. The two groups no longer seem alike, as the range of scores for Group A covers a distance of 2000 SI points, whereas for Group B the distance is only 1000. In thus using the range, a measure of variability has been applied to indicate the spread of all the scores. *Similarity can be shown between groups only when both the central tendency and the variability of the scores are approximately the same.*

There are three measures of variability in common use as follows: (1) the range, (2) the quartile deviation, and (3) the standard deviation. These will be discussed in the order listed.

The Range

In the preceding illustration, the range was used to indicate the variability of all the scores. Its use as a measure of variability, however, is unreliable when frequent or extreme gaps occur in the distribution, as it takes into account only the extreme scores. In the illustration above, for example, one or two extreme scores in Group A could distort the picture and make the variability appear greater than it actually is for the bulk of the scores. In order to avoid this condition, the other measures of variability cut off the extreme scores and consider only the scatter or spread of those in the center of the distribution.

The Quartile Deviation

The quartile deviation, or Q, indicates the scatter or spread of the middle 50 per cent of the scores taken from the median. Thus, in an effort to eliminate the effect of extreme scores on the measure of variability, this measure cuts 25 per cent from each end. The formula for calculating Q is as follows:

$$Q = \frac{Q_3 - Q_1}{2}.$$

As both Q_3 and Q_1 were calculated in the preceding section, the additional mathematical process is quite simple. Table XI indicates this procedure with the 62 weights. The third and first quartiles, 115.13 and 78.79, respectively, are taken from Table X. The distance

434

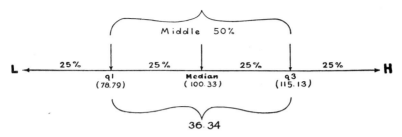

Figure A.1.   Relationships of Interquartile Range.

between the two, or the distance from the first to the third quartile, is 36.34, a distance frequently referred to as the *interquartile range*. One-half of this distance, or Q, is 18.17. This relationship is shown in Figure A.1, using the quartiles, median, and quartile deviation found in the sample problem. In interpreting the quartile deviation, or Q, this value is marked off in plus and minus distances from the median. It will be noted that 100.33, the median, plus 18.77, the quartile deviation, does not equal the actual Q_3; nor does 100.33 minus 18.17 equal the actual Q_1. Only in absolutely normal or symmetrical distributions will this occur.

The Standard Deviation (Short Method)

Like the mean, as a measure of central tendency, the standard deviation, or SD (also designated by the Greek sigma sign, σ), is the most reliable of the measures of variability and consequently is usually employed in advanced statistics and in research. The SD or σ, may be defined as that measure which indicates the scatter or spread of the middle 68.26 per cent of the scores taken from the mean of the distribution.

The formula for calculating the standard deviation by the short method, that is, in calculating it from a guessed average in a frequency table rather than from the actual average, is:

$$\sigma = \sqrt{\frac{\Sigma f d^2}{N} - \left(\frac{\Sigma f d}{N}\right)^2} \times SI$$

It will readily be seen from the formula and from Table XI, where the standard deviation is computed, that the only computation that is new at this point is $\Sigma f d^2$. The steps to be followed in finding SD are as follows:

1. Calculate the *fd* column, as previously described in the discussion of the mean.

2. Add another column (*fd²*), which is calculated by multiplying each figure in the *d* column by the corresponding figure in the *fd* column. Add this column serially, since all the signs are now positive. This will be Σfd^2.

TABLE XI

CALCULATION OF MEASURES OF VARIABILITY FROM DATA GROUPED INTO A
FREQUENCY TABLE
(Data from Table X)

Scores	f	d	fd	fd²
150–159	1	5	5	25
140–149	2	4	8	32
130–139	4	3	12	36
120–129	5	2	10 —	20
110–119	8	1	8 (+43)	8
100–109	12	0	0	0
90– 99	8	−1	−8	8
80– 89	6	−2	−12	24
70– 79	7	−3	−21	63
60– 69	4	−4	−16	64
50– 59	3	−5	−15 —	75
40– 49	2	−6	−12 (−84)	72
	N = 62		−41	427

Quartile Deviation:

$$Q = \frac{Q_3 - Q_1}{2}$$

$Q_3 = 115.13$ (Table XI)
$Q_1 = 78.79$ (Table XI)

$$Q = \frac{115.13 - 78.79}{2} = \frac{36.34}{2} = 18.17.$$

Standard Deviation (short method):

$$\sigma = \sqrt{\frac{\Sigma fd^2}{N} - \left(\frac{\Sigma fd}{N}\right)^2} \times SI$$

$$\frac{\Sigma fd^2}{N} = \frac{427}{62} = 6.89.$$

$$\left(\frac{\Sigma fd}{N}\right)^2 = \left(\frac{-41}{62}\right)^2 = (.66)^2 = .44$$

$$= \sqrt{6.89 - .44} \times 10$$
$$= 2.54 \times 10 = 25.4$$

3. Compute a correction $(\Sigma fd/N)^2$. This is to be subtracted from $\Sigma fd^2/N$, because the computations are being made from a guessed average rather than exactly at the mean.

4. Substitute in the formula and complete the computations.

With a few cases, SD may be computed from the following formula:

$$\sqrt{\frac{\Sigma d^2}{N}}$$

In this case, "d" is the actual deviation of each score from the calculated mean.

The Use of the Measures of Variability

The *range* is a rough measure of variability and is useful when a knowledge of the total spread of the scores is wanted. It is, however, unreliable when frequent or extreme gaps occur in the distribution.

The *quartile deviation* may be computed quickly and easily, and, like the median, is not affected by extreme scores in the distribution. It is also valuable when only the concentration of scores around the central tendency is sought. It is used in conjunction with the median only.

The *standard deviation* should be used when the most reliable measure of variability is wanted. Like the mean, it is affected by extreme scores in the distribution.

Equating Groups

In experimental research, it is often necessary to equate two or more groups on the basis of test scores. This is usually done by a process of matching, that is, of placing individuals with like scores (approximately) in opposite groups. When this process is completed, it is necessary to show statistically that the two groups are similar in so far as the test scores are concerned. This similarity is usually shown by giving the mean and the standard deviation of the test scores for each group. If these are nearly alike, equation is accepted. Thus, it can be demonstrated that not only are the central groupings the same, but that the scatter or spread of the scores in the different groups is also comparable, a fact that takes into account the possibility of extreme deviations.

To illustrate this procedure, the process of equating two groups adopted by Shay [2] in conducting his experiment on the progressive

---

[2] Clayton T. Shay, "The Progressive-Part vs. Whole Method of Learning Motor Skills," *Research Quarterly*, Vol. V, No. 4 (December 1934), p. 62.

part versus the whole method of learning motor skills is cited. As one phase of the experiment, Shay equated two groups of college students, using both *Rogers Strength Index* and the *Brace Scale of Motor Ability*, with the results shown in Table XII. From the previous discussion of the characteristics of the mean and the standard deviation, one can be very sure that the two groups involved are very well equated *in so far as the test results are concerned*, as both the means and standard deviations are approximately the same for both groups.

TABLE XII

SHAY'S EQUATION OF TWO GROUPS ACCORDING TO THE ROGERS STRENGTH
INDEX AND THE BRACE SCALE OF MOTOR ABILITY

	Group A	Group B
ROGERS STRENGTH INDEX:		
Mean	1800	1794
Standard Deviation	269	287
BRACE SCALE OF MOTOR ABILITY:		
Mean	64.76	64.50
Standard Deviation	10.76	10.44

The process of equating groups is of particular significance to the physical educator, for he may frequently wish to equate the competing powers of intramural teams or of groups within a physical education class. For this purpose he can follow out the process of matching scores, checking his work by computing means and standard deviations.

THE NORMAL PROBABILITY CURVE

An understanding of the characteristics of the normal probability curve is essential to the student of measurement. Upon it is based an understanding of reliability, that important phase of statistics dealing with the interpretation of statistical results. It is only through measures of reliability that the true value of such obtained measures as means, standard deviations, and coefficients of correlation can be understood.

The Principle of the Normal Curve

The principle of the normal curve is based upon the probable occurrence of an event when that probability depends upon chance. For example, in flipping a coin, the chances are even, or one in two, that it will come down heads, and there is the same probability that it will come down tails. If two coins are flipped, there are four possibilities, as follows:

(1)	(2)	(3)	(4)
a *b*	*a* *b*	*a* *b*	*a* *b*
H H	H T	T H	T T

Thus, the chances of both coins falling heads is one in four; of one head and one tail, one chance in two; and of both tails, one chance in four. If this line of reasoning were to be carried still further, it would be found that there is one chance in eight of getting all heads when three coins are flipped, and one chance in 1024 when ten coins are tossed.

This same ratio of chance probabilities in flipping coins is found in the binomial expansion theorem. For example, in expanding the binomial $(H + T)^2$, we get: $H^2 + 2HT + T^2$; and for $(H + T)^{10}$: $H^{10} + 10H^9T + 45H^8T^2 + 120H^7T^3 + 210H^6T^4 + 252H^5T^5 + 210H^4T^6 + 120H^3T^7 + 45H^2T^8 + 10HT^9 + T^{10}$.

If a graph were plotted showing the chance possibilities when ten coins are tossed, the result would be a normal probability curve, as shown in Figure A.2, with ten heads and ten tails at opposite extremes of the curve and with five heads and five tails in the center. This curve represents the distribution of measures which are dependent upon chance.

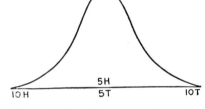

Figure A.2.   Theoretical Curve for Coin Tossing.

This theory of normal distribution, as applied to the chance occurrence of heads and tails in coin tossing, is also applied to the chance occurrence of human characteristics. Heredity, environment, and training are the factors upon which depend the amount of any human attribute: biological, anthropometrical, psychological, social, and economic. These factors are very much a matter of chance, and the scores of those various attributes will cluster about an average and will be distributed in much the same way as were the heads and tails in tossing coins.

The occurrence of the normal curve, however, whether it be in coin tossing or in the occurrence of human attributes, depends upon two very important factors, as follows:

1. The occurrence of the event must depend upon *chance*. If it can be shown that skill enters into tossing coins, then a normal distribution will not result. Also, the *motor ability* of physical education majors could not be used to represent the general run of students, as this particular group is a highly selected one physically —selection thereby not depending upon chance occurrence.

2. A *large number* of observations must be made. One would not expect an even distribution of heads and tails with only a few tosses; but, with a large number of trials, the distribution would begin to take on a normal aspect. The same rule applies to human attributes. For example, a teacher would not be justified in grading students on a normal curve when the class is small and she has only a few observations upon which to base her grades. It would be possible for the entire class to be exceptionally good, exceptionally poor, or quite a normal group. Then, too, in this instance, the teacher should consider the matter of selection as previously discussed. For example, the children of university professors or professional people would be expected to have greater intellectual ability on the whole than would the children from slum areas. Grading on the normal curve, however, may be justified when a large, unselected group is used, as there is a good possibility that the ability of the group is clustered around the center with a few exceptionally brilliant students and with a like number of dull ones.[3]

The Characteristics of the Normal Curve

Central tendency. In the normal probability curve, the mean, the median, and the mode are all exactly in the center of the distribution and hence are numerically equal. This must be true, as it has been shown that the normal probability curve is perfectly symmetrical bilaterally, and, as a consequence, all of the measures of central tendency must fall in the middle of the curve.

Measures of variability. In the normal curve, the measures of variability include certain constant fractional amounts of the total area of the curve. Special reference will be given to the standard deviation, as follows:

If an SD, which indicates the scatter or spread of the middle 68.26 per cent of the scores, is laid off in plus and minus distances on

---

[3] Normality of distributions may be tested by various methods described in statistics books, particularly by measures of skewness, kurtosis, and chi-square.

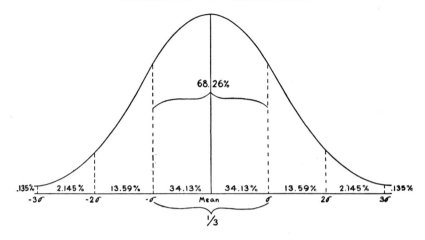

Figure A.3.   Properties of the Normal Curve in Terms of Standard Deviation.

a normal curve, it will take up the middle one-third of the base line. Thus, as shown in Figure A.3, there are, for practical purposes, three SD's in a complete distribution. Within the limits of three standard deviations lie 99.73 per cent of the scores.

Proportional Areas of the Normal Curve

Tables are available that give the proportion of the area between the mean and any point on the base line, measured in units of standard deviation. Table XIII shows the fractional parts of the total area under the normal probability curve corresponding to distances on the base line between the mean and successive points from the mean in units of standard deviation.

By the use of Table XIII, it is possible to compare any two scores. Knowing the raw score, the standard deviation, and the mean, it is possible to tell the percentage of cases that would fall above or below a certain score. The table shows that the area between the mean and two standard deviations is 47.72 per cent of the total. An individual who is two sigmas above the mean on a tennis test, for example, will have a tennis score not only higher than the 50 per cent below the mean but also higher than the 47.72 per cent who fall within the mean and the two sigmas, or he will have a score that is higher than 97.72 per cent of the group. Many other problems can be worked out from this table, such as those showing the percentage differences

441

ELEMENTS OF STATISTICS

TABLE XIII

<small>PERCENTAGE PARTS OF THE TOTAL AREA UNDER THE NORMAL PROBABILITY CURVE CORRESPONDING TO DISTANCES ON THE BASE LINE BETWEEN THE MEAN AND SUCCESSIVE POINTS FROM THE MEAN IN UNITS OF STANDARD DEVIATION [4]</small>

Example: Between the mean and a point 1.57 sigma is found 44.18 per cent of the entire area under the curve.

Units	.00	.01	.02	.03	.04	.05	.06	.07	.08	.09
0.0	00.00	00.40	00.80	01.20	01.60	01.99	02.39	02.79	03.19	03.59
0.1	03.98	04.38	04.78	05.17	05.57	05.96	06.36	06.75	07.14	07.53
0.2	07.93	08.32	08.71	09.10	09.48	09.87	10.26	10.64	11.03	11.41
0.3	11.79	12.17	12.55	12.93	13.31	13.68	14.06	14.43	14.80	15.17
0.4	15.54	15.91	16.28	16.64	17.00	17.36	17.72	18.08	18.44	18.79
0.5	19.15	19.50	19.85	20.19	20.54	20.88	21.23	21.57	21.90	22.24
0.6	22.57	22.91	23.24	23.57	27.89	24.22	24.54	24.86	25.17	25.49
0.7	25.80	26.11	26.42	26.73	27.04	27.34	27.64	27.94	28.23	28.52
0.8	28.81	29.10	29.39	29.67	29.95	30.23	30.51	30.78	31.06	31.33
0.9	31.59	31.86	32.12	32.38	32.64	32.90	33.15	33.40	33.65	33.89
1.0	34.13	34.38	34.61	34.85	35.08	35.31	35.54	35.77	35.99	36.21
1.1	36.43	36.65	36.86	37.08	37.29	37.49	37.70	37.90	38.10	38.30
1.2	38.49	38.69	38.88	39.07	39.25	39.44	39.62	39.80	39.97	40.15
1.3	40.32	40.49	40.66	40.82	40.99	41.15	41.31	41.47	41.62	41.77
1.4	41.92	42.07	42.22	42.36	42.51	42.65	42.79	42.92	43.06	43.19
1.5	43.32	43.45	43.57	43.70	43.83	43.94	44.06	44.18	44.29	44.41
1.6	44.52	44.63	44.74	44.84	44.95	45.05	45.15	45.25	45.35	45.45
1.7	45.54	45.64	45.73	45.82	45.91	45.99	46.08	46.16	46.25	46.33
1.8	46.41	46.49	46.56	46.64	46.71	46.78	46.86	46.93	46.99	47.06
1.9	47.13	47.19	47.26	47.32	47.38	47.44	47.50	47.56	47.61	47.67
2.0	47.72	47.78	47.83	47.88	47.93	47.98	48.03	48.08	48.12	48.17
2.1	48.21	48.26	48.30	48.34	48.38	48.42	48.46	48.50	48.54	48.57
2.2	48.61	48.64	48.68	48.71	48.75	48.78	48.81	48.84	48.87	48.90
2.3	48.93	48.96	48.98	49.01	49.04	49.06	49.09	49.11	49.13	49.16
2.4	49.18	49.20	49.22	49.25	49.27	49.29	49.31	49.32	49.34	49.36
2.5	49.38	49.40	49.41	49.43	49.45	49.46	49.48	49.49	49.51	49.52
2.6	49.53	49.55	49.56	49.57	49.59	49.60	49.61	49.62	49.63	49.64
2.7	49.65	49.66	49.67	49.68	49.69	49.70	49.71	49.72	49.73	49.74
2.8	49.74	49.75	49.76	49.77	49.77	49.78	49.79	49.79	49.80	49.81
2.9	49.81	49.82	49.82	49.83	49.84	49.84	49.85	49.85	49.86	49.86
3.0	49.865									
3.1	49.903									
3.2	49.93129									
3.3	49.95166									
3.4	49.96631									
3.5	49.97674									
3.6	49.98409									
3.7	49.98922									
3.8	49.99277									
3.9	49.99519									

[4] An adaptation from: Karl Pearson, *Tables for Statisticians and Biometricians* (Cambridge: Cambridge University Press, 1924).

between two means or the percentage of students that should receive each mark in grading a class (marking on the normal curve).

The T-Score and the Sigma Score

Both the T-scale, as originated by McCall, and the sigma scale itself are based upon SD values of the distribution. Unlike the percentile scale, where the distances on the base line are close together near the mean and spread out at the extremities of the distribution, sigma values are based upon equal distances on the base line of the normal curve. Zero in the percentile table is located at the lowest score in the data from which the table is constructed, with 100 placed at the highest score. Zero in the sigma table is located at a point three sigmas below the mean, with 100 at three sigmas above the mean. Thus, the lowest score is zero, the mean is 50, and the highest sigma value is 100. Zero in the T-scale is located five sigmas below the mean, with 100 at five sigmas above the mean. The unit of measure, or one "T," is .1 of the sigma of the distribution. The mean T-score, therefore, is 50, and each 10 points above and below this point represent one sigma. In practice, however, T-scores will usually be found to range between 15 and 85. The T-scale technique has the advantage of placing both zero and 100 at points so far below and above what could possibly be expected in future performances that one is very unlikely to find scores that cannot be placed on the scale.

The only items needed in constructing a Sigma Table or a T-scale when distributions are normal are the mean and the standard deviation.[5] The mean is a given value of 50 in both instances (50th sigma value and 50th T-score, respectively). The standard deviation is added to and subtracted from this amount for each σ distance above and below the mean. The only difference between the two scoring tables is that Sigma Tables range between three sigmas below and three above the average and the T-scale ranges between five sigmas below and five above the average. A T-scale in decile units appears in Table XIV.[6]

---

[5] When data are not normally distributed, other techniques are necessary to construct T-scales and sigma scales. Standard books on statistics should be consulted for this process.

[6] The method described here is an approximation only. For more refined procedures, standard statistics texts should be consulted.

Of course, if T-scales are prepared for all units between zero and 100, the T for any given score may readily be found. From the data appearing in Table XIV, however, this would be impossible. A score of 163, for example, falls between the T's of 50 and 60; interpolation thus becomes necessary. An easy and accurate method for completing such interpolations based upon an algebraic equation appears in the table.

A third type of scoring table based upon standard deviation distances is the Hull scale, which extends three and one-half sigmas either side of the mean. It goes beyond the somewhat narrow limits of the sigma scale, but does not leave the ends of the scale so gen-

TABLE XIV

CALCULATION OF A T-SCALE FROM DATA GIVEN IN THE TABLE

Mean Weight = 150
Standard Deviation = 20

Thus,
T-score of 50 = 150
Add or subtract 20 for each decile point.

Decile Table

T_{50} = 150		T	Score
T_{60} = 150 + 20 = 170		100	250
T_{70} = 170 + 20 = 190		90	230
T_{80} = 190 + 20 = 210		80	210
T_{90} = 210 + 20 = 230		70	190
T_{100} = 230 + 20 = 250		60	170
T_{50} = 150		50	150
T_{40} = 150 − 20 = 130		40	130
T_{30} = 130 − 20 = 110		30	110
T_{20} = 110 − 20 = 90		20	90
T_{10} = 90 − 20 = 70		10	70
T_{0} = 70 − 20 = 50		0	50

To Calculate T of a Given Score
Score given = 163

$$13:20::\chi:10$$

$$\frac{13}{20} = \frac{\chi}{10} \text{ or } \frac{13 \times 10}{20} = \chi$$

$$\chi = 6.5$$

$$50 + 6.5 = 56.5$$

	170	60
20 13 {	163	χ	10
	150	50

erally unused as does the T-scale. As a result, it has considerable merit for wider use as a scale.

Standard Scores

Another method of scoring, the *standard score*, is occasionally used in testing. The standard score is the standing deviation unit above or below the mean. Thus, a standard score of 0.42 made by a given pupil can be interpreted as a score $\frac{42}{100}$ of a standard deviation distance above the mean score made by the group; a standard score of -2.00, as a score two standard deviations below the mean score.

The formula for obtaining standard scores follows directly from the definition and may be written:

$$Z = \frac{X - M}{\sigma},$$

where $Z =$ a standard score
$X =$ a test score
$M =$ mean of the test scores

For example, the standard score for a pupil making a score of 60 on a given test, in which the mean score is 70 and the standard deviation is 20, would be computed as follows:

$$Z = \frac{70 - 60}{20} = \frac{10}{20} = 0.5.$$

MEASURES OF RELIABILITY

Meaning of Reliability

In statistical work, the true measure of any quality is very seldom obtained. For example, in the development of norms, it is impractical to obtain the true average upon which these norms are based. In order to determine, for example, the true average weight of 12-year-old boys, it would be necessary to measure the weight of every boy 12 years of age in the entire population. This, of course, would be an impossible situation. The usual procedure is to depend upon a random sampling, and to assume that this sample represents the whole. After this sample is taken, a measure of reliability may be applied to the mean in order to determine now near it is to the true mean (the mean of the entire population). The reliability of the mean, therefore, indicates within what limits an obtained mean approximates the corresponding true mean. What is true for the reliability of the mean is also true for all of the measures used in statistics; consequently, there are statistical methods for determining the reliability of the mean, the median, the standard deviation, the coefficient of correlation, and so forth.

Three major factors influence the reliability of a measure, or, to express it differently, show how nearly an obtained mean approximates the true measure. The *first* of these is the sample itself. How truly random is it? As has been previously shown, normal probability is definitely lacking if the factor of *selection* enters into the picture. In a random sample, therefore, boys should not be selected from one town or from near-by towns, nor should school boys in cities only be selected. To be truly representative, the sampling must include boys in school and out, from both urban and rural areas, and so forth. The more successful one is in securing an "unselected" group, the more nearly representative will his group be of all the boys of 12 years of age in the country.

The *second* factor influencing the reliability of a measure is the number of cases contained in the sample. It can readily be demonstrated that an obtained mean may be changed by the addition of one new case to the distribution, and that this new case will affect the mean much more when it is based upon a few scores than when a large number is involved. For example, the addition of one extreme score to a group of 10 measures will cause a greater change in the obtained mean than the addition of a similar score to a group of 1000 measures, as each case counts for less in the larger group.

It is also true that the reliability of an average will increase not in proportion to the number of measures upon which it is based, but upon the *square root* of the number. Thus, the reliability of the mean obtained from 50 cases is not twice that from 25, but rather 100 cases would be needed to obtain twice the reliability of 25. To illustrate:

$$\sqrt{25} = 5; \sqrt{100} = 10.$$

The *third* factor affecting the reliability of a measure is the variability of the distribution. The more variable the distribution, the greater the possibility of extreme scores appearing in the untested population, or the greater the distance scores may be from the mean. It is readily seen that the farther removed scores are from the average, the greater will be the possible pull on the mean of scores not measured (which those measured represent). For example, the effect of a score of 200 is greater on a mean of 100 than is a score of 125. Therefore, the more variable the distribution, the less reliable will be the results, and consequently, the greater will be the measure of reliability. It should be pointed out, too, that this factor of variability is entirely dependent upon the nature of the variable being considered, and it can in no way be controlled by the experimenter. For example, a variable such as the weight of 12-year-old boys is naturally much greater than is the variable of height for these same boys: an unavoidable situation, as heights simply do not vary to the same extent.

Thus, the reliability of the mean, or of any other statistical concept, depends first upon the representatives of the sampling itself. When this condition has been met, the other two factors affecting the reliability of measures, the number of scores and the variability of the distribution, can be accounted for in a formula. The measure of reliability usually used today is the *standard error,* and this may be applied, with appropriate formulae, to all statistical devices. For the purposes of this text, however, the reliability of the mean, of the difference between means, and of the coefficient of correlation only will be considered.

Reliability of the Mean

The standard error of the mean. The formula for the standard error of the mean is:

$$\sigma_M = \frac{\sigma_{\text{dist.}}}{\sqrt{N}}.$$

Taking data from Tables IX and XI, $M = 97.89$, $\sigma = 25.4$, and $N = 62$. Substituting in the formula:

$$\sigma_M = \frac{25.4}{\sqrt{62}} = 3.23.$$

It will readily be noted in the standard error of the mean that the larger the number of scores and the smaller the deviation of the score, the less will be the measure, or the greater the reliability of the obtained mean.

Interpretation. In interpreting the measures of reliability, it should be understood that the results obtained from calculating the mean do not give an absolutely accurate value true in all cases, but simply the obtained figures from a random sampling of the much larger population. Random samplings are relative affairs. Returning to the illustration of the weights of 12-year-old boys, if successive sam-

447

plings of these weights were taken with a different group of boys each time, the means would not always be precisely the same. Some of these means might agree, but many more would not. If additional random samplings were taken until there were, say, 100 samplings, and if the means of these 100 samplings were plotted on a graph, the results would approximate a normal curve, the mean of all the means would be located in the center, and the other means would be clustered around this center within the limits of the standard error of the distribution.

For example, using the figures in the sample problem calculated above, if 97.89 should have been the mean of many samples, 68.26 per cent of them would fall between 97.89 ± 3.23; and nearly all of them would fall between 97.89 ± 3 × 3.23, in accordance with the known qualities of normal distributions.

However, conclusions must be drawn from only *one* sampling and not from many. This is done in terms of probability. The chances are 68.26 in 100, therefore, that the true mean lies between 97.89 ± 3.23; and one can be practically certain (99.73 chances in 100) that it lies between 97.89 ± 3 × 3.23. For these chance relationships, consult Table XIII.

The interpretation of reliability given here provides only a rough guide to judge the statistical adequacy of a given sample. With the concepts of the null hypothesis, now generally approved, various "levels of confidence," or "accuracy limits," have been proposed. Fisher has proposed two such limits, called respectively the .05 and the .01 levels, which are accepted as standard for most experimental work. From Table XIII, it will be seen that 95 per cent of the normal distribution lies within the limits ± $1.96\sigma_M$; hence, the odds are 95 in 100 that any sample mean will be within these limits. This is the .05 level. For the .01 level, 99 per cent of the normal distribution lies between ± $2.58\sigma_M$; hence, the chances are 99 in 100 that any sample mean will lie within these limits. For small samples, the situation is quite complicated, so it will not be discussed here.

Reliability of the Difference Between Two Means

In studying the position at which the strength of the knee extensor muscles could be applied most effectively, Harrell [7] measured

---

[7] Dean U. Harrell, "Further Refinement of Objective Orthopedic Strength Tests." Unpublished master's thesis, Springfield College, Springfield, Mass., 1949.

with the tensiometer the amount of strength applied when the body was placed in two different positions. The mean for Position 1 was 112.94 pounds; for Position 2, 147.94 pounds. The question may logically be raised: Is this difference of 35 pounds statistically significant? The answer can only be found in terms of reliability. The results were as follows:

Position 1	Position 2
$M_1 = 112.94$	$M_2 = 147.94$
$\sigma_{M_1} = 3.20$	$\sigma_{M_2} = 6.55$

The formula for calculating the standard error of a difference between two means is

$$\sigma_d = \sqrt{\sigma^2 M_1 + \sigma^2 M_2}$$
$$= \sqrt{3.20^2 + 6.55^2} = 7.29.$$

The actual difference between the means of the two groups is designated by d. Hence, $d = 35 \pm 7.29$. The reliability of the difference between two means is interpreted in the same way in which the reliability of the mean is interpreted. Thus, the chances are 68.26 in 100 that the true difference lies between 35 ± 7.29; and one may be practically certain that it lies between $35 \pm 3 \times 7.29$.

Also, *statistically*, one may be practically certain from the evidence given that there is a definite difference in favor of Position 2, as $\pm 3 \times 7.29 = \pm 21.87$, which, subtracted from 35, the practical lower limit of probability, does not reach zero. The ratio between the difference and its measure of reliability is known as the *critical ratio*. Of course, the larger the critical ratio, the greater is the statistical significance of the difference. However, in order for the difference to be really significant, it should be 3 times its standard error, d/σ_d, as 3 times the standard error just reaches zero, indicating a favorable difference throughout. The concept of the null hypothesis, previously mentioned, however, provides for acceptable differences below this point.

CORRELATION

Meaning of Correlation

Up to this point, in considering statistics, one variable only has been dealt with. The next step will consider the degree of relationship between two variables, that is, correlation. There are various methods of computing correlations, but the standard method is known as the *product-moment* method, and is signified by the symbol "*r*," also known as the "Pearson-*r*," after its originator. Such other correlation methods as the "rank-difference" and the "Spearman footrule" have been devised for computing correlations when the number of cases is small. Because of the limitations of the latter methods, however, the product-moment correlation only will be presented in this text.

The range of the possible degree of correlations extends from a +1.00 through .00 to a −1.00, all divisions of the scale being used (such as .95, .137, −.17, and so forth). A +1.00 indicates a perfect positive correlation: a large amount of one variable is found with a large amount of the other; a small amount of one with a small amount of the other; and these are in direct proportion throughout all ranges of their distributions. A −1.00 is just as significant a correlation as is a +1.00, but the proportions are in reverse: a large amount of one variable is found with a small amount of the other, and these variables are also in direct proportion throughout all ranges of their distribution.

In a zero (.00) correlation, however, no relationship exists: an individual with a high score in one variable may appear anywhere on the scale for the opposite variable. With high positive or negative correlations, one could predict with considerable accuracy an individual's score in one variable by merely knowing his score in the other. With zero or near-zero correlations, such prediction would be impossible—would, in fact, be entirely a matter of chance.

To illustrate: If a +1.00 were obtained by correlating strength and intelligence, it would mean that the strongest individuals were the most brilliant and the weakest were the least brilliant. If a −1.00 correlation were obtained from the same two variables, it would indicate that the weakest individuals were the most brilliant and the strongest individuals were low in intelligence (the old expression of "a strong back and a weak mind"). With a zero correlation, however, the strongest individual may appear anywhere on the intelligence scale and the weak individual likewise: no relationship exists.

Computing Zero-Order Correlations

The procedures for calculating a coefficient of correlation by the product-moment method (r) may best be described by showing the actual computations involved. The following 90 pairs of arch-angles of college freshmen will serve as a problem to illustrate these techniques.

The problem is to determine the correlation between the arch heights (as determined by arch-angles) of the right and left feet of college freshmen. The steps, illustrated in Table XV, are as follows:

1. Construct a scattergram by preparing a double-entry table, as follows:

   a. Decide upon the intervals to be used for each one of the variables. This is done in the manner previously described for setting up a frequency table. Care should be taken to obtain approximately the same number of intervals for both variables; the size of the intervals will not necessarily be the same (although this is true in the sample problem, as the variabilities are the same), a step of 4 being used in both instances.

   b. List the intervals for one variable on the left (Y-variable) of the diagram, and the other at the top (X-variable). For the Y-variable, the intervals should run from high at the top to low at the bottom, in the accepted manner for frequency tables; and for the X-variable, from low at the left to high at the right.

R	L	R	L	R	L	R	L	R	L	R	L
19	16	32	22	57	42	39	37	28	32	45	47
54	50	49	45	39	41	36	38	39	39	48	46
44	47	46	42	35	50	41	48	35	41	27	26
56	56	46	47	33	27	37	42	50	48	50	46
43	41	41	41	45	39	46	48	50	58	40	45
46	50	49	48	36	30	28	21	49	42	45	45
49	53	47	45	20	18	37	43	34	46	47	46
40	42	43	41	31	33	20	18	44	45	35	33
32	36	27	35	47	56	38	35	54	54	50	52
37	40	41	35	50	54	47	50	43	41	45	41
44	35	43	38	38	51	29	31	41	43	42	44
45	47	43	43	50	43	47	44	48	48	31	29
38	35	55	53	37	34	42	48	51	51	44	44
45	49	47	30	25	47	47	48	48	48	45	43
44	45	43	44	41	31	53	47	40	40	39	41

   c. Starting with the first pair of arch-angles, 19 for the right foot and 16 for the left, make a tally in the proper square for them. The square for Pair No. 1 has been heavily ruled in Table XV. The tallies are placed in the upper left-hand corners of the squares.

d. Complete the scattergram with frequency columns: "*fy*" at the right of the scattergram for the *Y*-variable (right foot, in this instance); and "*fx*" at the bottom of the scattergram for the *X*-variable (left foot).

2. Guess as a mean for each variable the mid-point of an interval approximately in the middle of each distribution. Rule off with heavy lines the squares in the row and the column in which these guessed averages lie, as indicated in Table XV. Then compute the correction (c, or $\Sigma fd/N$) for each variable, C_x and C_y,[8] and the standard deviation

$$\sqrt{\frac{\Sigma fd^2}{N} - \left(\frac{\Sigma fd}{N}\right)^2}$$

of each variable, σx and σy,[9] in terms of deviation units, that is, without multiplying by the size of the interval. In making these computations, the following columns are necessarily adjacent to the scattergram: d, fd, and fd^2, placed on the right side for the *Y*-variable and at the bottom for the *X*-variable. So far, in calculating r, with the exception of the construction of the scattergram, no new statistical work has been presented.

3. The final step in the problem is to compute $\Sigma x'y'$. A definition of $x'y'$ is "the deviation of the various scores from the two guessed averages"; it is obtained by multiplying the deviation of the scores from one guessed average by the deviation from the other, in terms of deviation units (that is, without considering the size of the step). This procedure may be outlined as follows:

a. The lines representing the two guessed averages divide the scattergram into four quadrants: upper right, upper left, lower right, lower left. Squares on the right of the guessed average for the *X*-variable are positive; squares on the left, negative. Squares above the guessed average for the *Y*-variable are positive; squares below, negative. Therefore, all squares in the upper right and lower left quadrants are positive, as plus times plus and minus times minus equal plus, or positive; and all squares in the upper left and lower right quadrants are negative, as plus times minus equals minus, or negative.

---

[8] See the computation of the mean.
[9] See the computation of the standard deviation.

CALCULATION OF THE COEFFICIENT OF CORRELATION BY THE
PEARSON "r" METHOD FROM DATA GIVEN IN THE TEXT

X-VARIABLE: LEFT FOOT — Y-VARIABLE: RIGHT FOOT

$$c_y = \frac{92}{90} = 1.022$$

$$c_x = \frac{87}{90} = .967$$

$$\sigma_y = \sqrt{\frac{454}{90} - (1.022)^2} = 2.0$$

$$\sigma_x = \sqrt{\frac{535}{90} - (.967)^2} = 2.238$$

$$r = \frac{\dfrac{\Sigma X'y'}{N} - c_x c_y}{\sigma_x \sigma_y} = \frac{\dfrac{398}{90} - (.967 \times 1.022)}{2.238 \times 2.0} = .767$$

Correlation scatter table (marginal totals):

Y \ X	fy	dy	fdy	fdy²	x'-	y'+
56-59	2	5	10	50		30
52-55	4	4	16	64		52
48-51	14	3	42	126		120
44-47	23	2	46	92	2	76
40-43	16	1	16	16	3	20
36-39	13	0	(130 / -38 / +92)			
32-35	7	-1	-7	7	6	8
28-31	6	-2	-12	24		26
24-27	2	-3	-6	18		12
20-23	2	-4	-8	32		40
16-19	1	-5	-5	25		25
Totals	90		-38	454	-11	409 / -11 / 398

X class	16-19	20-23	24-27	28-31	32-35	36-39	40-43	44-47	48-51	52-55	56-59
fx	3	2	3	4	9	7	20	21	13	5	3
dx	-5	-4	-3	-2	-1	0	1	2	3	4	5
fdx	-15	-8	-9	-8	-9	0	20	42	39	20	15
fd²x	75	32	27	16	9	0	20	84	117	80	75

(Case No. 1 indicated in the body of the scatter at column 16-19, row 20-23.)

453

b. In case No. 1, the square deviation, or product deviation from the two guessed averages, is $(+5 \times +5) = 25$, as the square deviates five squares from both guessed averages, the final deviation being the product of these two distances. The figure 25, therefore, represents the value of the square, and is placed in its lower left-hand corner, as shown in Table XV. The values of all the squares are determined in like manner.

c. As there are more scores in some squares than in others, this fact must now be taken into account. For example, in the square representing Case No. 1, there is one frequency. Its product-moment, therefore, will be 1×25, or 25. If, however, there had been two frequencies in the square, its product-moment would be 2×25, or 50. In the square immediately above Case No. 1, there are two frequencies and a square deviation value of 20; its product-moment, therefore, is 2×20, or 40.

d. When the product-moments of all the squares have been computed, with due regard for plus and minus signs, the entries in the $x'y'$ column can be made. It will be noted that all the product-moments in Table XV have been circled to facilitate addition. Add the product-moments for each step of the Y-variable, placing the sum of the positive values under the plus sign, and the sum of the negative values under the minus sign. The algebraic sum of this column, then, is the difference between positive and negative values, 398 for the problem in question. This procedure may be duplicated for the X-variable columns to check the work: the two answers should agree.

4. Compute the coefficient of correlation, r, by means of the formula:

$$r = \frac{\dfrac{\Sigma x'y'}{N} - c_x c_y}{\sigma_x \sigma_y}.$$

The corrections, $c_x c_y$, and the standard deviations, $\sigma_x \sigma_y$, are in terms of deviation units and are not multiplied by units representing the size of the step interval.

Interpreting Coefficients of Correlation

Coefficients of correlation should not be confused with per cent relationships. A correlation of $+.50$ is not halfway to perfect correlation; nor is a correlation of $.80$ only twice as significant as one of

454

.40. Actually, there are three ways of interpreting correlations, as follows:

1. *General terms.* The correlation may be considered in such general terms as "good," "fair," "poor," "no correlation," or, "high," "low," "insignificant," and so forth; depending upon the size of *r*. Although this method is frequently used, it is obviously a very rough one and lacking in precision of definition.

2. *Predictive Index.*[10] Coefficients of correlation may be reduced to "percentages," or *Predictive Indices*, by the following formula:

$$PI = 1 - \sqrt{1 - r^2}.$$

When this formula is applied, the following results are obtained:

r	P.I.
.10	.005
.20	.020
.30	.046
.40	.083
.50	.134
.60	.200
.70	.286
.80	.400
.90	.564
.95	.688
.99	.859
1.00	1.000

Predictive Indices are interpreted in terms of their per cent of prediction value better than pure chance. Thus, a correlation of .50 is 13.3 per cent better than chance in predicting performance.

In physical education, the Predictive Index has been used quite largely to compare the significance of two or more coefficients. For example, *r*'s of .40 and .80 have PI's of .083 and .400, respectively; by comparing the PI's, therefore, a coefficient of .80 is seen to be nearly five times as significant as one of .40.

3. *Statistical significance.* With low correlations, it often becomes important to determine whether or not a significant relationship actually exists. The concept of the null hypothesis, with .05 and .01 levels of confidence, mentioned previously in connection with the reliability of the mean, is applicable to coefficients of correlation as

---

[10] The "Predictive Index" was first used by E. M. Bailor, in *Content and Form in Tests of Intelligence* (New York: Teachers College, Columbia University, 1925), pp. 25-29. It is the reciprocal of Truman Kelly's coefficient of alienation.

well; furthermore, it is the method in common use today to indicate statistical significance.

Tables are included in statistics textbooks, which provide the amount of the correlation necessary for significance, depending on the number of cases in the computations. For example, with 102 cases, an r of .195 is significant at the .05 level; an r of .254 is significant at the .01 level. Thus, only correlations as high as these could occur by sampling error 5 times in 100 at the .05 level and once in 100 at the .01 level.

Special Correlation Methods

Various methods of computing correlation have been devised for special conditions. Several of the more commonly used ones are described briefly below.

Rank-difference method. The rank-difference method, designated as rho (ρ), is designed to correlate two variables when the number of cases is small and when it would be cumbersome and impractical to use the more detailed product-moment method described above. In this situation, rho may be corrected for r by the use of a specially prepared table.

Biserial r. Occasionally it is useful to ascertain a relationship existing between two variables when only one of them is expressed in two categories. This method was utilized by Larson and McCurdy, for example, when they correlated the results of their "Organic Efficiency Test" with a criterion consisting of two groups, infirmary patients and varsity swimmers.

Tetrachoric correlation. This method of correlation is used when both variables are dichotomies (two categories each).

Coefficient of contingency. Whenever a relationship exists between two distributions, either one of which is not a variable, the usual methods of correlation are unsatisfactory. As an illustration: to determine the relationship between the extracurricular activities of college students and the type of position held five years after graduation. The coefficient of contingency indicates whether resultant frequencies are distributed as might be expected from mere chance or whether there is a tendency for certain characteristics in the one distribution to be associated with the characteristics in the other.

Modified Spearman-Brown Prophecy Formula. The Spearman-Brown Prophecy Formula is used frequently in the construction of objective written tests, particularly those of the true-false type. In securing reliability for these tests, the answers to the odd questions may be correlated with the answers to the even questions. However, as the length of a test affects its reliability, and the odd-even correlation represents only one-half of the entire test, a correction for the full-length test becomes necessary. The Prophecy Formula is designed to make this correction. A modified formula proposed by Wert [11] is as follows:

$$r = \frac{2r_{oe}}{1 + r_{oe}} \cdot \qquad (r = \text{coefficient of reliability;}$$
$$r_{oe} = \text{correlation: odds and evens})$$

With an odd-even correlation of .60,

$$r = \frac{2(.60)}{1 + .60} = .75.$$

Wert also proposes an *Index of Reliability*, which is the square root of the coefficient of reliability. Thus,

$$\sqrt{.75} = .87.$$

Multiple and partial correlation. So far, all measures of relationship that have been considered deal with two variables only. It is not only possible but often quite useful to estimate relationships when three or more variables are concerned.

The coefficient of multiple correlation has been developed for the purpose of indicating the degree to which values of one variable may correlate with two or more other variables. For example, how well does broad-jumping ability correlate with sprinting ability and leg strength?

The coefficient of partial correlation determines the net relationship between two variables when the influence of one or more other factors is excluded.

---

[11] James E. Wert, *Educational Statistics* (New York: McGraw-Hill Book Company, Inc., 1938), p. 211.

Scoring Tables

TABLE XVI

RATING TABLE FOR CRAMPTON BLOOD-PTOSIS TEST[*]

Heart Rate Increase	Systolic Blood Pressure										
	Increase						Decrease				
	+10	+8	+6	+4	+2	0	−2	−4	−6	−8	−10
0 to 4	100	95	90	85	80	75	70	65	60	55	50
5 to 8	95	90	85	80	75	70	65	60	55	50	45
9 to 12	90	85	80	75	70	65	60	55	50	45	40
13 to 16	85	80	75	70	65	60	55	50	45	40	35
17 to 20	80	75	70	65	60	55	50	45	40	35	30
21 to 24	75	70	65	60	55	50	45	40	35	30	25
25 to 28	70	65	60	55	50	45	40	35	30	25	20
29 to 32	65	60	55	50	45	40	35	30	25	20	15
33 to 36	60	55	50	45	40	35	30	25	20	15	10
37 to 40	55	50	45	40	35	30	25	20	15	10	5
41 to 44	50	45	40	35	30	25	20	15	10	5	0

[*] C. Ward Crampton, "A Test of Condition," Medical News, Vol. LXXXVII (September 1905), p. 529.

TABLE XVII

Scoring Table for Schneider's Cardiovascular Test [*]

A. Reclining Pulse Rate		B. Pulse Rate Increase on Standing				
Rate	Points	0–10 Beats, Points	11–18 Beats, Points	19–26 Beats, Points	27–34 Beats, Points	35–42 Beats, Points
50– 60	3	3	3	2	1	0
61– 70	3	3	2	1	0	−1
71– 80	2	3	2	0	−1	−2
81– 90	1	2	1	−1	−2	−3
91–100	0	1	0	−2	−3	−3
101–110	−1	0	−1	−3	−3	−3

C. Standing Pulse Rate		D. Pulse Rate Increase Immediately after Exercise				
Rate	Points	0–10 Beats, Points	11–20 Beats, Points	21–30 Beats, Points	31–40 Beats, Points	41–50 Beats, Points
60– 70	3	3	3	2	1	0
71– 80	3	3	2	1	0	0
81– 90	2	3	2	1	0	−1
91–100	1	2	1	0	−1	−2
101–110	1	1	0	−1	−2	−3
111–120	0	1	−1	−2	−3	−3
121–130	0	0	−2	−3	−3	−3
131–140	−1	0	−3	−3	−3	−3

E. Return of Pulse Rate to Standing Normal after Exercise		F. Systolic Pressure, Standing, Compared with Reclining	
Seconds	Points	Change in Mm.	Points
0– 30	3	Rise of 8 or more	3
31– 60	2	Rise of 2–7	2
61– 90	1	No rise	1
91–120	0	Fall of 2–5	0
After 120: 2–10 beats above normal	−1	Fall of 6 or more	−1
After 120: 11–30 beats above normal	−2		

[*] E. C. Schneider, "A Cardiovascular Rating as a Measure of Physical Fatigue and Efficiency," *Journal of American Medical Association,* Vol. 74 (May 29, 1920), page 1507.

SCORING TABLES

TABLE XVIII

WELLESLEY WEIGHT PREDICTION TABLE FOR COLLEGE WOMEN[*]

Sum of Skeletal Measures	Predicted Weight in Pounds	Sum of Skeletal Measures	Predicted Weight in Pounds	Sum of Skeletal Measures	Predicted Weight in Pounds
88.0	74.5	103.0	113.5	118.0	152.5
88.5	76.0	103.5	115.0	118.5	154.0
89.0	77.0	104.0	116.0	119.0	155.0
89.5	78.5	104.5	117.5	119.5	156.5
90.0	79.5	105.0	118.5	120.0	157.5
90.5	81.0	105.5	120.0	120.5	159.0
91.0	82.5	106.0	121.5	121.0	160.5
91.5	83.5	106.5	122.5	121.5	161.5
92.0	85.0	107.0	124.0	122.0	163.0
92.5	86.0	107.5	125.0	122.5	164.0
93.0	87.5	108.0	126.5	123.0	165.5
93.5	89.0	108.5	128.0	123.5	167.0
94.0	90.0	109.0	129.0	124.0	168.0
94.5	91.5	109.5	130.5	124.5	169.5
95.0	92.5	110.0	131.5	125.0	170.5
95.5	94.0	110.5	133.0	125.5	172.0
96.0	95.5	111.0	134.5	126.0	173.5
96.5	96.5	111.5	135.5	126.5	174.5
97.0	98.0	112.0	137.0	127.0	176.0
97.5	99.0	112.5	138.0	127.5	177.0
98.0	100.5	113.0	139.5	128.0	178.5
98.5	102.0	113.5	141.0	128.5	180.0
99.0	103.0	114.0	142.0	129.0	181.0
99.5	104.5	114.5	143.5	129.5	182.5
100.0	105.5	115.0	144.5	130.0	183.5
100.5	107.0	115.5	146.0	130.5	185.0
101.0	108.5	116.0	147.5	131.0	186.5
101.5	109.5	116.5	148.5	131.5	187.5
102.0	111.0	117.0	150.0		
102.5	112.0	117.5	151.0		

[*] Ludlum, F. E., and Elizabeth Powell, "Chest-Height-Weight Tables for College Women." *Research Quarterly*, Vol. XI, No. 3 (October 1940), p. 55.

TABLE XIX

Strength Index Norms for Boys (Belt)

AGE / WEIGHT

WEIGHT	8	8-6	9	9-6	10	10-6	11	11-6	12	12-6	13	13-6	14	14-6	15	15-6	16	16-6	17	17-6	18	WEIGHT
180															2664	2813	2917	2993	3056	3105	3159	180
178															2632	2778	2880	2954	3016	3064	3118	178
176															2601	2743	2843	2916	2976	3023	3077	176
174														2363	2569	2708	2805	2877	2936	2983	3035	174
172														2336	2537	2674	2768	2838	2896	2942	2994	172
170														2308	2505	2639	2731	2799	2856	2901	2953	170
168														2280	2474	2604	2694	2761	2816	2860	2911	168
166													2067	2253	2442	2569	2657	2722	2776	2819	2870	166
164													2043	2225	2410	2534	2620	2683	2736	2779	2829	164
162													2020	2198	2378	2499	2583	2645	2696	2738	2787	162
160												1848	1996	2170	2346	2465	2546	2606	2656	2697	2746	160
158												1827	1972	2142	2315	2430	2509	2567	2616	2656	2704	158
156											1718	1807	1949	2115	2283	2395	2472	2528	2576	2615	2663	156
154											1699	1786	1925	2087	2251	2360	2435	2490	2536	2575	2622	154
152											1680	1766	1902	2060	2219	2325	2398	2451	2496	2534	2580	152
150										1610	1661	1745	1878	2032	2188	2291	2361	2412	2456	2493	2539	150
148										1591	1642	1724	1854	2004	2156	2256	2324	2373	2416	2452	2498	148
146										1573	1623	1704	1831	1977	2124	2221	2287	2335	2376	2411	2456	146
144									1525	1554	1604	1683	1807	1949	2092	2186	2250	2296	2336	2371	2415	144
142									1506	1536	1585	1663	1784	1922	2060	2151	2213	2257	2296	2330	2374	142
140								1470	1487	1517	1566	1642	1760	1894	2029	2116	2176	2219	2256	2289	2332	140
138								1451	1468	1498	1547	1621	1736	1866	1997	2082	2139	2180	2216	2248	2291	138
136							1401	1431	1449	1480	1528	1601	1713	1839	1965	2047	2102	2141	2176	2207	2249	136
134							1382	1412	1430	1461	1509	1580	1689	1811	1933	2012	2065	2102	2136	2167	2208	134
132							1362	1392	1411	1443	1490	1560	1666	1784	1901	1977	2028	2064	2096	2126	2167	132
130						1318	1343	1372	1392	1424	1471	1539	1642	1756	1870	1942	1991	2025	2056	2085	2125	130
128					1273	1299	1324	1353	1373	1405	1452	1518	1618	1728	1838	1907	1956	1986	2016	2044	2084	128
126				1227	1255	1280	1304	1333	1354	1387	1433	1498	1595	1701	1806	1873	1917	1948	1976	2003	2043	126
124			1185	1209	1236	1261	1285	1314	1334	1368	1414	1477	1571	1673	1774	1838	1879	1909	1936	1963	2001	124
122		1146	1169	1192	1218	1242	1266	1294	1315	1350	1395	1457	1548	1646	1743	1803	1842	1870	1896	1922	1960	122
120		1130	1152	1174	1199	1223	1246	1275	1296	1331	1376	1436	1524	1618	1711	1768	1805	1831	1856	1881	1919	120
118	1092	1114	1135	1156	1181	1204	1227	1255	1277	1312	1357	1415	1500	1590	1679	1733	1768	1793	1816	1840	1877	118
116	1077	1098	1119	1139	1162	1185	1208	1235	1258	1294	1338	1395	1477	1563	1647	1699	1731	1754	1776	1799	1836	116
114	1061	1082	1102	1121	1144	1166	1188	1216	1239	1275	1319	1374	1453	1535	1615	1664	1694	1715	1736	1759	1795	114
112	1046	1066	1085	1104	1125	1146	1169	1196	1220	1257	1300	1354	1430	1508	1584	1629	1657	1677	1696	1718	1753	112
110	1030	1050	1069	1086	1107	1127	1150	1177	1201	1238	1281	1333	1406	1480	1552	1594	1620	1638	1656	1677	1712	110
108	1014	1034	1052	1063	1088	1108	1130	1157	1182	1219	1262	1312	1382	1452	1520	1559	1583	1599	1616	1636	1670	108
106	999	1018	1035	1051	1070	1089	1111	1138	1163	1201	1243	1292	1359	1425	1488	1524	1546	1560	1576	1595	1629	106
104	983	1002	1018	1033	1051	1070	1092	1118	1144	1182	1224	1271	1335	1397	1457	1490	1509	1522	1536	1555	1588	104
102	968	986	1002	1016	1033	1051	1072	1099	1125	1164	1205	1251	1312	1370	1425	1455	1472	1483	1496	1514	1546	102
100	952	970	985	998	1014	1032	1053	1079	1106	1145	1186	1230	1288	1342	1393	1420	1435	1444	1456	1473	1505	100
98	936	954	968	980	995	1013	1034	1059	1087	1126	1167	1209	1264	1314	1361	1385	1398	1405	1416	1432	1464	98
96	921	938	952	963	977	994	1014	1040	1068	1108	1148	1189	1241	1287	1329	1350	1361	1367	1376	1391	1422	96
94	905	922	935	945	958	975	995	1020	1049	1089	1129	1168	1217	1259	1298	1316	1324	1328	1336	1351		94
92	890	906	918	928	940	956	976	1001	1030	1071	1110	1148	1194	1232	1266	1281	1287	1289	1296	1310		92
90	874	890	902	910	921	937	956	981	1011	1052	1091	1127	1170	1204	1234	1246	1250	1251	1256			90
88	858	874	885	892	903	918	937	962	992	1033	1072	1106	1146	1176	1202	1211	1213	1212	1216			88
86	843	858	868	875	884	898	918	942	973	1015	1053	1086	1123	1149	1171	1176	1176	1173	1176			86
84	827	842	851	857	866	879	898	923	954	996	1034	1065	1099	1121	1139	1141	1139	1134	1136			84
82	812	826	835	840	847	860	879	903	935	978	1015	1045	1076	1094	1107	1107	1102	1096				82
80	796	810	818	822	829	841	860	883	916	959	996	1024	1052	1066	1075	1072	1065	1057				80
78	780	794	801	804	810	822	840	864	897	940	977	1003	1028	1038	1043	1037	1028	1018				78
76	765	778	785	787	792	803	821	844	878	922	958	983	1005	1011	1012	1002	991					76
74	749	762	768	769	773	784	802	825	858	903	939	962	981	983	980	967	953					74
72	734	746	751	752	755	765	782	805	839	885	920	942	958	956	948	933						72
70	718	730	735	734	736	746	763	786	820	866	901	921	934	928	916	898						70
68	702	714	718	716	718	727	744	766	801	847	882	900	910	900	885							68
66	687	698	701	699	708	724	746	782	829	863	880	887	873									66
64	671	682	684	681	681	689	705	727	763	810	844	859	863	845								64
62	656	666	668	664	662	669	686	707	744	792	825	839	840									62
60	640	650	651	646	650	666	688	725	773	806	818											60
58	624	634	634	628	625	631	647	668	706	754	787	797										58
56	609	618	618	611	607	612	628	649	687	736	768											56
54	593	602	601	593	588	593	608	629	668	717	749											54
52	578	586	584	576	570	574	589	610	649	699												52
50	562	570	568	558	551	555	570	590	630	680												50
	8	8-6	9	9-6	10	10-6	11	11-6	12	12-6	13	13-6	14	14-6	15	15-6	16	16-6	17	17-6	18	
*	7.80	8.00	8.35	8.80	9.26	9.54	9.67	9.78	9.52	9.30	9.50	10.30	11.80	13.80	15.89	17.41	18.52	19.36	20	20.40	20.68	

* Weight Deviation Multiplier.   *Reproduced with permission of Frederick Rand Rogers.*

1. Norms for individuals whose weights are above limits for which norms are included are calculated by adding to the norm for any chosen weight the pound difference between that weight and the individual's weight *times* the Weight Deviation Multiplier.

TABLE XX

STRENGTH INDEX NORMS FOR MEN (BELT)

AGE	18	19	20	21	22	23	24	25	26	27	28	29	30	31	32	33	34	35	36	37	38	AGE
230													3845	3796	3755	3722	3690	3664	3642	3621	3601	230
228													3808	3759	3719	3686	3653	3628	3606	3585	3565	228
226													3771	3723	3682	3649	3617	3592	3570	3549	3529	226
224													3734	3686	3646	3613	3581	3555	3534	3513	3493	224
222													3697	3650	3609	3577	3545	3519	3498	3477	3457	222
220												3706	3660	3613	3573	3541	3509	3483	3462	3441	3421	220
218												3669	3623	3576	3537	3504	3473	3447	3426	3405	3385	218
216												3632	3586	3540	3500	3468	3437	3411	3390	3369	3349	216
214											3650	3595	3549	3503	3464	3432	3401	3375	3354	3333	3313	214
212											3613	3557	3512	3467	3427	3396	3365	3339	3318	3297	3277	212
210										3626	3575	3520	3476	3430	3391	3359	3329	3303	3282	3261	3241	210
208										3588	3538	3483	3439	3393	3355	3323	3292	3267	3246	3225	3205	208
206										3550	3500	3416	3402	3357	3318	3287	3256	3231	3210	3189	3169	206
204									3567	3512	3162	3408	3365	3320	3282	3251	3220	3195	3174	3153	3133	204
202								3580	3529	3474	3425	3371	3328	3284	3245	3214	3184	3159	3138	3117	3097	202
200							3594	3541	3490	3436	3387	3334	3291	3247	3209	3178	3148	3123	3102	3081	3061	200
198						3603	3554	3502	3451	3398	3349	3297	3254	3210	3173	3142	3112	3087	3066	3045	3025	198
196					3596	3562	3514	3462	3413	3360	3312	3260	3217	3174	3136	3105	3076	3051	3030	3009	2989	196
194				3564	3554	3521	3474	3423	3374	3322	3274	3222	3180	3137	3100	3069	3040	3015	2994	2973	2953	194
192			3515	3522	3512	3480	3433	3384	3335	3284	3236	3185	3143	3101	3063	3033	3004	2979	2958	2937	2917	192
190			3473	3480	3471	3439	3393	3344	3297	3246	3199	3148	3107	3064	3027	2997	2968	2943	2922	2901	2881	190
188		3112	3131	3138	3429	3398	3353	3305	3258	3208	3161	3111	3070	3027	2991	2960	2931	2907	2886	2865	2845	188
186	3283	3371	3389	3396	3387	3357	3313	3265	3220	3170	3124	3073	3033	2991	2954	2924	2895	2871	2850	2829	2809	186
184	3242	3329	3347	3354	3315	3316	3273	3226	3181	3132	3086	3036	2996	2954	2918	2888	2859	2835	2814	2793	2773	184
182	3201	3287	3306	3312	3304	3275	3233	3187	3142	3094	3048	2999	2959	2918	2882	2852	2823	2799	2778	2757	2737	182
180	3159	3246	3261	3270	3262	3234	3192	3147	3104	3056	3011	2962	2922	2881	2845	2815	2787	2763	2742	2721	2701	180
178	3118	3204	3222	3228	3220	3193	3152	3108	3065	3018	2973	2924	2885	2844	2809	2779	2751	2727	2706	2685	2665	178
176	3077	3162	3180	3186	3179	3152	3112	3069	3026	2980	2935	2887	2848	2808	2772	2743	2715	2691	2670	2649	2629	176
174	3035	3121	3138	3144	3137	3112	3072	3029	2988	2942	2898	2850	2811	2771	2736	2707	2679	2654	2634	2613	2593	174
172	2994	3079	3096	3102	3095	3071	3032	2990	2949	2904	2860	2813	2774	2735	2699	2670	2643	2618	2598	2577	2557	172
170	2953	3037	3055	3060	3054	3030	2992	2951	2910	2866	2822	2775	2738	2698	2663	2634	2607	2582	2562	2541	2521	170
168	2911	2996	3013	3018	3012	2989	2951	2911	2872	2828	2785	2738	2701	2661	2627	2598	2570	2546	2526	2505	2485	168
166	2870	2954	2971	2976	2970	2948	2911	2872	2833	2790	2747	2701	2664	2625	2590	2562	2534	2510	2490	2469	2449	166
164	2829	2912	2929	2934	2928	2907	2871	2833	2794	2752	2709	2664	2627	2588	2554	2525	2498	2474	2454	2433	2413	164
162	2787	2871	2887	2892	2887	2866	2831	2793	2756	2714	2672	2626	2590	2552	2517	2489	2462	2438	2418	2397	2377	162
160	2746	2829	2845	2850	2845	2825	2791	2754	2717	2676	2634	2589	2553	2515	2481	2453	2426	2402	2382	2361	2341	160
158	2704	2788	2804	2808	2803	2784	2751	2714	2679	2638	2597	2552	2516	2478	2445	2417	2390	2366	2346	2325	2305	158
156	2663	2746	2762	2766	2762	2743	2710	2675	2640	2600	2559	2515	2479	2442	2408	2380	2354	2330	2310	2289	2269	156
154	2622	2704	2720	2724	2720	2702	2670	2636	2601	2562	2521	2477	2442	2405	2372	2344	2318	2294	2274	2253	2233	154
152	2580	2663	2678	2682	2678	2661	2630	2596	2563	2524	2484	2440	2405	2369	2335	2308	2282	2259	2238	2217	2197	152
150	2539	2621	2636	2640	2637	2620	2590	2557	2524	2486	2446	2403	2369	2332	2299	2272	2246	2222	2202	2181	2161	150
148	2198	2579	2594	2598	2595	2579	2550	2518	2485	2448	2408	2366	2332	2295	2263	2235	2209	2186	2165	2145	2125	148
146	2156	2538	2553	2556	2553	2538	2510	2478	2447	2410	2371	2329	2295	2258	2226	2199	2173	2150	2129	2109	2089	146
144	2415	2496	2511	2514	2511	2497	2470	2439	2408	2372	2333	2291	2258	2222	2190	2163	2137	2114	2093	2073	2053	144
142	2374	2454	2469	2472	2470	2456	2429	2400	2369	2334	2295	2254	2221	2186	2153	2126	2101	2078	2057	2037	2017	142
140	2332	2413	2427	2430	2428	2415	2389	2360	2331	2296	2258	2217	2184	2149	2117	2090	2065	2042	2021	2001	1981	140
138	2291	2371	2385	2388	2386	2374	2349	2321	2292	2258	2220	2180	2147	2112	2081	2054	2029	2006	1985	1965	1945	138
136	2249	2330	2343	2346	2345	2333	2309	2281	2254	2220	2183	2142	2110	2076	2044	2018	1993	1970	1949	1929	1909	136
134	2208	2288	2301	2304	2303	2292	2269	2242	2215	2182	2145	2105	2073	2039	2008	1981	1957	1934	1913	1893	1873	134
132	2167	2246	2260	2262	2261	2251	2229	2203	2176	2144	2107	2068	2036	2003	1971	1945	1921	1898	1877	1857	1837	132
130	2125	2205	2218	2220	2220	2210	2188	2163	2138	2106	2070	2031	2000	1966	1935	1909	1885	1862	1841	1821	1801	130
128	2084	2163	2176	2178	2178	2169	2148	2124	2099	2068	2032	1993	1963	1929	1899	1873	1848	1826	1805	1785	1765	128
126	2043	2121	2134	2136	2136	2128	2108	2085	2060	2030	1994	1956	1926	1893	1862	1836	1812	1790	1769	1749	1729	126
124	2001	2080	2092	2094	2094	2088	2068	2045	2022	1992	1957	1919	1889	1856	1826	1800	1776	1753	1733	1713	1693	124
122	1960	2038	2050	2052	2053	2047	2028	2006	1983	1954	1919	1882	1852	1820	1789	1764	1740	1717	1697	1677	1657	122
120	1919	1996	2009	2010	2011	2006	1988	1967	1944	1916	1881	1844	1815	1783	1753	1728	1704	1681	1661	1641	1621	120
118	1877	1955	1967	1968	1969	1965	1947	1927	1906	1878	1844	1807	1778	1746	1717	1691	1668	1645	1625	1605	1585	118
116	1836	1913	1925	1926	1928	1924	1907	1888	1867	1840	1806	1770	1741	1710	1680	1655	1632	1609	1589	1569		116
114	1795	1871	1883	1884	1886	1883	1867	1849	1828	1802	1768	1733	1704	1673	1644	1619	1596	1573	1553			114
112	1753	1830	1841	1812	1844	1842	1827	1809	1790	1764	1731	1695	1667	1637	1607	1583	1560	1537				112
110	1712	1788	1799	1800	1803	1801	1787	1770	1751	1726	1693	1658	1631	1600	1571	1546	1524					110
108	1670	1747	1758	1758	1761	1760	1747	1730	1713	1688	1656	1621	1594	1563	1535	1510						108
106	1629	1705	1716	1716	1719	1719	1706	1691	1674	1650	1618	1584	1557	1527	1498							106
104	1588	1663	1674	1674	1677	1678	1666	1652	1635	1612	1580	1546	1520	1490								104
102	1546	1622	1632	1632	1637	1636	1626	1612	1597	1574	1543	1509	1483	1454								102
100	1505	1580	1590	1590	1594	1596	1586	1573	1558	1536	1505	1472	1446									100
	18	19	20	21	22	23	24	25	26	27	28	29	30	31	32	33	34	35	36	37	38	
*	20.68	20.82	20.92	21	20.85	20.48	20.08	19.68	19.32	19	18.82	18.62	18.45	18.30	18.20	18.13	18.05	18.02	18.01	18	18	

* Weight Deviation Multiplier.   *Reproduced with permission of Frederick Rand Rogers.*

1. Norms for individuals whose weights are above limits for which norms are included are calculated by adding to the norm for any chosen weight the pound difference between that weight and the individual's weight *times* the Weight Deviation Multiplier.

2. Norms for men over 38 years of age may be calculated roughly by subtracting twenty points from the 38-year norm for each year over 38.

SCORING TABLES

TABLE XXI

STRENGTH INDEX NORMS FOR GIRLS (BELT)

AGE

WEIGHT	8	8-6	9	9-6	10	10-6	11	11-6	12	12-6	13	13-6	14	14-6	15	15-6	16	16-6	17	17-6	18	WEIGHT
180															2810	2933	2990	2981	2960	2912	2835	180
178														2721	2796	2885	2910	2934	2912	2865	2790	178
176													2598	2681	2752	2837	2890	2884	2863	2819	2745	176
174												2192	2560	2610	2707	2789	2840	2835	2815	2772	2700	174
172											2364	2457	2523	2600	2663	2711	2790	2785	2766	2726	2655	172
170										2250	2332	2422	2186	2559	2619	2693	2710	2735	2718	2679	2610	170
168										2220	2300	2387	2449	2518	2575	2645	2690	2685	2670	2632	2565	168
166									2083	2190	2268	2352	2112	2478	2531	2597	2610	2635	2621	2586	2520	166
164									2058	2160	2236	2318	2374	2137	2486	2519	2590	2586	2573	2539	2475	164
162								1923	2030	2130	2204	2283	2337	2397	2442	2501	2510	2536	2524	2493	2430	162
160							1818	1897	2002	2100	2172	2218	2300	2356	2398	2153	2190	2186	2176	2446	2385	160
158							1793	1871	1974	2070	2140	2213	2263	2315	2354	2405	2410	2136	2428	2399	2310	158
156						1736	1769	1845	1946	2040	2108	2178	2226	2275	2310	2357	2390	2386	2379	2353	2295	156
154						1711	1744	1818	1919	2010	2076	2144	2188	2234	2265	2309	2310	2337	2331	2306	2250	154
152					1681	1687	1720	1792	1891	1980	2044	2109	2151	2194	2221	2261	2290	2287	2282	2260	2205	152
150				1625	1657	1663	1695	1766	1863	1950	2012	2074	2114	2153	2177	2213	2240	2237	2234	2213	2160	150
148			1524	1602	1633	1639	1670	1740	1835	1920	1980	2039	2077	2112	2133	2165	2190	2187	2186	2166	2115	148
146			1502	1578	1609	1615	1646	1714	1807	1890	1948	2004	2040	2072	2089	2117	2140	2137	2137	2120	2070	146
144		1419	1479	1555	1584	1590	1621	1687	1780	1860	1916	1970	2002	2031	2044	2069	2090	2088	2089	2073	2025	144
142	1340	1398	1457	1531	1560	1566	1597	1661	1752	1830	1884	1915	1965	1991	2000	2021	2040	2038	2010	2027	1980	142
140	1319	1376	1435	1508	1536	1542	1572	1635	1724	1800	1852	1900	1928	1950	1956	1973	1990	1988	1992	1980	1935	140
138	1298	1354	1413	1485	1512	1518	1547	1609	1696	1770	1820	1865	1891	1909	1912	1925	1940	1938	1944	1933	1890	138
136	1278	1333	1391	1461	1488	1494	1523	1583	1668	1740	1788	1830	1854	1869	1868	1877	1890	1888	1895	1887	1845	136
134	1257	1311	1368	1438	1463	1469	1498	1556	1641	1710	1756	1796	1816	1828	1823	1829	1840	1839	1817	1840	1810	134
132	1237	1290	1316	1414	1439	1445	1474	1530	1613	1680	1724	1761	1779	1788	1779	1781	1790	1789	1798	1791	1755	132
130	1216	1268	1324	1391	1415	1421	1419	1504	1585	1650	1692	1726	1742	1747	1735	1733	1740	1739	1750	1717	1710	130
128	1195	1246	1302	1368	1391	1397	1424	1478	1557	1620	1660	1691	1705	1706	1691	1685	1690	1689	1702	1700	1665	128
126	1175	1225	1280	1344	1367	1373	1400	1452	1529	1590	1628	1656	1668	1666	1647	1637	1640	1639	1653	1654	1620	126
124	1154	1203	1257	1321	1342	1348	1375	1425	1502	1560	1596	1622	1630	1625	1602	1589	1590	1590	1605	1607	1575	124
122	1134	1182	1235	1297	1318	1324	1351	1399	1474	1530	1564	1587	1593	1585	1558	1541	1510	1510	1516	1561	1530	122
120	1113	1160	1213	1274	1294	1300	1326	1373	1446	1500	1532	1552	1556	1544	1514	1493	1190	1490	1508	1514	1485	120
118	1092	1138	1191	1251	1270	1276	1301	1347	1418	1470	1500	1517	1519	1503	1470	1445	1440	1440	1466	1467	1440	118
116	1072	1117	1169	1227	1246	1252	1277	1321	1390	1440	1468	1482	1482	1163	1426	1397	1390	1390	1411	1421	1395	116
114	1051	1095	1146	1204	1221	1227	1252	1294	1363	1410	1436	1448	1444	1422	1381	1349	1340	1341	1363	1374	1350	114
112	1031	1074	1124	1180	1197	1203	1228	1268	1335	1380	1441	1413	1407	1382	1337	1301	1290	1291	1314	1328	1305	112
110	1010	1052	1102	1157	1173	1179	1203	1242	1307	1350	1372	1378	1370	1341	1293	1253	1210	1241	1266	1281	1260	110
108	989	1030	1080	1134	1149	1155	1178	1216	1279	1320	1340	1343	1333	1300	1249	1205	1190	1191	1218	1234	1215	108
106	969	1009	1058	1110	1125	1131	1154	1190	1251	1290	1308	1308	1296	1260	1205	1157	1140	1141	1169	1188	1170	106
104	948	987	1035	1087	1100	1106	1129	1163	1224	1260	1276	1274	1258	1219	1160	1109	1090	1092	1121	1141	1125	104
102	928	966	1013	1063	1076	1082	1105	1137	1196	1230	1244	1239	1221	1179	1116	1061	1040	1042	1072	1095	1080	102
100	907	944	991	1040	1052	1058	1080	1111	1168	1200	1212	1204	1184	1138	1072	1013	990	992	1024	1048	1035	100
98	886	922	969	1017	1028	1034	1055	1085	1140	1170	1180	1169	1147	1097	1028	965	940	942	976	1001	990	98
96	866	901	947	993	1004	1010	1031	1059	1112	1140	1148	1134	1110	1057	984	917	890	892	927	935	945	96
94	845	879	924	970	979	985	1006	1032	1085	1110	1116	1100	1072	1016	936	869	840	813	879	908	900	94
92	825	858	902	946	955	961	982	1006	1057	1080	1084	1065	1035	976	895	821	790	793	830	862	855	92
90	804	836	880	923	931	937	957	980	1029	1050	1052	1030	998	935	851	773	740	743	782	815	810	90
88	783	814	858	900	907	913	954	1001	1020	1020	995	961	894	807	725	690	693	734	768	765		88
86	763	793	836	876	883	889	908	928	973	990	988	960	924	854	763	677	640	643	685	722	720	86
84	742	771	813	853	858	864	883	901	946	960	956	926	886	813	718	629	590	594	637	675	675	84
82	722	750	791	829	834	840	859	875	918	930	924	891	849	773	674	581	540	544	588	629	630	82
80	701	728	769	806	810	816	834	849	890	900	892	856	812	732	630	533	490	494	540	582	585	80
78	680	706	747	783	786	792	809	823	862	870	860	821	775	691	586	485	440	444	492	535		78
76	660	685	725	759	762	768	785	797	834	840	828	786	738	651	542	437	390	394	443	489		76
74	639	663	702	736	737	743	760	770	807	810	796	752	700	610	497	389	340	345	395			74
72	619	642	680	712	713	719	736	744	779	780	764	717	663	570	453	341	290	295	346			72
70	598	620	658	689	689	695	711	718	751	750	732	682	626	529	409	293	240	245				70
68	577	598	636	666	665	671	686	692	723	720	700	647	589	488	365	245	190					68
66	557	577	614	642	641	647	662	666	695	690	668	612	552	448	321	197	140					66
64	536	555	591	619	616	622	637	639	668	660	636	578	514	407	276	149						64
62	516	534	569	595	592	598	613	613	640	630	604	543	477	367	232							62
60	495	512	547 · 572	568	574	588	587	612	600	572	508	440	326									60
58	474	490	525	549	544	550	563	561	584	570	540	473	403									58
56	454	469	503	525	520	526	539	535	556	540	508	438										56
54	433	447	480	502	495	501	514	508	529	510	476											54
52	413	426	458	478	471	477	490	482	501	480												52
50	392	404	436	455	447	453	465	456	473													50
*	10.3	10.8	11.1	11.7	12.1	12.1	12.3	13.1	13.9	15	16	17.4	18.6	20.3	22.1	24	25	24.9	24.2	23.3	22.5	*
	8	8-6	9	9-6	10	10-6	11	11-6	12	12-6	13	13-6	14	14-6	15	15-6	16	16-6	17	17-6	18	

* Weight Deviation Multiplier.

Reproduced with permission of Frederick Rand Rogers.

SCORING TABLES

TABLE XXII

Strength Index Norms for Women (Belt)

AGE

WEIGHT	18	19	20	21	22	23	24	25	26	27	28	29	30	31	32	33	34	35	36	37	38	WEIGHT
220													3035	3017	3000	2994	2978	2975	2972	2969	2955	220
218												3017	2998	2981	2964	2958	2942	2939	2936	2933	2919	218
216											3001	2980	2962	2944	2928	2922	2906	2903	2900	2897	2883	216
214										2985	2964	2944	2925	2908	2891	2885	2870	2867	2864	2861	2848	214
212										2948	2927	2907	2889	2871	2855	2849	2834	2831	2828	2825	2812	212
210										2946	2890	2870	2852	2835	2819	2813	2798	2795	2792	2789	2776	210
208								2943	2908	2874	2853	2833	2815	2799	2783	2777	2762	2759	2756	2753	2740	208
206								2905	2871	2837	2816	2796	2779	2762	2747	2741	2726	2723	2720	2717	2704	206
204							2913	2867	2833	2799	2779	2760	2742	2726	2710	2704	2690	2687	2684	2681	2669	204
202							2875	2829	2796	2762	2742	2723	2706	2689	2674	2668	2651	2651	2648	2645	2633	202
200						2873	2836	2791	2758	2725	2705	2686	2669	2653	2638	2632	2618	2615	2612	2609	2597	200
198							2834	2797	2753	2720	2688	2668	2649	2632	2617	2602	2596	2582	2579	2576	2561	198
196					2844	2795	2759	2715	2683	2651	2631	2612	2596	2580	2566	2560	2546	2543	2540	2537	2525	196
194					2804	2756	2720	2677	2645	2613	2594	2576	2559	2544	2529	2523	2510	2507	2504	2501	2490	194
192				2822	2765	2717	2682	2639	2608	2576	2557	2539	2523	2507	2193	2187	2174	2171	2168	2465	2454	192
190				2782	2725	2678	2643	2601	2570	2539	2520	2502	2186	2171	2157	2151	2138	2135	2132	2429	2418	190
188			2808	2742	2685	2639	2604	2563	2532	2502	2483	2465	2449	2435	2421	2415	2402	2399	2396	2393	2382	188
186			2766	2701	2646	2600	2566	2525	2495	2465	2446	2428	2413	2398	2385	2379	2366	2363	2360	2357	2316	186
184		2804	2725	2661	2606	2561	2527	2487	2457	2427	2409	2392	2376	2362	2318	2312	2330	2327	2324	2321	2311	184
182	2880	2761	2683	2620	2567	2522	2489	2419	2420	2390	2372	2355	2310	2325	2312	2306	2294	2291	2288	2285	2275	182
180	2835	2718	2642	2580	2527	2483	2450	2411	2382	2353	2335	2318	2303	2289	2276	2270	2258	2255	2252	2249	2239	180
178	2790	2675	2601	2540	2487	2444	2411	2373	2344	2316	2298	2281	2266	2253	2240	2234	2222	2219	2216	2213	2203	178
176	2745	2632	2559	2199	2448	2105	2373	2335	2307	2279	2261	2244	2230	2216	2204	2198	2186	2183	2180	2177	2167	176
174	2700	2590	2518	2459	2408	2366	2334	2297	2269	2241	2224	2208	2193	2180	2167	2161	2150	2147	2144	2141	2132	174
172	2655	2517	2476	2118	2369	2327	2296	2259	2232	2204	2187	2171	2157	2143	2131	2125	2114	2111	2108	2105	2096	172
170	2610	2501	2435	2378	2329	2288	2257	2221	2194	2167	2150	2134	2120	2107	2095	2089	2078	2075	2072	2069	2060	170
168	2565	2161	2394	2338	2289	2249	2218	2183	2156	2130	2113	2097	2083	2071	2059	2053	2012	2039	2036	2033	2021	168
166	2520	2118	2352	2297	2250	2210	2180	2145	2119	2093	2076	2060	2047	2034	2023	2017	2006	2003	2000	1997	1988	166
164	2475	2376	2311	2257	2210	2171	2141	2107	2081	2055	2039	2024	2010	1998	1986	1980	1970	1967	1964	1961	1953	164
162	2430	2333	2269	2216	2171	2132	2103	2069	2044	2018	2002	1987	1974	1961	1950	1944	1931	1928	1925	1917		162
160	2385	2290	2228	2176	2131	2093	2064	2031	2006	1981	1965	1950	1937	1925	1914	1908	1898	1895	1892	1889	1881	160
158	2310	2247	2187	2136	2091	2054	2025	1993	1968	1944	1928	1913	1900	1889	1878	1872	1862	1859	1856	1853	1845	158
156	2295	2204	2145	2095	2052	2015	1987	1955	1931	1907	1891	1876	1864	1852	1812	1836	1826	1823	1820	1817	1809	156
154	2250	2162	2104	2055	2012	1976	1948	1917	1893	1869	1854	1810	1827	1816	1805	1799	1790	1787	1784	1781	1774	154
152	2205	2119	2062	2014	1973	1937	1910	1879	1856	1832	1817	1803	1791	1779	1769	1763	1754	1751	1748	1745	1738	152
150	2160	2076	2021	1974	1933	1898	1871	1841	1818	1795	1780	1766	1754	1743	1733	1727	1718	1715	1712	1709	1702	150
148	2115	2033	1980	1934	1893	1859	1832	1803	1780	1758	1743	1729	1717	1707	1697	1691	1682	1679	1676	1673	1666	148
146	2070	1990	1938	1893	1854	1820	1794	1765	1743	1721	1706	1692	1681	1670	1661	1635	1646	1643	1640	1637	1630	146
144	2025	1948	1897	1853	1814	1781	1755	1727	1705	1683	1669	1656	1644	1634	1624	1618	1610	1607	1604	1601	1595	144
142	1980	1905	1855	1812	1775	1742	1717	1689	1668	1646	1632	1619	1608	1597	1588	1582	1574	1571	1568	1565	1559	142
140	1935	1862	1814	1772	1735	1703	1678	1651	1630	1609	1595	1582	1571	1561	1552	1546	1538	1535	1532	1529	1523	140
138	1890	1819	1773	1732	1695	1664	1639	1613	1592	1572	1558	1545	1525	1516	1510	1502	1499	1496	1493	1487		138
136	1845	1776	1731	1691	1656	1625	1601	1575	1555	1535	1521	1508	1498	1488	1480	1474	1466	1463	1460	1457	1451	136
134	1800	1734	1690	1651	1616	1586	1562	1537	1517	1497	1484	1472	1461	1452	1443	1437	1430	1427	1424	1421	1416	134
132	1755	1691	1618	1610	1577	1524	1499	1480	1460	1447	1435	1425	1415	1407	1401	1394	1391	1388	1385	1380		132
130	1710	1648	1607	1570	1537	1508	1485	1461	1442	1423	1410	1398	1388	1379	1371	1365	1358	1355	1352	1319	1314	130
128	1665	1605	1566	1530	1497	1469	1446	1423	1404	1386	1373	1361	1351	1343	1335	1329	1322	1319	1316	1313	1308	128
126	1620	1562	1524	1489	1458	1430	1408	1385	1367	1349	1336	1324	1315	1306	1299	1293	1286	1283	1280	1277	1272	126
124	1575	1520	1483	1449	1418	1391	1369	1347	1329	1311	1299	1288	1278	1270	1262	1256	1250	1247	1244	1241	1236	124
122	1530	1477	1441	1408	1379	1352	1331	1309	1292	1274	1262	1251	1242	1233	1226	1220	1214	1211	1208	1205	1201	122
120	1485	1434	1400	1368	1339	1313	1292	1271	1254	1237	1225	1211	1205	1197	1190	1184	1178	1175	1172	1169	1165	120
118	1440	1391	1359	1328	1299	1274	1253	1233	1216	1200	1188	1177	1168	1154	1148	1142	1139	1136	1133	1129		118
116	1395	1348	1317	1287	1260	1235	1215	1195	1179	1163	1151	1140	1132	1124	1118	1112	1106	1103	1100	1097	1093	116
114	1350	1306	1276	1247	1220	1196	1176	1157	1141	1125	1114	1104	1095	1088	1081	1075	1070	1067	1064	1061	1053	114
112	1305	1263	1234	1206	1181	1157	1138	1119	1104	1088	1077	1067	1059	1051	1045	1039	1031	1028	1025	1022		112
110	1260	1220	1193	1166	1141	1118	1099	1081	1066	1051	1040	1030	1022	1015	1009	1003	998	995	992	989	986	110
108	1215	1177	1152	1126	1101	1079	1060	1043	1028	1014	1003	993	985	979	973	967	962	959	956			108
106	1170	1134	1110	1085	1062	1040	1022	1005	991	977	966	956	949	942	937	931	926	923				106
104	1125	1092	1069	1045	1022	1001	983	967	953	939	929	920	912	906	900	894	890					104
102	1080	1049	1027	1004	983	962	945	929	916	902	892	883	876	869	864	858						102
100	1035	1006	986	964	943	923	906	891	878	865	855	846	839	833	828							100
98	990	963	945	924	903	884	867	853	840	828	818	809	802	797								98
96	945	920	903	883	864	845	829	815	803	791	781	772	766									96
94	900	878	862	843	824	806	790	777	765	753	744	736										94
92	855	835	820	802	785	767	752	739	728	716	707											92
90	810	792	779	762	745	728	713	701	690													90
	18	19	20	21	22	23	24	25	26	27	28	29	30	31	32	33	34	35	36	37	38	
*	22.5	21.4	20.7	20.2	19.8	19.5	19.3	19	18.8	18.6	18.5	18.4	18.3	18.2	18.1	18.1	18	18	18	18	17.9	

* Weight Deviation Multiplier.

SCORING TABLES

TABLE XXIII—A

OREGON SIMPLIFICATION OF STRENGTH AND PHYSICAL FITNESS INDICES
TABLES FOR COMPUTATION OF REGRESSION EQUATION
UPPER ELEMENTARY SCHOOL BOYS

Equation: SI = 1.05 (Leg Lift) + 1.35 (Back Lift) + 10.92 (Push-ups) + 133

1.05 (Leg Lift)

	0	10	20	30	40	50	60	70	80	90
100	105	116	126	137	147	158	168	179	189	200
200	210	221	231	242	252	263	273	284	294	305
300	315	326	336	347	357	368	378	389	399	410
400	420	431	441	452	462	473	483	494	504	515
500	525	536	546	557	567	578	588	599	609	620
600	630	641	651	662	672	683	693	704	714	725
700	735	746	756	767	777	788	798	809	819	830
800	840	851	861	872	882	893	903	914	924	935

1.35 (Back Lift)

	0	10	20	30	40	50	60	70	80	90
		14	27	41	54	68	81	95	108	122
100	135	149	162	176	189	203	216	230	243	257
200	270	284	297	311	324	338	351	365	378	392
300	405	419	432	446	459	473	486	500	513	527

10.92 (Push-ups)

	0	1	2	3	4	5	6	7	8	9
		11	22	33	44	55	66	76	87	98
10	109	120	131	142	153	164	175	186	197	207
20	218	229	240	251	262	273	284	295	306	317

SCORING TABLES

TABLE XXIII–B

OREGON SIMPLIFICATION OF STRENGTH AND PHYSICAL FITNESS INDICES
TABLES FOR COMPUTATION OF REGRESSION EQUATION
JUNIOR HIGH SCHOOL BOYS

A Equation: 1.33 (Leg Lift) + 1.20 (Arm Strength) + 286

1.33 (Leg Lift)

	0	10	20	30	40	50	60	70	80	90
300	399	412	426	439	452	466	479	492	505	519
400	532	545	559	572	585	599	612	625	638	652
500	665	678	692	705	718	732	745	758	771	785
600	798	811	825	838	851	865	878	891	904	918
700	931	944	958	971	984	998	1011	1024	1037	1051
800	1064	1077	1091	1104	1117	1131	1144	1157	1170	1184
900	1197	1210	1224	1237	1250	1264	1277	1290	1303	1317
1000	1330	1343	1357	1370	1383	1397	1410	1423	1436	1450
1100	1463	1476	1490	1503	1516	1530	1543	1556	1569	1583
1200	1596	1609	1623	1636	1649	1663	1676	1689	1702	1716
1300	1729	1742	1756	1769	1782	1796	1809	1822	1835	1849
1400	1862	1875	1889	1902	1915	1929	1942	1955	1968	1982
1500	1995	2008	2022	2035	2048	2062	2075	2088	2101	2115
1600	2128	2141	2155	2168	2181	2195	2208	2221	2234	2248
1700	2261	2274	2288	2301	2314	2328	2341	2354	2367	2381
1800	2394	2407	2421	2434	2447	2461	2474	2487	2500	2514

1.20 (Rogers Arm Strength)

	0	10	20	30	40	50	60	70	80	90
		12	24	36	48	60	72	84	96	108
100	120	132	144	156	168	180	192	204	216	228
200	240	252	264	276	288	300	312	324	336	348
300	360	372	384	396	408	420	432	444	456	468
400	480	492	504	516	528	540	552	564	576	588
500	600	612	624	636	648	660	672	684	696	708

TABLE XXIII–C

OREGON SIMPLIFICATION OF STRENGTH AND PHYSICAL FITNESS INDICES
TABLES FOR COMPUTATION OF REGRESSION EQUATION
JUNIOR HIGH SCHOOL BOYS

B Equation: 1.12 (Leg Lift) + .99 (Arm Strength) + 5.19 (Right Grip) + 129

1.12 (Leg Lift)

	0	10	20	30	40	50	60	70	80	90
300	336	347	358	370	381	392	403	414	426	437
400	448	459	470	482	493	504	515	526	538	549
500	560	571	582	594	605	616	627	638	650	661
600	672	683	694	706	717	728	739	750	762	773
700	784	795	806	818	829	840	851	862	874	885
800	896	907	918	930	941	952	963	974	986	997
900	1008	1019	1030	1042	1053	1064	1075	1086	1098	1109
1000	1120	1131	1142	1154	1165	1176	1187	1198	1210	1221
1100	1232	1243	1254	1266	1277	1288	1299	1310	1322	1333
1200	1344	1355	1366	1378	1389	1400	1411	1422	1434	1445
1300	1456	1467	1478	1490	1501	1512	1523	1534	1546	1557
1400	1568	1579	1590	1602	1613	1624	1635	1646	1658	1669
1500	1680	1691	1702	1714	1725	1736	1747	1758	1770	1781
1600	1792	1803	1814	1826	1837	1848	1859	1870	1882	1893
1700	1904	1915	1926	1938	1949	1960	1971	1982	1994	2005
1800	2016	2027	2038	2050	2061	2072	2083	2094	2106	2117

0.99 (Rogers Arm Strength)

	0	10	20	30	40	50	60	70	80	90
		10	20	30	40	50	59	69	79	89
100	99	109	119	129	139	149	158	168	178	188
200	198	208	218	228	238	248	257	267	277	287
300	297	307	317	327	337	347	356	366	376	386
400	396	406	416	426	436	446	455	465	475	485
500	495	505	515	525	535	545	554	564	574	584

TABLE XXIII–C (*Cont.*)

OREGON SIMPLIFICATION OF STRENGTH AND PHYSICAL FITNESS INDICES
TABLES FOR COMPUTATION OF REGRESSION EQUATION
JUNIOR HIGH SCHOOL BOYS

B Equation: 1.12 (Leg Lift) + .99 (Arm Strength) + 5.19 (Right Grip) + 129

5.19 (Right Grip)

	0	1	2	3	4	5	6	7	8	9
30	156	161	166	171	176	182	187	192	197	202
40	208	213	218	223	228	234	239	244	249	254
50	260	265	270	275	280	285	291	296	301	306
60	311	317	322	327	332	337	343	348	353	358
70	363	368	374	379	384	389	394	400	405	410
80	415	420	426	431	436	441	446	452	457	462
90	467	472	477	483	488	493	498	503	509	514
100	519	524	529	535	540	545	550	555	561	566
110	571	576	581	586	592	597	602	607	612	618
120	623	628	633	638	644	649	654	659	664	670
130	675	680	685	690	695	701	706	711	716	721
140	727	732	737	742	747	753	758	763	768	773
150	779	784	789	794	799	804	810	815	820	825

SCORING TABLES

TABLE XXIII–D

Oregon Simplification of Strength and Physical Fitness Indices Tables for Computation of Regression Equation Senior High School Boys

A *Equation:* 1.22 (Leg Lift) + 1.23 (Arm Strength) + 499

1.22 (Leg Lift)

	0	10	20	30	40	50	60	70	80	90
300	366	378	390	403	415	427	439	451	464	476
400	488	500	512	525	537	549	561	573	586	598
500	610	622	634	647	659	671	683	695	708	720
600	732	744	756	769	781	793	805	817	830	842
700	854	866	878	891	903	915	927	939	952	964
800	976	988	1000	1013	1025	1037	1049	1061	1074	1086
900	1098	1110	1122	1135	1147	1159	1171	1183	1196	1208
1000	1220	1232	1244	1257	1269	1281	1293	1305	1318	1330
1100	1342	1354	1366	1379	1391	1403	1415	1427	1440	1452
1200	1464	1476	1488	1501	1513	1525	1537	1549	1562	1574
1300	1586	1598	1610	1623	1635	1647	1659	1671	1684	1696
1400	1708	1720	1732	1745	1757	1769	1781	1793	1806	1818
1500	1830	1842	1854	1867	1879	1891	1903	1915	1928	1940
1600	1952	1964	1976	1989	2001	2013	2025	2037	2050	2062
1700	2074	2086	2098	2111	2123	2135	2147	2159	2172	2184
1800	2196	2208	2220	2233	2245	2257	2269	2281	2294	2306
1900	2318	2330	2342	2355	2367	2379	2391	2403	2416	2428
2000	2440	2452	2464	2477	2489	2501	2513	2525	2538	2550

1.23 (Rogers Arm Strength)

	0	10	20	30	40	50	60	70	80	90
		12	25	37	49	62	74	86	98	111
100	123	135	148	160	172	185	197	209	221	234
200	246	258	271	283	295	308	320	332	344	357
300	369	381	394	406	418	431	443	455	467	480
400	492	504	517	529	541	554	566	578	590	603
500	615	627	640	652	664	677	689	701	713	726
600	738	750	763	775	787	800	812	824	836	849
700	861	873	886	898	910	923	935	947	959	972
800	984	996	1009	1029	1033	1046	1058	1070	1082	1095

SCORING TABLES

TABLE XXIII–E

OREGON SIMPLIFICATION OF STRENGTH AND PHYSICAL FITNESS INDICES
TABLES FOR COMPUTATION OF REGRESSION EQUATION
SENIOR HIGH SCHOOL BOYS

B Equation: 1.07 (Leg Lift) + 1.06 (Arm Strength) + 1.42 (Back Lift) + 194

1.07 (Leg Lift)

	0	10	20	30	40	50	60	70	80	90
300	321	332	342	353	364	375	385	396	407	417
400	428	439	449	460	471	482	492	503	514	524
500	535	546	556	567	578	589	599	610	621	631
600	642	653	663	674	685	696	706	717	728	738
700	749	760	770	781	792	803	813	824	835	845
800	856	867	877	888	899	910	920	931	942	952
900	963	974	984	995	1006	1017	1027	1038	1049	1059
1000	1070	1081	1091	1102	1113	1124	1134	1145	1156	1166
1100	1177	1189	1198	1209	1220	1231	1241	1252	1263	1273
1200	1284	1295	1305	1316	1327	1338	1348	1359	1370	1380
1300	1391	1402	1412	1423	1434	1445	1455	1466	1477	1487
1400	1498	1509	1519	1530	1541	1552	1562	1573	1584	1594
1500	1605	1616	1626	1637	1648	1659	1669	1680	1691	1701
1600	1712	1723	1733	1744	1755	1766	1776	1787	1798	1808
1700	1819	1830	1840	1851	1862	1873	1883	1894	1905	1915
1800	1926	1937	1947	1958	1969	1980	1990	2001	2012	2022
1900	2033	2044	2054	2065	2076	2087	2097	2108	2119	2129
2000	2140	2151	2161	2172	2183	2194	2204	2215	2226	2236

TABLE XXIII–E (*Cont.*)

OREGON SIMPLIFICATION OF STRENGTH AND PHYSICAL FITNESS INDICES
TABLES FOR COMPUTATION OF REGRESSION EQUATION
SENIOR HIGH SCHOOL BOYS

B Equation: 1.07 (Leg Lift) + 1.06 (Arm Strength) + 1.42 (Back Lift) + 194

1.06 (Rogers Arm Strength)

	0	10	20	30	40	50	60	70	80	90
	11	21	32	42	53	64	74	85	95	
100	106	117	127	138	148	159	170	180	191	201
200	212	223	233	244	254	265	276	286	297	307
300	318	329	339	350	360	371	382	392	403	413
400	424	435	445	456	466	477	488	498	509	519
500	530	541	551	562	572	583	594	604	615	625
600	636	647	657	668	678	689	700	710	721	731
700	742	753	763	774	784	795	806	816	827	837
800	848	859	869	880	890	901	912	922	933	943

1.42 (Back Lift)

	0	10	20	30	40	50	60	70	80	90
200	284	298	312	327	341	355	369	383	398	412
300	426	440	454	469	483	497	511	525	540	554
400	568	582	596	611	625	639	653	667	682	696
500	710	724	738	753	767	781	795	809	824	838
600	852	866	880	895	909	923	937	951	966	980

472

SCORING TABLES

TABLE XXIV

T-Scores for Navy Standard Physical Fitness Test*

T-Score	Squat Thrusts	Sit-Ups	Push-Ups	Squat Jump	Pull-Ups
100	48	205	89	127	37
99		200	86-8	123	
98	47	190-5	84-5	120	36
97		185	82-3	117	35
96		180	80-1	114	
95	46	170-5	78-9	111	34
94		165	76-7	108	33
93		160	74-5	106	32
92	45	155	73	103	31
91		150	71-2	100	30
90	44	145	69-70	98	29
89		140	67-8	95	
88		135	66	93	28
87	43	130	64-5	90	27
86		125	63	88	
85		120	61-2	86	26
84	42	115	60	83	
83			58-9	81	25
82	41	110	57	79	24
81		105	55-6	77	
80		100	54	75	23
79	40	97-9	53	73	22
78		92-6	52	71	
77		89-91	51	69	21
76	39	86-8	50	68	
75		82-5	49	66	20
74	38	79-81	48	64	19
73		77-8	47	63	
72		74-6	45-6	61	18
71	37	72-3	44	59	
70		69-71	43	58	17
69		67-8	42	56	
68	36	65-6	41	55	16
67		63-4		54	
66	35	61-2	40	52	15
65		59-60	39	51	
64		57-8	38	49	14
63	34	55-6	37	48	
62		54	36	47	13
61	33	52-3		46	
60		51	35	45	
59		49-50	34	43	12
58	32	47-8	33	42	
57		46	32	41	
56	31	44-5		40	11
55		43	31	39	
54		42	30	38	
53	30	40-1	29	37	10

---

* *Physical Fitness Manual for the U. S. Navy,* Chapter IV. Washington, D. C.: Bureau of Naval Personnel, Training Division, Physical Section, 1943.

TABLE XXIV (*Cont.*)

T-Score	Squat Thrusts	Sit-Ups	Push-Ups	Squat Jump	Pull-Ups
52		39		36	
51	29	38	28	35	
50		36-7		34	9
49	28	35	27	33	
48		34	26		
47		33		32	8
46	27	32	25	31	
45		31		30	
44	26	29-30	24	29	
43		28	23		7
42	25	27		28	
41		26		27	
40		25	22		6
39	2⁴		21	26	
38		24		25	
37	23				5
36		23	20	24	
35	22	22		23	
34			19		4
33	21	21	18	22	
32		20			
31	20	19	17	21	
30					
29	19	18		20	
28		17	16	19	**3**
27	18	16			
26			15		
25	17			18	
24		15	14		
23	16			17	**2**
22		14			
21	15		13	16	
20		13			
19	14		12	15	**1**
18		12			
17	13				
16			11	14	
15	12	11			
14	11				
13			10	13	
12	10	10			
11			9		
10	9			12	
9	8	9			
8			8		
7	7			11	
6	6				
5	5	8	7		
4	4				
3			6	10	
2	3				
1	2	7			

SCORING TABLES

TABLE XXV

INDIANA MOTOR FITNESS INDEX
SCALE SCORES FOR COLLEGE MEN*

Scale score	Raw scores					Scale score
	Chins	Straddle chins	Push-ups	Vertical jump	Standing broad jump	
100	17	35	36	29.75	110	100
99				29.50		99
98				29.25	109	98
97		34	35	29.00		97
96	16				108	96
95			34	28.75		95
94		33		28.50	107	94
93						93
92		32	33	28.25	106	92
91	15			28.00		91
90			32		105	90
89		31		27.75		89
88				27.50	104	88
87			31	27.25		87
86	14	30				86
85			30	27.00	103	85
84				26.75		84
83		29			102	83
82			29	26.50		82
81	13	28		26.25	101	81
80			28			80
79				26.00	100	79
78		27		25.75		78
77			27	25.50	99	77
76						76
75	12	26	26	25.25	98	75
74				25.00		74
73		25			97	73
72			25	24.75		72
71				24.50	96	71
70	11	24	24	24.25		70
69					95	69
68				24.00		68
67		23	23	23.75	94	67
66						66

TABLE XXV (*Cont.*)

INDIANA MOTOR FITNESS INDEX
SCALE SCORES FOR COLLEGE MEN*

Scale score	Raw scores					Scale score
	Chins	Straddle chins	Push-ups	Vertical jump	Standing broad jump	
65	10	22	22	23.50	93	65
64				23.25		64
63					92	63
62		21	21	23.00		62
61				22.75	91	61
60	9		20	22.50		60
59		20			90	59
58				22.25		58
57		19	19	22.00	89	57
56						56
55			18	21.75	88	55
54	8	18		21.50		54
53					87	53
52			17	21.25		52
51		17		21.00	86	51
50			16	20.75		50
49	7	16			85	49
48				20.50		48
47			15	20.25	84	47
46		15				46
45			14	20.00	83	45
44	6			19.75		44
43		14		19.50	82	43
42			13			42
41		13		19.25	81	41
40			12	19.00		40
39	5				80	39
38		12		18.75		38
37			11	18.50	79	37
36						36
35		11	10	18.25	78	35
34	4			18.00		34
33		10		17.75	77	33
32			9			32
31				17.50	76	31

TABLE XXV (*Cont.*)

INDIANA MOTOR FITNESS INDEX
SCALE SCORES FOR COLLEGE MEN [*]

Scale score		Raw scores				Scale score
	Chins	Straddle chins	Push-ups	Vertical jump	Standing broad jump	
30		9	8	17.25		30
29						29
28	3			17.00	75	28
27		8	7	16.75		27
26				16.50	74	26
25		7	6			25
24				16.25	73	24
23	2			16.00		23
22		6	5		72	22
21				15.75		21
20			4	15.50	71	20
19		5				19
18	1			15.25	70	18
17		1	3	15.00		17
16				14.75	69	16
15			2			15
14		3		14.50	68	14
13				14.25		13
12			1		67	12
11		2		14.00		11
10				13.75	66	10
9		1		13.50		9
8					65	8
7				13.25		7
6				13.00	64	6
5						5
4				12.75	63	4
3				12.50		3
2					62	2
1				12.25		1

[*] Karl W. Bookwalter, "Further Studies of Indiana University Motor Fitness Index," *Bulletin of the School of Education*, Indiana University, Vol. XIX, No. 5 (September 1943).

SCORING TABLES

TABLE XXVI

Scale Score	SS	SM	SH	MS	MM	MH	TS	TM	TH	Total	Scale Score
100	165	177	142	149	174	149	172	150	181	174	100
95-9	155-64	166-76	134-41	140-48	163-73	139-48	161-71	141-49	169-80	163-73	95-99
90-4	145-54	156-65	125-33	131-39	153-62	130-38	151-60	132-40	156-68	152-62	90-94
85-9	135-44	145-55	116-24	122-30	142-52	120-29	141-50	123-31	144-55	142-51	85-89
80-4	125-34	134-44	107-15	113-21	132-41	111-19	130-40	114-22	131-43	130-41	80-84
75-9	115-24	123-33	99-06	104-12	121-31	102-10	120-29	105-13	118-30	120-29	75-79
70-4	105-14	112-22	90-98	95-03	110-20	92-01	110-19	96-04	106-17	110-19	70-74
65-9	95-04	101-11	81-89	86-94	100-09	83-91	99-09	88-95	93-05	99-09	65-69
60-4	85-94	90-00	72-80	77-85	89-99	73-82	89-98	79-87	81-92	88-98	60-64
55-9	75-84	80-89	64-71	68-76	79-88	64-72	79-88	70-78	68-80	78-87	55-59
50-4	65-74	69-79	55-63	59-67	68-78	55-63	69-78	61-69	56-67	67-77	50-54
45-9	55-64	58-68	46-54	50-58	57-67	45-54	58-66	52-60	43-55	56-66	45-49
40-4	45-54	47-57	37-45	41-49	47-56	36-44	48-57	43-51	31-42	45-55	40-44
35-9	35-44	36-46	29-36	32-40	36-46	26-35	38-47	34-42	18-30	35-44	35-39
30-4	25-34	25-35	20-28	23-31	26-36	17-25	27-37	27-33	6-17	24-34	30-34
25-9	15-24	14-24	11-19	14-22	15-25	8-16	17-26	18-26	0- 5	13-23	25-29
20-4	5-14	4-13	2-10	5-13	4-14	0- 7	7-16	9-17		3-12	20-24
15-9	0- 4	0- 3	0- 1	0- 4	0- 3		0- 6	0- 8		0- 2	15-19
10-4											10-14
5-9											5- 9
0-4											0- 4

Row groupings (left margin): Superior (100–75-9), Good (70-4–60-4), Average (55-9–40-4), Poor (35-9–25-9), Inferior (20-4–0-4)

478

SCORING TABLES

TABLE XXVII

ACHIEVEMENT SCALES FOR BOYS IN
INDIANA STATE PHYSICAL FITNESS TEST

	Scale Score	Up to 779	780-814	815-849	850-884	885-919	920-and up	Total	Scale Score
Superior	100	167	180	186	211	214	214	203	100
	95-9	159-66	171-79	177-85	200-10	203-13	203-13	192-02	95-99
	90-4	151-58	162-70	168-76	189-99	192-02	192-02	182-91	90-94
	85-9	143-50	152-61	158-67	178-88	181-91	181-91	171-81	85-89
	80-4	135-42	143-51	149-57	167-77	170-80	171-80	161-70	80-84
	75-9	127-34	134-42	140-48	156-66	158-69	160-70	151-60	75-79
Good	70-4	119-26	124-33	131-39	146-55	147-57	149-59	140-50	70-74
	65-9	112-18	113-23	122-30	135-45	136-46	138-48	130-39	65-69
	60-4	104-11	106-14	112-21	124-34	125-35	127-37	119-29	60-64
Average	55-9	96-03	96-05	103-11	113-23	114-24	117-26	109-18	55-59
	50-4	88-95	87-95	94-02	102-12	103-13	106-16	99-08	50-54
	45-9	80-87	78-86	85-93	91-01	91-02	95-05	88-98	45-49
	40-4	72-79	69-77	76-84	80-90	80-90	84-94	78-87	40-44
Poor	35-9	64-71	59-68	66-75	69-79	69-79	73-83	67-77	35-39
	30-4	56-63	50-58	57-65	58-68	58-68	63-72	57-66	30-34
	25-9	48-55	41-49	48-56	47-57	47-57	52-62	47-56	25-29
Inferior	20-4	40-47	31-40	39-47	36-46	36-46	41-51	36-46	20-24
	15-9	33-39	22-30	30-38	25-35	25-35	30-40	26-35	15-19
	10-4	25-32	13-21	20-29	14-24	13-24	19-29	15-25	10-14
	5-9	17-24	3-12	11-19	3-13	2-12	9-18	5-14	5- 9
	0-4	9-16	0- 2	2-10	0- 2	0- 1	0- 8	0- 4	0- 4

SCORING TABLES

TABLE XXVIII

			Classification Index Groupings				
	Scale Score	Up to 609	610– 644	645– 679	680– 714	715– 749	750 and over	Scale Score
	100	109	124	124	140	145	159	100
	99	108	122	122	138	144	158	99
	98	106	121	121	136	142	156	98
	97	105	119	119	135	140	154	97
	96	104	118	118	133	139	152	96
E	95	102	116	116	132	137	151	95
X	94	101	115	115	130	135	149	94
C	93	100	113	113	128	134	147	93
E	92	99	111	112	127	132	145	92
L	91	97	110	111	125	130	144	91
L	90	96	108	109	123	129	142	90
	89	95	107	108	122	127	140	89
E	88	93	105	106	120	125	138	88
N	87	92	104	105	118	124	136	87
T	86	91	102	103	117	122	135	86
	85	90	101	102	115	120	133	85
	84	88	99	100	113	119	131	84
	83	87	98	99	112	117	129	83
	82	86	96	97	110	115	128	82
	81	85	95	96	108	114	126	81
	80	83	93	94	107	112	124	80
	79	82	92	93	105	110	122	79
	78	81	90	92	103	109	121	78
	77	79	89	90	102	107	119	77
	76	78	87	89	100	105	117	76
	75	77	86	87	99	104	115	75
	74	76	84	86	97	102	114	74
	73	74	83	84	95	100	112	73
G	72	73	81	83	94	99	110	72
O	71	72	80	81	92	97	108	71
O	70	70	78	80	90	95	107	70
D	69	69	77	78	89	94	105	69
	68	68	75	77	87	92	103	68
	67	67	74	76	85	90	101	67
	66	65	72	74	84	89	100	66
	65	64	71	73	82	87	98	65
	64	63	69	71	80	85	96	64
	63	61	68	70	79	84	94	63
	62	60	66	68	77	82	92	62
	61	59	65	67	75	80	91	61

TABLE XXVIII (*Cont.*)

Classification Index Groupings

	Scale Score	Up to 609	610–644	645–679	680–714	715–749	750 and over	Scale Score
	60	58	63	65	74	79	89	60
	59	56	62	64	72	77	87	59
	58	55	60	62	70	75	85	58
	57	54	59	61	69	74	84	57
	56	53	57	59	67	72	82	56
	55	51	56	58	66	70	80	55
	54	50	54	57	64	69	78	54
F	53	49	53	55	62	67	77	53
A	52	47	51	54	61	65	75	52
I	51	46	50	52	59	64	73	51
R	50	45	48	51	57	62	71	50
	49	44	47	49	56	60	70	49
	48	42	45	48	54	59	68	48
	47	41	44	46	52	57	66	47
	46	40	42	45	51	55	64	46
	45	38	41	43	49	54	63	45
	44	37	39	42	47	52	61	44
	43	36	38	40	46	50	59	43
	42	35	36	39	44	49	57	42
	41	33	34	38	42	45	54	41
	40	32	33	36	41	44	52	40
	39	31	31	35	39	42	50	39
	38	29	30	33	37	40	48	38
	37	28	28	32	36	39	47	37
	36	27	27	30	34	37	45	36
	35	26	25	29	33	35	43	35
	34	24	24	27	31	34	41	34
P	33	23	22	26	29	32	40	33
O	32	22	21	24	28	30	38	32
O	31	21	19	23	26	29	36	31
R	30	19	18	21	24	27	34	30
	29	18	16	20	23	25	33	29
	28	17	15	19	21	24	31	28
	27	15	13	17	19	22	29	27
	26	14	12	16	18	20	27	26
	25	13	10	14	16	19	26	25
	24	12	9	13	14	17	24	24
	23	10	7	11	13	15	22	23
	22	9	6	10	11	14	20	22
	21	8	4	8	9	12	19	21

481

TABLE XXVIII (*Cont.*)

INDIANA PHYSICAL FITNESS TEST STATE NORMS FOR ELEMENTARY BOYS
(GRADES 4–8)*

Classification Index Groupings

	Scale Score	Up to 609	610–644	645–679	680–714	715–749	750 and over	Scale Score
	20	6	3	7	8	10	17	20
	19	5	1	5	6	9	15	19
	18	4		4	4	7	13	18
	17	3		3	3	5	12	17
	16	1		1	1	3	10	16
	15					2	8	15
I	14					1	6	14
N	13						4	13
F	12						3	12
E	11						1	11
R	10							10
I	9							9
O	8							8
R	7							7
	6							6
	5							5
	4							4
	3							3
	2							2
	1							1

* G. C. Franklin and N. G. Lehsten, "Indiana Physical Fitness Test for the Elementary Level," *The Physical Educator,* Vol. V, No. 3 (May 1948), pages 42–43.

SCORING TABLES

TABLE XXIX

INDIANA PHYSICAL FITNESS TEST STATE NORMS FOR ELEMENTARY GIRLS
(GRADES 4–8)*

Classification Index Groupings

	Scale Score	Up to 609	610– 644	645– 679	680– 714	715– 749	750 and over	Scale Score
	100	110	121	146	154	129	105	100
	99	108	119	144	152	128	104	99
	98	107	118	142	150	126	103	98
	97	106	116	141	148	124	102	97
	96	104	115	139	146	123	100	96
E	95	103	114	137	144	121	99	95
X	94	101	112	136	142	120	98	94
C	93	100	111	134	140	118	97	93
E	92	98	109	132	138	116	96	92
L	91	97	108	131	136	115	94	91
L	90	96	106	129	134	113	93	90
E	89	94	105	127	132	112	92	89
N	88	93	103	126	130	110	91	88
T	87	91	102	124	128	109	89	87
	86	90	101	122	126	107	88	86
	85	88	99	121	124	105	87	85
	84	87	98	119	122	104	85	84
	83	86	96	117	120	102	84	83
	82	84	95	116	118	101	83	82
	81	83	93	114	116	99	82	81
	80	81	92	112	114	98	81	80
	79	80	91	111	112	96	80	79
	78	79	89	109	110	94	78	78
	77	77	88	107	108	93	77	77
	76	76	86	106	105	91	76	76
	75	74	85	104	103	90	75	75
	74	73	83	102	101	88	73	74
	73	71	82	101	99	86	72	73
G	72	70	81	99	97	85	71	72
O	71	69	79	97	95	83	70	71
O	70	67	78	96	93	82	68	70
D	69	66	76	94	91	80	67	69
	68	64	75	92	89	79	66	68
	67	63	73	91	87	77	65	67
	66	61	72	89	85	75	64	66
	65	60	71	87	83	74	62	65
	64	59	69	86	81	72	61	64
	63	57	68	84	79	71	60	63
	62	56	66	82	77	69	59	62
	61	54	65	81	75	68	57	61

TABLE XXIX (*Cont.*)

Indiana Physical Fitness Test State Norms for Elementary Girls
(Grades 4–8)*

Classification Index Groupings

	Scale Score	Up to 609	610–644	645–679	680–714	715–749	750 and over	Scale Score
	60	53	63	79	73	66	56	60
	59	52	62	77	71	64	55	59
	58	50	61	76	69	63	54	58
	57	49	59	74	67	61	53	57
	56	47	58	72	65	60	51	56
	55	46	56	71	63	58	50	55
	54	44	55	69	61	56	49	54
	53	43	53	67	59	55	48	53
F	52	42	52	66	57	53	46	52
A	51	40	51	64	55	52	45	51
I	50	39	49	63	53	50	44	50
R	49	37	48	61	51	49	43	49
	48	36	46	59	49	47	41	48
	47	35	45	58	47	45	40	47
	46	33	43	56	45	44	39	46
	45	32	42	54	43	42	38	45
	44	30	41	53	41	41	37	44
	43	29	39	51	38	39	35	43
	42	27	38	49	36	37	34	42
	41	26	36	48	34	36	33	41
	40	25	35	46	32	34	32	40
	39	23	33	44	30	33	30	39
	38	22	32	43	28	31	29	38
	37	20	31	41	26	30	28	37
	36	19	29	39	24	28	27	36
	35	17	28	38	22	26	25	35
	34	16	26	36	20	25	24	34
	33	15	25	34	18	23	23	33
P	32	13	23	33	16	22	22	32
O	31	12	22	31	14	20	21	31
O	30	10	21	29	12	19	19	30
R	29	9	19	28	10	17	18	29
	28	8	18	26	8	15	17	28
	27	6	16	24	6	14	16	27
	26	5	15	23	4	12	14	26
	25	3	13	21	2	11	13	25
	24	2	12	19	1	9	12	24
	23		11	18		7	11	23
	22		9	16		6	9	22
	21		8	14		4	8	21

TABLE XXIX (Cont.)

INDIANA PHYSICAL FITNESS TEST STATE NORMS FOR ELEMENTARY GIRLS
(GRADES 4–8)*

Classification Index Groupings

Scale Score	Up to 609	610–644	645–679	680–714	715–749	750 and over	Scale Score
20		6	13		3	7	20
19		5	11		1	6	19
18		3	9			5	18
17		2	8			3	17
16		1	6			2	16
15			4			1	15
I 14			3				14
N 13			1				13
F 12							12
E 11							11
R 10							10
I 9							9
O 8							8
R 7							7
6							6
5							5
4							4
3							3
2							2
1							1

* G. C. Franklin and N. G. Lehsten, "Indiana Physical Fitness Test for the Elementary Level," *The Physical Educator*, Vol. V, No. 3 (May 1948), pages 44-45.

TABLE XXX

INDIANA PHYSICAL FITNESS TEST

HEIGHT-WEIGHT CLASS DIVISIONS OF SECONDARY SCHOOL GIRLS

	Height		Weight		
	Feet & Inches	Inches	Slender	Medium	Heavy
Short	4-7	55	up to 82	83-111	112 up
	4-8	56	up to 79	80-102	103 up
	4-9	57	up to 82	83-107	108 up
	4-10	58	up to 85	86-110	111 up
	4-11	59	up to 91	92-112	113 up
	5-0	60	up to 96	97-117	118 up
	5-1	61	up to 99	100-120	121 up
Medium	5-2	62	up to 103	104-124	125 up
	5-3	63	up to 106	107-127	128 up
	5-4	64	up to 110	111-132	133 up
Tall	5-5	65	up to 113	114-136	137 up
	5-6	66	up to 116	117-140	141 up
	5-7	67	up to 120	121-143	144 up
	5-8	68	up to 120	121-152	153 up
	5-9	69	up to 126	127-153	154 up
	5-10	70	up to 125	126-154	155 up
	5-11 up	71 up	up to 124	125-160	161 up

Direction: Read down the height column until the girl's height is reached. Next read to the right to the weight column containing the girl's weight for that height. Her classification is the height group and weight group combined. (Example: A girl whose height is 65 inches and whose weight is 137 is a Tall Heavy (TH).)

Code for Classification:

SS—Short Slender   MS—Medium Slender   TS—Tall Slender
SM—Short Medium   MM—Medium Medium   TM—Tall Medium
SH—Short Heavy   MH—Medium Heavy   TH—Tall Heavy

486

TABLE XXXI

OREGON MOTOR FITNESS TEST
NORMS FOR SECONDARY SCHOOL BOYS
BY GRADES

Points	Jump and Reach in Inches						Number of Pull-ups						Potato Race in Seconds					
	7th	8th	9th	10th	11th	12th	7th	8th	9th	10th	11th	12th	7th	8th	9th	10th	11th	12th
100	28	29	33		37		17		22	23	26		22	23	21			24
96	27	28	32	34	36	39	16	18	21	21	25	26	23	24	22	23	23	
92	26	27	31	32	35	37	15	17	19	20	24	24	24	25	23	24	24	25
88	25	26	30	31	34	36	14	15	17	19	22	23	26	26	24	25	25	26
84	24	25	29	30	32	34	13	14	16	18	20	21	27	27	25	26	26	27
80	23	24	27	29	31	33	12	13	14	16	19	20	28	28	26	27	27	
76	21	23	26	27	29	32	11	12	13	15	17	18	30	29	27	28	28	28
72	20	22	25	26	28	31	9	11	12	13	16	16	31	30	29	29	29	29
68	19	21	24	25	27	29	8	10	10	12	14	15	32	31	30	30	30	30
64	17	19	22	24	25	27	7	9	9	10	13	13	33	32	31	31	31	
60	16	18	21	23	24	26	6	7	8	9	11	11	35	34	32	32		31
56	15	17	20	21	23	24	5	6	6	8	9	10	36	35	33	33	32	32
52		16	19	20	22	23	4	5	5	6	8	8	37	36	34	34	33	33
48	14	15	17	19	20	22	3	4	3	5	6	7	39	37	35	35	34	34
44	13	14	16	18	19	20	2	3	2	3	5	5	40	38	36	36	35	
40	12	13	15	16	18	19	1	2	1	2	3	3	41	39	38	37	36	35
36	10	11	14	15	17	17		1		1	1	2	42	40	39	38		36
32	9	10	13	14	16	16							44	41	40	39	37	
28	8	9	11	13	14	15							45	43	41	40	38	37
24	7	8	10	11	13	13							46	44	42	41	39	38
20	6	7	9	10	12	12							48	45	43	42	40	39
16	5	6	8	9	11	10							49	46	44	43	41	40
12	4	5	7	8	9	9							50	47	45			
8	3	3	5	7	8	8							51	48	47	44	42	41
4		1	4	5	7	6							53	49	48	45	43	42
1	2		3			5							54	50				

SCORING TABLES

TABLE XXXII

OREGON MOTOR FITNESS TEST
NORMS FOR SECONDARY SCHOOL GIRLS
BY GRADES

Points	Arm Flexed Hang in Seconds						Standing Broad Jump in Inches						Number of Crossed Arm Curl-ups					
	7th	8th	9th	10th	11th	12th	7th	8th	9th	10th	11th	12th	7th	8th	9th	10th	11th	12th
100	75	75	107	104	105	106	99	100	105	105	106	106	105	105	121	121	123	123
96	72	72	100	97	98	99	98	99	102	102	104	104	101	101	114	114	116	116
92	68	68	93	90	91	92	96	97	100	100	102	102	95	95	107	107	109	109
88	64	64	86	83	84	85	93	95	98	98	100	100	89	89	100	100	102	102
84	60	60	79	76	77	78	90	92	95	95	97	97	83	83	93	93	95	95
80	56	56	72	69	70	71	86	88	91	91	93	93	77	77	86	86	88	88
76	52	52	65	62	63	64	83	86	89	89	91	91	71	71	79	79	81	81
72	48	48	58	55	56	57	80	82	85	85	87	87	65	65	72	72	74	74
68	44	44	51	48	49	50	76	78	81	81	85	85	59	59	65	65	67	67
64	40	40	44	41	42	43	73	75	78	78	80	80	53	53	58	58	60	60
60	36	36	37	34	35	36	70	72	75	75	76	76	47	47	51	51	53	53
56	20	20	30	27	28	29	66	68	71	71	71	71	41	41	44	44	46	46
52	16	16	23	20	21	20	63	65	68	68	68	68	35	35	37	37	39	39
48	12	12	17	13	14	14	59	61	63	64	65	65	29	29	31	31	33	33
44	8	8	11	9	10	11	56	58	60	60	61	62	23	23	25	25	27	27
40	5	5	8	5	6	7	53	54	56	56	58	59	19	19	21	21	23	23
36	4	4	7	4	5	6	49	51	53	53	55	56	15	15	17	17	19	19
32	3	3	6	3	4	5	46	48	49	49	51	52	11	11	13	13	15	15
28	2	2	5	2	3	4	43	44	45	57	49	50	7	7	9	9	11	11
24	1	1	4	1	2	3	39	39	41	43	45	46	5	5	7	7	9	9
20			3		1	2	36	36	39	41	43	44	3	3	5	5	7	7
16			2			1	33	33	36	38	40	41	1	1	3	3	5	5
12			1				30	30	33	35	37	38			1	1	3	3
8							27	27	30	32	34	35					1	1
4							24	24	27	29	31	32						
1							22	22	25	27	29	30						

SCORING TABLES

TABLE XXXIII

Six-Sigma Scoring Chart for
NSWA Physical Performance Test[*]

Scale Score	Standing Broad Jump	Basket-ball Throw	Potato Race	Pull-ups	Push-ups	Sit-ups	10-Second Squat Thrust	30-Second Squat Thrust	Scale Score
100	7–9	78	8.4	47	61	65	9–1	24	100
95	7–7	75	8.6	45	58	61	9	23	95
90	7–4	72	8.8	42	54	57	8–3	22	90
85	7–2	68	9.0	39	51	54	8–1	21	85
80	6–11	65	9.4	37	47	50	8	20	80
75	6–9	62	9.6	34	43	46	7–3	19	75
70	6–7	59	10.0	32	39	43	7–1	18–2	70
65	6–4	56	10.2	29	36	39	7	18	65
60	6–2	53	10.4	26	32	36	6–2	17	60
55	6–0	50	10.6	24	28	33	6–1	16	55
50	5–9	46	11.0	21	25	29	6	15	50
45	5–7	43	11.2	18	21	25	5–2	14–2	45
40	5–5	40	11.6	16	17	22	5–1	14	40
35	5–2	37	11.8	13	13	18	4–3	13	35
30	5–0	34	12.0	10	10	15	4–2	12	30
25	4–9	31	12.4	8	6	11	4	11	25
20	4–7	27	12.6	5	2	7	3–3	10	20
15	4–4	24	13.0	3	1	3	3–2	9	15
10	4–2	21	13.2	1	0	1	3	8–2	10
5	4–0	18	13.4	0	0	0	2–3	7–2	5
0	3–9	15	13.6	0	0	0	2–2	7	0

[*] Eleanor Metheny, Chairman, "Physical Performance Levels for High School Girls," *Journal of Health and Physical Education,* Vol. XVI, No. 6 (June 1945).

TABLE XXXIV

PERCENTILE SCALE
COWELL SOCIAL ADJUSTMENT INDEX

Raw Score	Percentile Score	Raw Score	Percentile Score	Raw Score	Percentile Score
88	99.55	36	68.47	− 6	25.22
81	99.10	35	67.12	− 7	23.87
80	98.65	34	65.32	− 8	23.42
79	98.20	33	64.41	− 9	22.97
78	97.75	32	63.51	−12	22.52
77	97.30	31	61.26	−15	21.62
75	96.85	30	59.91	−16	21.17
74	96.40	29	59.01	−17	20.72
73	95.94	28	57.21	−18	19.82
72	95.50	27	56.31	−19	18.92
70	95.04	26	55.40	−20	18.47
68	94.59	25	54.95	−21	17.51
65	92.79	24	53.60	−23	16.22
63	92.34	23	52.70	−25	15.32
62	91.44	22	51.80	−26	13.96
61	90.54	21	50.90	−27	12.36
60	90.09	20	50.45	−28	12.16
59	89.19	18	48.65	−29	11.71
58	88.29	17	46.85	−35	10.81
57	86.49	16	45.94	−36	9.91
56	86.04	15	45.50	−39	8.56
55	85.14	14	45.04	−40	8.11
54	84.23	13	43.24	−42	7.66
52	83.33	12	41.44	−43	7.21
51	82.88	11	40.54	−44	6.76
50	82.43	10	40.09	−45	6.31
49	81.08	9	38.74	−46	5.40
48	80.18	8	37.84	−47	4.50
47	79.28	7	36.94	−49	4.05
46	78.38	6	35.59	−50	3.60
45	77.03	4	34.68	−54	3.15
44	74.77	3	33.33	−55	2.70
43	73.42	2	32.43	−58	1.80
42	72.97	1	30.63	−61	1.35
41	72.52	−1	29.73	−62	.90
40	72.07	−2	28.38	−71	.45
38	71.17	−3	27.48	−73	.00
37	69.37	−5	26.00		

n = 222

SCORING TABLES

TABLE XXXV

PERCENTILE SCALE
COWELL PERSONAL DISTANCE

Raw Score	Percentile Score	Raw Score	Percentile Score	Raw Score	Percentile Score
159	99.34	321	61.59	396	31.12
161	98.68	327	60.93	398	30.46
173	98.01	329	60.26	400	29.80
196	97.35	331	59.60	405	26.49
200	96.69	333	58.94	412	25.83
205	94.04	335	57.62	415	25.16
210	93.38	336	56.29	416	24.50
211	92.71	344	54.97	417	23.84
219	92.05	347	54.30	418	23.18
220	91.39	351	53.64	419	21.19
222	90.73	352	52.98	420	20.53
233	90.07	369	45.70	421	19.87
237	89.40	371	45.03	422	19.20
240	88.74	375	44.37	423	17.22
252	88.08	376	43.71	425	16.56
256	86.75	377	43.05	426	15.89
257	84.10	378	41.06	428	15.23
259	83.44	379	40.40	429	14.57
260	82.78	353	51.66	431	13.91
265	82.12	354	50.33	433	13.24
266	81.46	355	49.67	434	12.58
267	80.79	357	49.01	435	11.92
271	79.47	359	48.34	439	11.25
274	78.81	361	47.68	445	10.60
281	76.16	363	47.02	455	9.93
282	75.50	366	46.36	457	9.27
283	74.17	380	39.74	469	7.95
284	73.51	381	38.41	470	7.28
285	72.85	382	37.75	471	6.62
289	72.18	384	37.09	482	5.96
294	70.20	385	36.76	495	5.30
295	68.87	386	35.10	496	4.64
300	68.21	389	34.44	500	3.97
311	65.56	390	33.77	503	1.99
312	64.90	391	33.11	509	1.32
315	64.24	392	32.45	541	.66
319	62.91	395	31.79	636	.00

n = 151

TABLE XXXVI

CARPENTER'S MOTOR ABILITY TEST FOR FIRST THREE GRADES (BOYS) *

	0	1	2	3	4	5	6	7	8	9
600	115.94	116.24	116.54	116.84	117.14	117.44	117.75	118.05	118.35	118.65
590	112.93	113.23	113.53	113.83	114.13	114.44	114.74	115.04	115.34	115.64
580	109.92	110.22	110.52	110.82	111.13	111.43	111.73	112.03	112.33	112.63
570	106.91	107.21	107.51	107.82	108.12	108.42	108.72	109.02	109.32	109.62
560	103.90	104.20	104.51	104.81	105.11	105.41	105.71	106.01	106.31	106.61
550	100.90	101.20	101.50	101.80	102.10	102.40	102.70	103.00	103.30	103.60
540	97.80	98.19	98.49	98.79	99.09	99.39	99.69	99.99	100.29	100.59
530	94.88	95.18	95.48	95.78	96.08	96.38	96.68	96.98	97.28	97.59
520	91.87	92.17	92.45	92.77	93.07	93.37	93.67	93.97	94.28	94.58
510	88.86	89.16	89.46	89.76	90.06	90.36	90.66	90.97	91.27	91.57
500	85.85	86.15	86.45	86.75	87.05	87.35	87.66	87.96	88.26	88.56
490	82.84	83.14	83.44	83.74	84.04	84.35	84.65	84.95	85.25	85.55
480	79.83	80.13	80.43	80.73	81.04	81.34	81.64	81.94	82.24	82.54
470	76.82	77.12	77.42	77.73	78.03	78.33	78.63	78.93	79.23	79.53
460	73.81	74.11	74.42	74.72	75.02	75.32	75.62	75.92	76.22	76.52
450	70.81	71.11	71.41	71.71	72.01	72.31	72.61	72.91	73.21	73.51
440	67.80	68.10	68.40	68.70	69.00	69.30	69.60	69.90	70.20	70.50
430	64.79	65.09	65.39	65.69	65.99	66.29	66.59	66.89	67.19	67.50
420	61.78	62.08	62.38	62.68	62.98	63.28	63.58	63.88	64.19	64.49
410	58.77	59.07	59.37	59.67	59.97	60.27	60.57	60.88	61.18	61.48
400	55.76	56.06	56.36	56.66	56.96	57.26	57.57	57.87	58.17	58.47

* Aileen Carpenter, "Strength Testing in the First Three Grades," Research Quarterly, Vol. 13, No. 3 (October 1942), page 332.

TABLE XXXVII

Carpenter's Motor Ability Test for First Three Grades (Girls)*

	0	1	2	3	4	5	6	7	8	9
600	125.03	125.28	125.54	125.79	126.05	126.30	126.56	126.81	127.07	127.32
590	122.48	122.74	122.99	123.23	123.50	123.76	124.01	124.26	124.52	124.78
580	119.93	120.19	120.44	120.70	120.95	121.21	121.46	121.72	121.97	122.23
570	117.38	117.64	117.89	118.15	118.40	118.66	118.91	119.17	119.42	119.68
560	114.83	115.09	115.34	115.60	115.85	116.11	116.36	116.62	116.87	117.13
550	112.29	112.54	112.79	113.05	113.30	113.56	113.81	114.07	114.32	114.58
540	109.74	109.99	110.25	110.50	110.76	111.01	111.27	111.52	111.78	112.03
530	107.19	107.44	107.70	107.95	108.21	108.46	108.72	108.97	109.32	109.48
520	104.64	104.89	105.15	105.40	105.66	105.91	106.17	106.42	106.68	106.93
510	102.09	102.34	102.60	102.85	103.11	103.36	103.62	103.87	104.13	104.38
500	99.54	99.79	100.05	100.30	100.56	100.81	101.07	101.32	101.58	101.83
490	96.99	97.25	97.50	97.76	98.01	98.27	98.52	98.78	99.03	99.29
480	94.44	94.70	94.95	95.21	95.46	95.72	95.97	96.23	96.48	96.74
470	91.89	92.15	92.40	92.66	92.91	93.17	93.42	93.68	93.93	94.19
460	89.34	89.60	89.85	90.11	90.36	90.62	90.87	91.13	91.38	91.64
450	86.80	87.05	87.30	87.56	87.81	88.07	88.32	88.58	88.83	89.09
440	84.25	84.50	84.76	85.01	85.27	85.52	85.78	86.03	86.29	86.54
430	81.70	81.95	82.21	82.46	82.72	82.97	83.23	83.48	83.74	83.99
420	79.15	79.40	79.66	79.91	80.17	80.42	80.68	80.93	81.19	81.44
410	76.60	76.85	77.11	77.36	77.62	77.87	78.13	78.38	78.64	78.89
400	74.05	74.30	74.56	74.81	75.07	75.32	75.58	75.83	76.09	76.34

* Aileen Carpenter, "Strength Testing in the First Three Grades," Research Quarterly, Vol. 13, No. 3 (October 1942), page 331.

SCORING TABLES

TABLE XXXVIII

ACHIEVEMENT SCALES FOR THE NEWTON MOTOR ABILITY TEST
FOR HIGH SCHOOL GIRLS *

Point Score	Hurdles	Broad Jump	Scramble	Total Points	Point Score	Decile Score
100	7.2	83.0	10.4	275	100	
99	7.3	82.5	10.6	273	99	
98	7.4	82.0	10.7	270	98	
97			10.8	268	97	
96	7.5	81.5	10.9	265	96	
95	7.6	81.0	11.0	263	95	
94	7.7	80.5	11.2	260	94	
93		80.0	11.3	258	93	
92	7.8	79.5	11.4	255	92	
91	7.9	79.0	11.6	253	91	
90		78.5	11.7	250	90	
89	8.0		11.8	248	89	
88	8.1	78.0	11.9	245	88	
87	8.2	77.5	12.0	243	87	
86		77.0	12.2	240	86	
85	8.3	76.5	12.3	238	85	
84	8.4	76.0	12.4	235	84	
83	8.5	75.5	12.6	233	83	
82		75.0	12.7	230	82	
81	8.6		12.8	228	81	
80	8.7	74.5	12.9	225	80	
79	8.8	74.0	13.0	223	79	
78		73.5	13.2	220	78	
77	8.9	73.0	13.3	218	77	
76	9.0	72.5	13.4	215	76	
75		72.0	13.6	213	75	
74	9.1		13.7	210	74	
73	9.2	71.5	13.8	208	73	
72	9.3	71.0	13.9	205	72	
71		70.5	14.0	203	71	
70	9.4	70.0	14.2	200	70	
69	9.5	69.5	14.3	198	69	
68	9.6	69.0	14.4	195	68	
67			14.6	193	67	II
66	9.7	68.5	14.7	190	66	
65	9.8	68.0	14.8	188	65	
64		67.5	14.9	185	64	
63	9.9	67.0	15.0	183	63	
62	10.0	66.5	15.2	180	62	
61	10.1	66.0	15.3	178	61	III
60			15.4	175	60	
59	10.2	65.5	15.6	173	59	

494

TABLE XXXVIII (*Cont.*)

ACHIEVEMENT SCALES FOR THE NEWTON MOTOR ABILITY TEST
FOR HIGH SCHOOL GIRLS *

Point Score	Hurdles	Broad Jump	Scramble	Total Points	Point Score	Decile Score
58	10.3	65.0	15.7	170	58	
57	10.4	64.5	15.8	168	57	
56		64.0	15.9	165	56	IV
55	10.5	63.5	16.0	163	55	
54	10.6	63.0	16.2	160	54	
53		62.5	16.3	158	53	
52	10.7		16.4	155	52	V
51	10.8	62.0	16.6	153	51	
50	10.9	61.5	16.7	150	50	
49		61.0	16.8	148	49	
48	11.0	60.5	16.9	145	48	VI
47	11.1	60.0	17.1	143	47	
46	11.2	59.5	17.2	140	46	
45		59.0	17.3	138	45	
44	11.3		17.4	135	44	
43	11.4	58.5	17.6	133	43	VII
42	11.5	58.0	17.7	130	42	
41		57.5	17.8	128	41	
40	11.6	57.0	17.9	125	40	
39	11.7	56.5	18.1	123	39	
38		56.0	18.2	120	38	VIII
37	11.8		18.3	118	37	
36	11.9	55.5	18.4	115	36	
35	12.0	55.0	18.6	113	35	
34		54.5	18.7	110	34	
33	12.1	54.0	18.8	108	33	
32	12.2	53.5	18.9	105	32	IX
31	12.3	53.0	19.1	103	31	
30			19.2	100	30	
29	12.4	52.5	19.3	98	29	

TABLE XXXVIII (*Cont.*)

ACHIEVEMENT SCALES FOR THE NEWTON MOTOR ABILITY TEST
FOR HIGH SCHOOL GIRLS *

Point Score	Hurdles	Broad Jump	Scramble	Total Points	Point Score	Decile Score
28	12.5	52.0	19.4	95	28	
27		51.5	19.6	93	27	
26	12.6	51.0	19.7	90	26	
25	12.7	50.5	19.8	88	25	
24	12.8	50.0	19.9	85	24	
23			20.1	83	23	
22	12.9	49.5	20.2	80	22	
21	13.0	49.0	20.3	78	21	
20	13.1	48.5	20.4	75	20	
19		48.0	20.6	73	19	
18	13.2	47.5	20.7	70	18	
17	13.3	47.0	20.8	68	17	
16	13.4		20.9	65	16	
15		46.5	21.1	63	15	X
14	13.5	46.0	21.2	60	14	
13	13.6	45.5	21.3	58	13	
12		45.0	21.4	55	12	
11	13.7	44.5	21.6	53	11	
10	13.8	44.0	21.7	50	10	
9	13.9	43.5	21.8	48	9	
8		43.0	21.9	45	8	
7	14.0		22.1	43	7	
6	14.1	42.5	22.2	40	6	
5	14.2	42.0	22.3	38	5	
4		41.5	22.4	35	4	
3	14.3	41.0	22.6	33	3	
2	14.4	40.5	22.7	30	2	
1			22.8	28	1	
0	14.5	40.0	22.9	25	0	

* Elizabeth Powell and Eugene C. Howe, "Motor Ability Tests for High School Girls," *Research Quarterly*, Vol. 10, No. 4 (December 1939), pages 86–87.

TABLE XXXIX

McCLOY'S PROPOSED DIVISIONS FOR CLASSIFICATION INDICES*
Classification Index I—High School
Range 685–955

Class	For a Small Group	Class	For a Larger Group
A	890 and over	A	900 and over
B	860	B	845
C	830	C	815
D	800	D	785
E	770	E	755
F	740	F	725
G	739 and under	G	695
		H	665
		I	664 and under

Classification Index I—Junior High School
Range 540–900

Class	For All Groups
A	875 and over
B	845
C	815
D	785
E	755
F	725
G	695
H	665
I	664 and under

Classification Index II—College
Range 490–600

Class	For a Small Group	Class	For a Larger Group
A	570 and over	A	580 and over
B	550	B	560
C	530	C	540
D	529 and under	D	520
		E	519 and under

Classification Index III—Elementary School Only
Range 160–320

Class	For a Small Group	Class	For a Larger Group
A	275 and over	A	275 and over
B	260	B	263
C	245	C	255
D	230	D	245
E	215	E	235
F	200	F	225
G	185	G	215
H	184 and under	H	205
		I	195
		J	185
		K	184 and under

* C. H. McCloy, *Tests and Measurements in Health and Physical Education*, page 47.
New York: F. S. Crofts and Company, 1939.

TABLE XL

THE NEILSON AND COZENS CLASSIFICATION CHART FOR BOYS AND GIRLS*
(Elementary and Junior High School)

Exponent	Height in Inches	Age in Years	Weight in Pounds
1	50 to 51	10 to 10-5	60 to 65
2	52 to 53	10-6 to 10-11	66 to 70
3		11 to 11-5	71 to 75
4	54 to 55	11-6 to 11-11	76 to 80
5		12 to 12-5	81 to 85
6	56 to 57	12-6 to 12-11	86 to 90
7		13 to 13-5	91 to 95
8	58 to 59	13-6 to 13-11	96 to 100
9		14 to 14-5	101 to 105
10	60 to 61	14-6 to 14-11	106 to 110
11		15 to 15-5	111 to 115
12	62 to 63	15-6 to 15-11	116 to 120
13		16 to 16-5	121 to 125
14	64 to 65	16-6 to 16-11	126 to 130
15	66 to 67	17 to 17-5	131 to 133
16	68	17-6 to 17-11	134 to 136
17	69 and over	18 and over	137 and over

Sum of Exponents	Class	Sum of Exponents	Class
9 and below.................	A	25 to 29......................	E
10 to 14....................	B	30 to 34........	F
15 to 19....................	C	35 to 38.....................	G
20 to 24....................	D	39 and above................	H

* N. P. Neilson and F. W. Cozens, *Achievement Scales*. New York: A. S. Barnes and Company.

TABLE XLI

ACHIEVEMENT SCALES IN ARCHERY FOR WOMEN*

Scale	First Columbia Total Score (Target Score)	Final Columbia Record (Target Score)			
		Total Score	50 yards	40 yards	30 yards
100	436	466	150	176	194
99	430	460	148	174	192
98	424	455	146	171	190
97	418	449	143	169	187
96	412	443	141	167	185
95	406	438	139	164	183
94	400	432	137	162	181
93	394	426	135	160	179
92	388	420	132	157	176
91	382	415	130	155	174
90	376	409	128	153	172
89	370	403	126	150	170
88	364	398	124	148	168
87	358	392	121	146	165
86	352	386	119	143	163
85	346	381	117	141	161
84	340	375	115	139	159
83	334	369	113	136	157
82	328	363	110	134	154
81	322	358	108	132	152
80	316	352	106	129	150
79	310	346	104	127	148
78	304	341	102	125	146
77	298	335	99	122	143
76	292	329	97	120	141
75	286	324	95	118	139
74	280	318	93	115	137
73	274	312	91	113	135
72	268	306	88	111	132
71	262	301	86	108	130
70	256	295	84	106	128
69	250	289	82	104	126
68	244	284	80	101	124
67	238	278	77	99	121
66	232	272	75	97	119
65	226	267	73	94	117
64	220	261	71	92	115
63	214	255	69	90	113
62	208	249	66	87	110
61	202	244	64	85	108

* Scale constructed by F. W. Cozens, University of California at Los Angeles. Reproduced from: Edith I. Hyde, "An Achievement Scale in Archery," *Research Quarterly*, Vol. VII, No. 2 (May 1937), page 109.

TABLE XLI (*Cont.*)

Scale	First Columbia Total Score (Target Score)	Final Columbia Record (Target Score)			
		Total Score	50 yards	40 yards	30 yards
60	196	238	62	83	106
59	190	232	60	80	104
58	184	227	58	78	102
57	178	221	55	76	99
56	172	215	53	73	97
55	166	210	51	71	95
54	160	204	49	69	93
53	154	198	47	66	91
52	148	192	44	64	88
51	142	187	42	62	86
50	136	181	40	59	84
49	133	178	39	58	82
48	131	174	—	57	80
47	128	171	38	56	79
46	125	167	37	55	77
45	122	164	36	53	75
44	120	160	35	52	74
43	117	157	—	51	72
42	114	153	34	50	70
41	111	150	33	49	69
40	109	146	32	47	67
39	106	143	31	46	65
38	103	139	—	45	64
37	100	136	30	44	62
36	98	132	29	43	60
35	95	129	28	42	59
34	92	125	27	40	57
33	89	122	—	39	55
32	87	118	26	38	54
31	84	115	25	37	52
30	81	111	24	36	50
29	78	108	23	34	49
28	76	104	—	33	47
27	73	101	22	32	45
26	70	97	21	31	44
25	67	94	20	30	42
24	65	90	19	28	40
23	62	87	—	27	39
22	59	83	18	26	37
21	56	80	17	25	35

TABLE XLI (*Cont.*)

Scale	First Columbia Total Score (Target Score)	Final Columbia Record (Target Score)			
		Total Score	50 yards	40 yards	30 yards
20	54	76	16	24	34
19	51	73	15	23	32
18	48	69	—	21	30
17	45	66	14	20	29
16	43	62	13	19	27
15	40	59	12	18	25
14	37	55	11	17	24
13	34	52	—	15	22
12	32	48	10	14	20
11	29	45	9	13	19
10	26	41	8	12	17
9	23	38	7	11	15
8	21	34	—	9	14
7	18	31	6	8	12
6	15	27	5	7	10
5	12	24	4	6	9
4	10	20	3	5	7
3	7	17	—	4	5
2	4	13	2	2	4
1	1	10	1	1	2

TABLE XLII

SCALE SCORES FOR STROUP BASKETBALL TEST*

Shooting	Passing	Dribbling	Scale Score	Shooting	Passing	Dribbling	Scale Score
6	53	27	51	24	78	42	76
7	55		52				77
8	56	28	53	25	79	43	78
9	57	29	54	26	80		79
	59	30	55	27	81	44	80
10	60	31	56		82		81
11	61		57	28		45	82
12	62	32	58	29	83		83
13	64	33	59		84	46	84
14	65	34	60	30	85		85
	66		61		86	47	86
15	67	35	62	31	87		87
16	68		63	32	88	48	88
	69	36	64		89	49	89
17	70		65	33	90	50	90
		37	66	34	91		91
18	71		67	35	93	51	92
19	72	38	68	36	94		93
	73		69	37	95	52	94
20		39	70		97		95
21	74		71	38	98	53	96
	75	40	72	39	99		97
22	76		73	40	100	54	98
23	77	41	74	41	102	55	99
			75	42	103	56	100

* Frances Stroup, "Game Results as a Criterion for Validating Basketball Skill Test," *Research Quarterly*, Vol. XXVI, No. 3 (October 1955), p. 353.

SCORING TABLES

TABLE XLIII

T-Scores for the Borleske Touch Football Test*
Forward Pass for Distance
(Distance Measured to Nearest Yard)

Score in Yards	Frequency	T-Score
56–58	1	75
53–55	0	73
50–52	3	69
47–49	1	66
44–46	8	63
41–43	8	59
38–40	16	54
35–37	15	50
32–34	12	46
29–31	9	42
26–28	6	39
23–25	3	36
20–22	1	34
17–19	3	31
14–16	0	27
11–13	1	25
	$N = 87$	

Running Straightaway (Time Measured to Nearest Tenth-Second)			*Punt for Distance* (Distance Measured to Nearest Yard)		
Score in Seconds and Tenths	Frequency	T-Score	Score in Yards	Frequency	T-Score
			50.6–53.5	1	75
5.36–5.55	2	72.5	47.6–50.5	1	71
5.56–5.75	6	65.	44.6–47.5	1	69
5.76–5.95	8	60.5	41.6–44.5	14	62
5.96–6.15	15	56.	38.6–41.5	12	56
6.16–6.35	11	51.5	35.6–38.5	16	51
6.36–6.55	14	48	32.6–35.5	4	48
6.56–6.75	8	44	29.6–32.5	19	45
6.76–6.95	9	40.5	26.6–29.5	4	40
6.96–7.15	2	37.5	23.6–26.5	2	38
7.16–7.35	3	35	20.6–23.5	1	37
7.36–7.55	3	31.5	17.6–20.5	5	35
7.56–7.75	0	27.5	14.6–17.5	2	30
7.76–7.95	0	27.5	11.6–14.5	0	27
7.96–8.15	0	27.5	8.6–11.5	1	25
8.16–8.35	0	27.5		$N = 83$	
8.36–8.55	0	27.5			
8.56–8.75	0	27.5			
8.76–8.95	0	27.5			
8.96–9.15	1	00.0			
	$N = 82$				

* Frederick W. Cozens, "Ninth Annual Report of Committee on Curriculum Research of the College Physical Education Association: Part III," *Research Quarterly*, Vol. VIII, No. 2 (May 1937), page 73.

SCORING TABLES

TABLE XLIV

Fox Swimming Power Test for College Women[*]
T-Scores for Crawl and Side Strokes

T-Score	Crawl	Side Stroke	T-Score	Crawl	Side Stroke
	(Feet)	(Feet)		(Feet)	(Feet)
76	50	52	51	27	28
73	47–49	51	49	26	26–27
72	46	50	48	25	25
70		48–49	47		24
69	45	46–47	46	24	
68	44	45	45		23
67	43	44	44	23	22
66	40–42	43	43		21
65		42	42	22	
64	39		41	21	19–20
63		40–41	40	20	18
62	38	37–39	39		17
61	36–37	36	38	19	16
60	35	35	37		15
59	34	34	36	18	
57	33	33	35	17	14
56	32		34		9–13
55	31	32	33	16	8
54	30	31	32		7
53	28–29	30	30	15	6
52		29	27	9–14	
			24	8	5

[*] Margaret G. Fox, "Swimming Power Test," *Research Quarterly*, Vol. XXVIII, No. 3 (October 1957), p. 233.

SCORING TABLES

TABLE XLV

Sigma Scale	Test Score	Sigma Scale	Test Score	Sigma Scale	Test Score	Sigma Scale	Test Score
100	67	75	50	50	33	25	16
99	66	74	49	49	32	24	15
98	—	73	—	48	—	23	—
97	65	72	48	47	31	22	14
96	64	71	47	46	30	21	13
95	—	70	—	45	—	20	—
94	63	69	46	44	29	19	12
93	62	68	45	43	28	18	11
92	—	67	44	42	27	17	10
91	61	66	—	41	—	16	—
90	60	65	43	40	26	15	9
89	59	64	42	39	25	14	8
88	—	63	—	38	—	13	—
87	58	62	41	37	24	12	7
86	57	61	40	36	23	11	6
85	—	60	—	35	—	10	—
84	56	59	39	34	22	9	5
83	55	58	38	33	21	8	4
82	—	57	—	32	—	7	—
81	54	56	37	31	20	6	3
80	53	55	36	30	19	5	2
79	—	54	—	29	—	4	—
78	52	53	35	28	18	3	1
77	51	52	34	27	17	2	—
76	—	51	—	26	—	1	

* Joanna T. Dyer, "Revision of Backboard Test of Tennis Ability," *Research Quarterly*, Vol. IX, No. 1 (March 1938), page 25.

SCORING TABLES

TABLE XLVI

T-Scales for Mott's Table Tennis Backboard Test for
College Women *

T-Score	Raw Score	T-Score	Raw Score	T-Score	Raw Score
77	60	59	45	41	29
76		58		40	
75		57	44	39	28
74		56		38	27
73	58	55	43	37	26
72		54	42	36	
71	55	53	41	35	25
70		52	40	34	24
69	54	51		33	23
68	52	50	39	32	22
67	51	49	38	31	
66	50	48	37	30	
65	49	47	36	29	21
64	48	46	34-35	28	
63		45	33	27	
62	47	44	32	26	20
61		43	31	25	
60	46	42	30	24	16

* Jane A. Mott, "Table Tennis Backboard Test," *Journal of Health and Physical Education,* Vol. 17, No. 9 (November 1946), page 552.

SCORING TABLES

TABLE XLVII

SIGMA-SCALE VALUES, RUSSELL-LANGE VOLLEY BALL TEST FOR GIRLS IN JUNIOR HIGH SCHOOL*

Sigma Scale	Test Scores		Sigma Scale	Test Scores	
	Serve	Repeated Volleys		Serve	Repe ted Volleys
100	—	51	50	—	22
99	45	50	49	16	—
98	44	—	48	—	21
97	—	49	47	—	—
96	43	—	46	15	20
95	—	48	45	—	—
94	42	—	44	—	19
93	41	47	43	14	—
92	—	46	42	—	—
91	40	—	41	—	18
90	—	45	40	13	—
89	39	—	39	—	17
88	—	44	38	—	—
87	38	43	37	12	16
86	37	—	36	—	—
85	—	42	35	—	15
84	36	—	34	11	—
83	—	41	33	—	—
82	35	—	32	—	14
81	—	40	31	10	—
80	34	39	30	—	13
79	33	—	29	—	—
78	—	38	28	9	12
77	32	—	27	—	—
76	—	37	26	—	—
75	31	36	25	8	11
74	30	—	24	—	—
73	—	35	23	—	10
72	29	—	22	7	—
71	—	34	21	—	9
70	28	—	20	—	—
69	—	33	19	6	8
68	27	32	18	—	—
67	26	—	17	—	—
66	—	31	16	—	7
65	25	—	15	—	—
64	—	30	14	—	6
63	24	—	13	4	—
62	23	29	12	—	5
61	—	28	11	—	—
60	22	—	10	3	4
59	—	27	9	—	—
58	21	—	8	—	—
57	—	26	7	2	3
56	20	25	6	—	—
55	19	—	5	—	2
54	—	24	4	1	—
53	18	—	3	—	1
52	—	23	2	—	—
51	17	—	1	—	—

* Naomi Russell and Elizabeth Lange, "Achievement Tests in Volleyball for High School Girls," *Research Quarterly*, Vol. XI, No. 4 (December 1940), page 33.

Index

INDEX

INDEX

INDEX

INDEX

C